Sessions 1–60

Keyboarding
in the Medical Office

William Mitchell
Ronald Kapper

Paradigm PUBLISHING

Developmental Editor   Tom Modl

Production Editor   Courtney Kost

Medical Content Reviewer   Jerri Adler

Copy Editor   Cheryl Wilms

Indexer   Ina Gravitz

Cover and Text Designer   Leslie Anderson

Desktop Publisher   Lisa Beller

Reviewers/Consultants:

Sherrie Burke
Hillsborough Community College
Tampa, Florida

Stephanie Cox
York Technical Institute
Lancaster, Pennsylvania

Tracie Fuqua
Wallace State Community College
Hanceville, Alabama

Helen Hustead
Westmoreland County
Community College
Youngwood, Pennsylvania

Connie Lieseke
Olympic College
Bremerton, Washington

Terri Schuster
Southeastern Community College
West Burlington, Iowa

Deborah Westervelt
Allied College
Fenton, Missouri

The authors wish to acknowledge and thank the following sources for allowing them to adapt material for use in the production documents:

Arizona Cancer Research Center: Documents 34A, 34B, 34D, 34E, 36C, 44D, 51C, 55A, 55B, 56A, 58A, 59A, 59B; **Krames Communications:** Document 35D

Some material used in production documents has previously appeared in or been paraphrased from the following Paradigm texts: Warren, Eason, Burch, Ewens, *Medical Assisting*; Eitinger and Eitinger, *Medical Transcription, 2e Revised*; Rutkosky, Seguin, and Rutkosky, *Marquee Series: Using Computers in the Medical Office—Microsoft Word, Excel, PowerPoint®*; Shmaefsky, *Applied Anatomy and Physiology.*

Publishing Management Team:

Bob Cassel, Publisher; Janice Johnson, Vice President of Marketing;
Shelley Clubb, Electronic Design and Production Manager

Microsoft and Windows are registered trademarks of Microsoft Corporation. IBM is a registered trademark of IBM Corporation.

ISBN-13: 978-07638-2914-8 (textbook)
ISBN-10: 0-7638-2914-5

ISBN-13: 978-07638-2915-5 (textbook and user guide)
ISBN-10: 0-7638-2915-3

Order Number 00237

© 2007 by Paradigm Publishing Inc., a division of EMC Corporation
Published by EMC Corporation
875 Montreal Way
St. Paul, MN 55102
(800) 535-6865
E-mail: educate@emcp.com
Web site: www.emcp.com

Printed in the United States of America

10 9 8 7 6 5 4 3 2 1

Keyboarding in the Medical Office

Table of Contents

Introduction

Keyboarding in the Medical Office

Keyboarding in the Medical Office provides instruction in developing the basic keyboarding skills needed to key alphabetic, numeric, and special symbol characters, as well as teaching the skills needed to use a 10-key numeric keypad. It also provides instruction in basic word processing features, including creating, saving, deleting, and printing documents, and formatting memos, e-mail messages, letters, reports, manuscripts, and tables you are likely to create in a medical office setting.

LEARNING OUTCOMES

When you have completed this book, you will be able to demonstrate a basic-level mastery of keyboarding, which includes:

- Keying straight-copy alphanumeric material at an average rate of 40 words a minute (WAM) with one or fewer errors per minute
- Keying numeric copy using correct touch techniques on the 10-key numeric keypad at 25 WAM
- Using word-processing commands to perform the basic file management activities of creating, saving, deleting, printing, and closing documents
- Using keyboarding skills to compose coherent material with correct word usage at the word, sentence, paragraph, and document levels
- Using word processing skills to prepare correctly formatted memos, e-mail messages, letters, manuscripts, tables, and reports at 25 WAM

PROGRAM OVERVIEW

This textbook works in conjunction with Paradigm's Web-based keyboarding and word processing software, Paradigm Keyboarding with Snap (PKB). This software provides you with drill lines and timings for learning keys along with activities for learning language and composition skills. Included within PKB is the Paradigm Word Processor (PWP), which you will use for document production and management in Sessions 34–60.

SESSION STRUCTURE

Sessions 1–30 follow a basic pattern of On-Screen and Textbook exercises.

On-Screen Exercises

- **Warm-Up:** As the name implies, this introductory activity has you flexing your fingers and practicing key presses so you are ready to key quickly and efficiently when the new material is presented.
- **New Keys:** The computer keyboard is shown on the screen with the new keys highlighted along with instructions for which fingers to use on the new keys.
- **New Key Drills:** The Paradigm software presents a line at a time of words or sentences using the new keys. You are asked to key the lines so your brain and fingers learn where the keys are, and you don't have to look at the keyboard—eventually!
- **Thinking Drills:** These drills are designed to reinforce the English language skills, especially for English Language Learners. They teach you to compose sentences at the keyboard, and to think and key at the same time, eliminating the need to write down what you want to say on paper first. These drills begin in Session 3 and appear in most of the Sessions from 3–23.

Textbook Exercises

- **Reinforcement:** In this part of the session, you will key drills similar to those presented on the screen earlier, along with some new ones, in order to reinforce the learning you did on screen.
- **Timings:** This final session activity is an opportunity for you to determine your keyboarding speed and accuracy. The PKB software displays information about the length of the timing and the paragraph and page number in the text. The program's automatic timer begins when you strike the first key. When the time is up, the keyboard locks so you cannot continue. Immediately the software checks the accuracy and length of what you keyed and displays the results in WAM and errors at the bottom of the screen. The software also automatically saves this file to your directory, and you can print it when required. In addition, the software keeps a record of your timing scores. This record is called the "Student Report," and can be accessed from your Paradigm Keyboarding with Snap home page.
- **Ergonomic Tips:** An awareness and informational tip pertaining to ergonomics will appear at the end of each session.

Sessions 31–33 provide Skillbuilding Reinforcement exercises that allow you to focus on particular keys.

Sessions 34–60 introduce you to basic word processing procedures and teach you how to create memos, e-mail messages, letters, medical reports, manuscripts, and tables using the Paradigm Word Processor (PWP). Each session begins with a Warm-Up, a Timed Short Drill (in which you focus on either increasing your speed or accuracy), and several timings. You then create Production Documents, of which there are two kinds:

- **Checked Production Documents:** You create these documents in PWP, and the software automatically saves and names the file for you and checks it for errors by comparing it to a master document contained in the software. Your scores are saved to the Production Progress Report. (See your *Paradigm Keyboarding with Snap User Guide* for steps to access this report.)
- **Unchecked Production Documents:** You create these documents in a regular PWP editing window, and are responsible for naming, saving, closing, and deleting the documents. PKB does not check these documents for errors. However, you can measure your speed in creating these documents by using the WAM button. (See below for more details.)

All production exercises are based on medically related content and use medical terminology. They will also introduce formatting of various types of medical documents. These exercises will give you realistic work-environment experience while you learn document production skills.

Unit 7, Session 34, introduces basic word processing features using the Paradigm Word Processor (PWP) and developing effective proofreading techniques. There are five exercises involving paragraphs and sentences with medical related content that involve the use of basic word processing features and the development of basic proofreading techniques.

Unit 8, Sessions 35–38, is devoted to preparing memorandums and e-mails related to day-to-day activities within a medical facility. Memorandums are used primarily within the facility, whereas e-mail messages can be internal or external communications.

Unit 9, Sessions 39–44, includes letters between doctors and patients, patients and doctors, and doctors to doctors. One session is devoted to preparing letters of application and résumés for applying for a position as a medical assistant.

The emphasis in Unit 10, Sessions 45–53, is on a wide variety of medical reports and forms including HP (History and Physical) Exam Reports, Medical Consultant's Reports, SOAP (Subjective, Objective, Assessment, and Plan) Reports, Radiology Reports, Operative Reports, Discharge Summary Reports, and Medical Consent Forms. Before preparing Medical Reports, you will prepare a table consisting of the medical terms used in the report along with the definition of the terms. You also will create a template for each of the various types of medical reports. You then will use these templates to create various reports specific reports.

Unit 11, Manuscripts, Sessions 54–59, covers both unbound and bound manuscripts on a variety of medical topics. Title pages, text notes, and the preparation of bibliographies for the manuscripts are included.

Unit 12, Session 60, represents a Productivity Check and includes a medical related e-mail, letter, report, bound manuscript, and memorandum. Your Words-a-Minute (WAM) goal throughout Units 7–12 is to reach at least 25 WAM with all errors corrected.

Each session includes a Reinforcing Writing Skills section where you will compose a medical related document.

A comfortable and ergonomic work environment is essential to efficient keyboarding. Your workstation needs to contain only those items necessary for working on the sessions. Here is an Ergonomic Checklist to review before you begin (see also the following illustration):

- Align the front of the keyboard with the desk's front edge.
- Adjust the monitor so your line of sight is 10–20 degrees below the horizontal.
- Adjust your chair so that you sit about 16 to 24 inches from the screen and your chair seat is 16–19 inches from the floor.
- Sit up straight, back against the chair, feet flat on the floor.
- Place your fingers on the keys in a curved position. Raise your forearms and wrists slightly so that they are parallel to the keyboard. Do not rest your forearms on the keyboard!

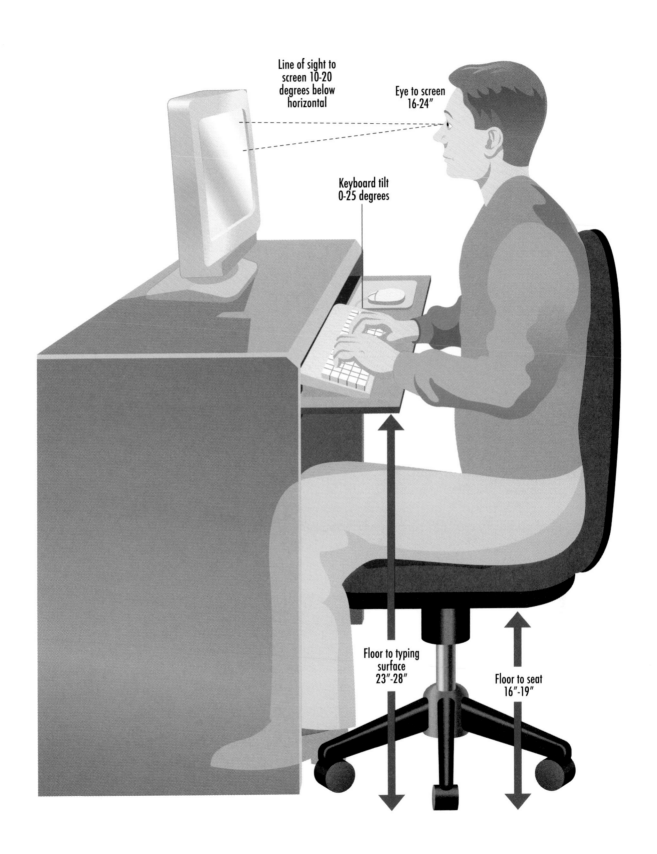

Line of sight to screen 10-20 degrees below horizontal

Eye to screen 16-24"

Keyboard tilt 0-25 degrees

Floor to typing surface 23"-28"

Floor to seat 16"-19"

HARDWARE AND SOFTWARE REQUIRED TO USE PKB

To use the PKB software, you will need the following equipment and configuration:

Processor	Intel Celeron 600Mhz or higher.
Operating System	Windows 2000 (with SP4) or Windows XP Home/Professional (with SP1 or higher)
RAM	128 MB minimum. (256 MB highly recommended on Windows XP)
Web Browser	Internet Explorer 6.0
Desktop Resolution	800 x 600 in 16 bit color

Security Information for Windows and Internet Explorer

1. Scripting and cookies must be enabled within Internet Explorer.
2. Pop-up blocking software must be disabled for www.keyboarding.emcp.com.
3. The web browser should permit signed ActiveX controls to be installed and activated.
4. Computer firewalls should be set to accept data transfer to and from www.keyboarding.emcp.com.
5. Administrative privileges are required to install the ActiveX control for the first time. (Win XP)
6. Power user (or higher) privileges are required to install the ActiveX control for the first time. (Win 2000)
7. Once the Active X control is installed, PKB can be run with the privileges of a guest account.

PREPARING INTERNET EXPLORER FOR VIEWING AND USING PKB

In order to use the PKB software that is part of your textbook package, you need to have access to a computer that is connected to the Internet, has either the Windows 2000 or Windows XP operating system, with the Internet Explorer 6.0 (or later) Web browser. You will need to make the adjustments in Internet Explorer to ensure that you can access and use PKB.

Disabling Pop-Up Blockers

Pop-up blockers need to be turned off in order for you to view PKB. If your computer has Windows XP with Service Pack 2 installed on it, you will need to take the following steps to ensure that PKB's popup windows are functional:

1. Click Tools on Internet Explorer's Menu bar.
2. Point to the Pop-up Blocker and click Pop-up Blocker Settings.
3. In the dialog that appears, type in **keyboarding.emcp.com** and click the Add button.

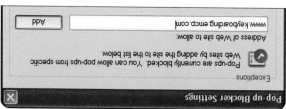

4. Click the Close button.

Installing the ActiveX Control

Take the following steps to ensure that your Internet Explorer's settings permit the ActiveX control needed so that the keyboarding software can be launched:

To ensure that ActiveX controls and plug-ins are enabled in Internet Explorer, take the following steps:

1. At the Internet Explorer Screen, click Tools and then click Internet Options.
2. Click the Security Tab.
3. Select Internet from the list of zones displayed. The security level for this zone should be set at "Medium." If not, follow any of the methods mentioned below.

Method I - Utilizing the Default Zone Security Settings (Recommended)

1. Click the Default Level button.
2. Verify that the security level slider is set to the Medium Security Level.
3. Click the Apply button, and then click OK.

Method 2 - Customizing the Internet Zone Security Settings

1. Click the Custom Level button.
2. Navigate to the section entitled ActiveX controls and plug-ins.
3. Locate the heading entitled Download signed ActiveX controls and click Prompt.

4. Locate the heading entitled Script ActiveX controls marked safe for scripting and click Enable.

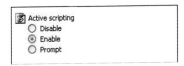

5. Navigate to the section entitled Downloads.
6. Locate the heading entitled File download and click Enable.

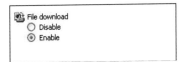

7. Navigate to the section entitled Scripting.
8. Locate the heading Script ActiveX and click Enable.

9. Click OK to save your changes.
10. Click OK again to shut the window.

Getting Started: Beginning a Session

Below are detailed instructions and illustrations for entering and exiting PKB. These instructions are also given in Session 1 and then repeated in the next two sessions.

1 Log on to the Internet if your computer is not already connected to it.

2 At the Windows desktop of your computer, double-click the *Internet Explorer* icon.

3 At the Internet Explorer screen, click on the entry in the Address text box.

4 Key **www.keyboarding.emcp.com** in the Address text box and click *GO*. The Paradigm Keyboarding with Snap home page appears.

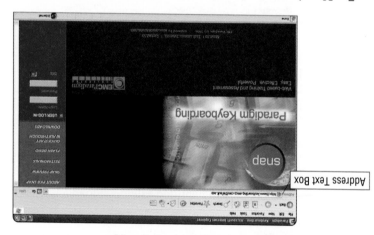

5 Your instructor has given you a **login name** that has been assigned for your class. The textbook package for your course includes a *Paradigm Keyboarding with Snap User Guide*. On the inside front cover of the *User Guide* is your unique PKB **password** that you will use with the login name from your instructor to access PKB. Enter your login name in the Login Name text box (lower right corner of the screen). Enter your password in the Password text box.

6 Click the arrow in the red box.

Note: If you enter either your login name or password incorrectly, you will receive an error message, stating that you need to try again. You must retype your login details exactly; login names and passwords are case sensitive. If you have forgotten your login name or password, please contact your instructor.

7 When you log into Paradigm Keyboarding for the first time, you will be asked to read and agree to the Paradigm Keyboarding End User License Agreement, and to verify certain details about your course. You will need to do this only once.
If the information displayed at this point is correct, click the Proceed button to continue.

Note: If the information displayed does not match your course details, click Cancel and contact your instructor to get the correct Login Name for your section. If you discover you are in the wrong section after you have already enrolled, ask your instructor to have you moved to the correct section.

8 Your Paradigm Keyboarding with Snap Welcome page appears.

9 Find the Session and exercise you want to launch in the Exercises table, and click the exercise name hyperlink once. The Launch Keyboarding dialog box appears.

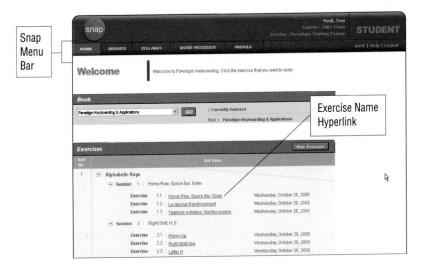

10 Click the Launch button.
11 The PKB Exercise screen appears.

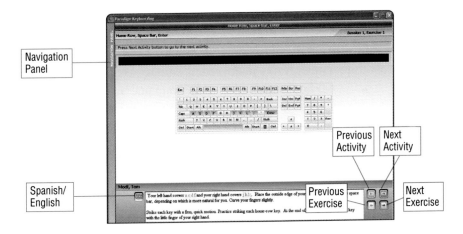

Essential Program Commands and Features

The PKB Exercise screen features the following buttons and functions:

Next Activity/Previous Activity These buttons take you to the next or previous activity within an exercise.

Next Exercise/Previous Exercise These buttons take you to the next or previous exercise of the program. These will provide the most common way of moving through the program.

Navigation Panel This feature allows you to move to any exercise within the program. Click on the orange panel on the left side of your screen with your mouse and a tree menu showing all the sessions and exercises in the program appears.

Spanish/English This toggle button allows you to view most software instructions in Spanish. Click the button to see instructions in Spanish. Click it again to see them in English.

When exercises are done from the text, two more icons appear at the bottom-left side of the screen. They are—

- A Timing button 🔘 where you can set a time length for a specified time period. At the end of the timing, the software calculates your Words-a-Minute (WAM) rate, and adds that to your work.

- A WAM button 🔘 where you have an open ended time frame; when you click on the Stop WAM 🔘 which replaced the WAM button, when the document or timing is completed, the software calculates your Words-a-Minute (WAM) rate.

- An important point to remember about these buttons is that the button does not work if the program is requiring some other specific response (for example, a dialog box is displayed and the program is waiting for you to respond). However, once the response has been completed, the PKB buttons will function.

Ending a Session

At the end of each session, you have three options: print any documents you have created, continue with the next session, or exit PKB.

Print

To print exercises proceed as follows:

1   Click the Close ☒ button in the top right corner of the PKB Exercise screen.
2   At your Paradigm Keyboarding with Snap Welcome page, point to Reports on the Snap menu bar, and click View Submissions Report.
3   At the View Submissions Report Wizard, click Show session files to see drill and reinforcement text, Show timings files to see the timings text, or Show production files or Show unchecked production files to see production documents.
4   Click Show Report.
5   Click the name of the file you want to print.
6   At the Word Processor dialog box, click Launch.
7   Click File, and then click Print.
8   At the Print dialog box, click OK.
9   Click the Close button ☒ to close the Paradigm Word Processor.
10 Click Home on the Snap menu bar to return to the Welcome page.

Continue

To continue on to the next session, click the Next Exercise ⬅ button.

Exit

To exit PKB, take the following steps:

1   Click the Close ☒ button in the top right corner of the PKB Exercise screen.
2   At your Paradigm Keyboarding with Snap Welcome page, click Logout.

PROGRAM HINTS

At this point, you are ready to begin working in the program. Here are some hints to help you move smoothly and efficiently through the sessions:

- Be sure the computer you are using has the proper settings for accessing the PKB software. See the section "Using the Paradigm Keyboarding with Snap Software" on page xii or your Paradigm Keyboarding with Snap User Guide for details.

- Whenever a dialog box is displayed, you must respond to it before trying to execute another program command.

- All session work is named and saved automatically:

  1 Warm-Ups, New-key drills, Thinking Drills, Timed Short Drills, and Reinforcement exercises are saved in a file called 000ses (where 000 is the session number and "ses" stands for session).

  2 Timings are saved in a file called 000tim (where 000 is the session number and "tim" stands for timing).

  3 Production documents that are electronically scored are saved in a file called 000prox (where 000 is the session number, "pro" stands for production, and the "x" is replaced with a letter denoting a document — e.g. document a, b, c, d, or e). A version of the file showing the results from the first time you checked it is also saved, with "chk" added after the document letter.

- Beginning in Session 34, all production documents composed and saved by the student are stored in a file 000wprx (where 000 is the session number and "wpr" stands for word processing reinforcement, and the "x" represents the alphabetic letter of the document— d, e, f, g).

- All printing is done using the Paradigm Word Processor (PWP), except in the Reinforcement activities, where you have the option of printing from the screen. You can access the files created by PKB through the View Submissions Report available through the Reports menu of your PKB Home page. (See the instructions above under "Ending a Session" on how to access this report and print files.)

- Certain type conventions have been used in the text:

  1 Command sequences are shown as follows: File→Open, where the underlined letter in the first word is the letter PWP underlines on the screen, the arrow indicates a drop-down menu, and the next command listed is the option to be selected from the drop-down menu.

  2 Key presses appear in bold type.

  3 Dialog box names, prompts, and filenames that appear on the screen are shown in italics.

  4 Command sequences the user keys are shown in bold italic type.

Now you are ready to proceed with Session 1. If you have any questions, contact your instructor.

1

ALPHABETIC KEYS

] WHAT DO POLYPS HAVE TO DO WITH CANCER? [bf

] Introduction [bf

¶ Colon polyps are abnormal growths in the lining of the large intestine. They are usually small and mushroom-like in appearance. These growths usually do not cause symptoms, so people who have them usually don't know it.

] Adenomatous Polyps [bf

¶ Polyps in and of themselves are not harmful. However, polyps can grow or change and turn cancerous. Adenomatous polyps are of particular concern. Most, if not all, colon cancers start from an adenomatous polyp. Currently, the only way to prevent colon cancer is to remove these potentially dangerous polyps before they turn into cancer.

] Locating Polyps [bf

¶ The best way to find a polyp is to take a look in the colon. This can be done with endoscopic procedures that use narrow, flexible tubes inserted in the rectum to directly view the lining of the colon. These instruments are equipped with lights, lenses, cameras, and special surgical instruments that are used to remove abnormal tissue. The best procedure to detect polyps is a colonoscopy, because it is the only procedure that examines the entire large intestine

] The Growth of Polyps [bf

¶ Much is yet to be learned about colon polyps, what causes them, and how they become cancerous. Polyps grow at different rates from person to person. However, it is estimated that for the average person, it may take three to five years to develop a sizable adenoma from normal tissue, and that it takes another five to ten years to transform from an adenoma to cancer. While some people form new, sizable polyps every one or two years, others may have only one or two polyps every five or ten years. There is considerable variation among individuals.

] Preventing Colon Cancer [bf

¶ The best way we know to prvent colon cancer is by having a regular colonoscopy and removing all adenomatous polyps. In addition, there is an ongoing research study using certain medications to prevent adenomatous polyps from recurring. If adenomatous polyps can be eliminated, then we may be able to prevent colon cancer. (Arizona Colon Cancer Group 4)

60.10

Document F

Evaluation of the Keyboarding Course for Medical Offices

Now that you have completed this keyboarding course, reflect on what you have learned and on how it was presented. At your keyboard, compose an evaluation of the course and this textbook and software. Format it as a memo to your instructor. Use headings to guide your reader through the evaluation.

Describe what you have accomplished. Did you meet the learning objectives listed in the preface? If not, why? Discuss the strengths and weaknesses of the textbook and the software program. How could they be improved? Then, pick your favorite session or activity and explain why you liked it.

Save the document as **060wprf**. Then print and close the document.

ENDING THE SESSION

Congratulations on completing this Keyboarding for the Medical Office course! If you need to print any Session 60 files, do so at this time. Delete all wpr files. Be sure to turn in all required materials to your instructor. Then exit the program.

HOME ROW, SPACE BAR, ENTER

Session Goals

ASDF JKL;
Space Bar, Enter Key

1.1- ON-SCREEN EXERCISES: GETTING STARTED
1.2

You will be using the Paradigm Keyboarding with Snap (PKB) Web-based software along with your textbook to do the exercises that will help you develop your keyboarding skills.

To access PKB, take the following steps:

1 Log on to the Internet if your computer is not already connected to it.

2 At the Windows desktop of your computer, double-click the *Internet Explorer* 🥏 icon.

3 At the Internet Explorer screen, click on the entry in the Address text box.

4 Key **www.keyboarding.emcp.com** in the Address text box and click *GO*. The Paradigm Keyboarding with Snap home page appears.

5 Your instructor has given you a Login Name that has been assigned for your class. The textbook package for your course includes a *Paradigm Keyboarding with Snap User Guide*. On the inside front cover of the *User Guide* is your unique PKB Password that you will use with the Login Name from your instructor to access PKB. Enter your login name in the Login Name text box (lower right corner of the screen). Enter your password in the Password text box.

6 Click the arrow in the red box. [→]

7 When you log into Paradigm Keyboarding for the first time, you will be asked to read and agree to the Paradigm Keyboarding End User License Agreement, and to verify certain details about your course. You will need to do this only once.

CLINICAL HISTORY: Acute pain.

PROCEDURE(S): Five-view lumbar spine examination.

FINDING: There is a moderate thoracolumbar curvature on frontal view. On lateral view there is 3 mm of retrospondylolisthesis of L4 on L5 and of L5 on S1. There is moderate to severe disc space narrowing throughout the lumbar spine. There is a mild compression deformity along the superior endplate at T9. There is a moderate compression deformity at L2. There is moderate to severe degenerative change at the facet joints at L3-4, L4-5, and L5-S1. An IVC filter is noted. Prominent aortic calcification is noted. There is a 1.5-mm rounded calcification in the right upper quadrant, probably reflecting a gallbladder stone.

IMPRESSION: Severe degenerative changes in the spine and nonspecific mild to moderate compression deformities at T9 and L2. These compression fractures are age indeterminate and could be correlated with MRI to evaluate for bone marrow edema, if this is clinically significant. Radiodensity in the right upper quadrant could relate to the gallbladder, such as a gallstone.

S. L. Cowen, M. D.

xx/060prod

60.9 **Document E**

Edited Bound Manuscript

1 At the *Session 60 Document E* screen, key document E by completing the following steps:
   a Read the document before keying to make sure all errors have been corrected in the editing process.
   b Follow the formatting guidelines presented in Session 55.
   c Change to double spacing.
   d Enter the title in all caps and bolded on Line 7.
   e Change the left and right margins to 1.25.
   f Number the pages in the upper right corner except for page 1.
   g Enter hard page breaks where appropriate.
2 After keying Document E, proofread and correct any errors.
3 Click the Check icon to name (**060proe**), save, and check the document.
4 Print the document.
5 To correct errors, click View Original. Make any necessary changes, then recheck the document.
6 Click Next Exercise.

If the information displayed at this point is correct, click the Proceed button to continue.

8   Your Paradigm Keyboarding with Snap Welcome page appears.

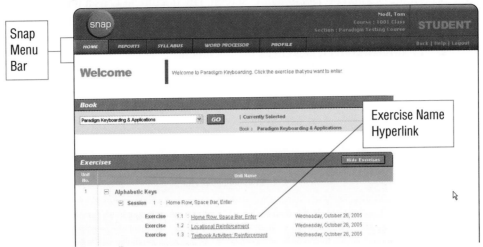

Find Exercise 1.1 in the Exercises table, and click <u>Home Row, Space Bar, Enter</u>. The Launch Keyboarding dialog box appears.

9   Click the Launch button.

10   The PKB Exercise screen appears.

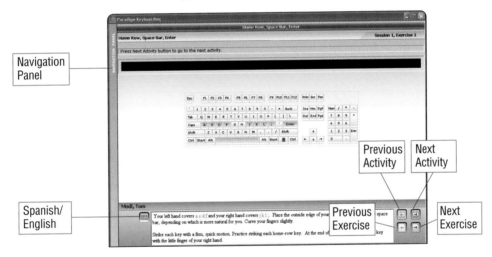

The PKB Exercise screen features the following buttons and functions:

Next Activity/Previous Activity 🔲🔲   These buttons take you to the next or previous activity within an exercise.

Next Exercise/Previous Exercise 🔲🔲   These buttons take you to the next or previous exercise of the program. These will provide the most common way of moving through the program.

Navigation Panel This feature allows you to move to any exercise within the program. Click on the orange panel with your mouse and a tree menu showing all the sessions and exercises in the program appears.

Spanish/English This toggle button allows you to view most software instructions in Spanish. Click the button to see instructions in Spanish. Click it again to see them in English.

Follow the instructions on screen to to complete Exercises 1.1 through 1.2. When you complete Exercise 1.2, Locational Reinforcement, there will be a message on the screen to return to page 4 in the text to complete Exercise 1.3, Textbook Reinforcement.

60.7

Document C

Creating a Radiology Report Form

1 At the *Session 60 Document C* screen, key document C as a template for a radiology report form. The template for this document is slightly different from the one prepared for Session 48, Document B.
2 Proofread, correct, and check the document.
3 The document will be saved automatically as **060proc**.
4 Click Next Exercise.

Document C

> ### SIMON IMAGING
> ### SUN CITY WEST, ARIZONA
>
> **NAME:**   **MEDICAL RECORD #:**
> **DATE:**   **DOB:**
> **PHYSICIAN:**   **PROCEDURE:**
>
> ### RADIOLOGY REPORT
>
> **CLINICAL HISTORY:**
> **PROCEDURE(S):**
> **FINDINGS:**
> **IMPRESSION:**
>
> _____

60.8

Document D

Radiology Report

1 At the *Session 60 Document D* screen, insert document 060proc. Enter the following information for the headings:
  a NAME: **Roberto Garcia**
  b MEDICAL RECORD #: **19373**
  c DATE: **09/25/Current year**
  d DOB: **06/23/1960**
  e PHYSICIAN: **S. L. Cowen, M.D.**
  f PROCEDURE: **Lumbar spine x-ray**
  Note: When entering the Name, Date, and Physician information, use your right arrow key to move past the colon, press the space bar once, and enter the data. For the other entries in the heading press the End key, then press the space bar once.
2 Check the document for errors that may have been overlooked before keying it.
3 Key the body of the radiology report.
4 Proofread and correct any errors.
5 Click the Check icon to name (**060prod**), save, and then print the document.
6 Click on View Original to correct any errors.
7 Click Next Exercise.

Welcome back! You have begun building your skill on the home keys, space bar, and Enter key. Everything you have keyed so far has been saved automatically in a file named 001ses. Now you will review the Session 1 keys.

Reviewing the Home Row Keys

Fingers

- Left hand on ASDF
- Right hand on JKL;
- Either left or right thumb on space bar
- Little finger of right hand for Enter

Students in Online Classes:

Whether working from the screen or text, keep your eyes on the copy; this will help you build speed.

Home Row Drill

- Key each line once.
- Keep eyes on copy.
- Press **Enter** at the end of each line. Press **Enter** twice between groups of lines.
- Repeat any group of 3 lines if you need more practice.

1 aaa sss ddd fff jjj kkk lll ;;; sd kl ;
2 aa ss dd ff jj kk ll ;; asdf jkl; af j;
3 a s d f j k l ; aa ss dd ff jj kk ll ;;

4 a ad a ad add add adds adds a ad add ad
5 a as as a ask ask asks asks a all all a
6 ad add as ask a; a; as adds asks a;; ad

7 fads fads fall fall falls falls fad fad
8 lass lass lad lad lads dad dads ask ask
9 falls flask alas fads dads asks all sad

Drill

Key the following drill. Press **Enter** after each line.

1 all all
2 sad sad dad dad

3 fad fad alas alas
4 fall fall lad lad add add

make sure all parts of the document are included such as dates, filnames, and copy notations. Read the document before keying it to check spelling, punctuation, and misspelled words. If you are to prepare a memo, a block-style letter, a report, or an unbound manuscript, make sure you know the formatting elements and guidelines. If you are unsure, check the appropriate sessions in the text for a quick review.

60.5

Document A

E-Mail Message

1 At the *Session 60 Document A* screen, key document A as an e-mail message.
2 Proofread and correct any errors.
3 Click Check to name (**060proa**), save, and check the letter.
4 To print the message with errors highlighted, click the Print button.
5 To correct errors, click View Original. Make changes, then recheck the document.
6 Click Next Exercise.

Document A

TO: AstroClinicDistributionList@emcp.com /C: mlopez23@emcp.com /SUBJECT: NOTICE TO ALL EMPLOYEES/Dr. St. Claire will be presenting information on diabetes at the monthly meeting of the Astro Medical Clinic. You are invited to attend this presentation, which will take place Wednesday, October 15, from 7 to 8:30 p.m., in Room 224 at the Astro Clinic./The presentation will include information on the prevalence of diabetes among people of different age and ethnic groups, health complications related to diabetes, and treatment and prevention of diabetes. For more information on the presentation, please contact Marie Lopez at extension 9445.

60.6

Document B

Letter to Patient

1 Be sure to read the letter in the text before keying it; it may contain spelling errors. You are to format the letter using the block-style letter (all parts begin at the left margin) and ensure that all parts of the letter are included.
2 At the *Session 60 Document B* screen, key document B, a letter from a doctor to a patient.
3 Proofread and correct any errors.
4 Click Check to name (**060prob**), save, and check the letter.
5 To print the letter with any errors highlighted, click the Print button.
6 To correct any errors, click View Original. Make changes, then recheck the document.
7 Click Next Exercise.

Document B

Mr. Ed Dawson/14630 W. El Capitan Circle/Sun City, AZ 85374/Dear Mr. Dawson:/Your oral disease has been diagnosed as lichen planus: an inflammatory dieseae of the mucosa of the mouth. Please follow the enclosed diet as needed./The condition in rare instances could be pre-malignant and should be checked by our office or your dentist at least once a year. Any suspicious areas you happen to notice should be biopsied at once./We have no cure for this disease, but we do have medications that will help treat the symptoms. If you develop a lot of pain, soreness, ulcerations, discomfort or bleeding, please call us at 623-555-9199 for an appointment./Sincerely,/Gary K. Holyoak, DMD/Enclosure

Additional Drill

Key the following drill. Press *Enter* after each line.

1 a all all a alas alas a as ad add ask a

2 ask ask asks asks all all alas alas all

3 ad add as ask all alas adds asks all ad

4 dad dad dads dads sad sad fad fad fads

5 flak flak flask flask lad lad lads lads

ENDING THE SESSION

Now that you have completed this session, you have three options:

1 Print any documents you have created.
2 Continue with the next session.
3 Exit Snap Paradigm Keyboarding.

Print

To print Exercises 1.1–1.3 proceed as follows:

1 Click the Close ☒ button in the top right corner of the PKB Exercise screen.
2 At your Paradigm Keyboarding with Snap Welcome page, point to Reports on the Snap menu bar, and click View Submissions Report.
3 At the View Submissions Report Wizard, click Show session files.
4 Click Show Report.
5 Click 001ses.rtf.
6 At the Word Processor dialog box, click Launch.
7 Click File, and then click Print.
8 At the Print dialog box, click OK.
9 Click the Close button to close the Paradigm Word Processor.
10 Click Home on the Snap menu bar to return to the Welcome page.

Continue

To continue on the next session, click the Next Exercise ⬛ button **twice**. This will take you to Exercise 2.2. (You will bypass Exercise 2.1 Warmup since you are already warmed up.)

Exit

To exit, do the following:

1 Click the Close ☒ button in the top right corner of the screen.
2 At your Paradigm Keyboarding with Snap Welcome page, click Logout.

Ergonomic Tip

Sit upright in your seat using back of the chair for lumbar support to eliminate lower back pain and strain.

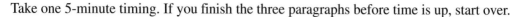

Goal: 35 WAM/1 error

SI: 1.55

Take one 5-minute timing. If you finish the three paragraphs before time is up, start over.

1   Sailing has played an important part in this country's heritage, both in commerce and in sport. Naval architects and shipbuilders are well known because of the beautiful and speedy ships that have sailed the oceans of the world. Full-rigged clipper ships such as the great "Flying Cloud" have set many speed records on the water route between San Francisco and the Orient. Building speedy ships has been a major objective of American yacht designers. A number of fine designers of yachts have earned much recognition, praise, and popularity for their grand designs of winning yachts.

     Enthusiasm for sailing as a new hobby progressed fast during the thirties; amateur sailors from England and America have competed in a series of races for many years. The boats used in earlier races were class sloops which measured up to 135 feet in length. Today, the big races are run in twelve-meter sloops averaging 70 feet in length; the ships are fine precision machines which have been designed for close-course match racing.

     Until 1945, sailboats were very few in number when compared with the total ownership of sailboats today. Within the past few decades, many new materials have allowed boats to be made more easily and less expensively. Fiberglass was the fabric which revolutionized the boat industry. Fiberglass has made the task of molding the hull of a boat easier and very efficient. A builder no longer has to utilize wooden planks in boat construction. Mass production of many boats is now an economical process. A number of boat owners prefer the fiberglass as it requires less upkeep and is not expensive to maintain.

TEXTBOOK EXERCISES: PRODUCTIVITY CHECK

Now that you have completed the instructional activities for creating memos, e-mail messages, letters, tables, reports, and manuscripts, it is time to assess how accurately and quickly you can key these documents.

The goal for memos, e-mails, letters, business reports, and manuscripts is 25 WAM or higher with all errors corrected. The time used in calculating your WAM rate for all types of documents includes the following:

- Formatting the document.
- Accessing the word processing features.
- Keying the document.
- Correcting any errors.

The completed document must be "mailable." To reach the highest possible WAM rate, be sure to read the instructions for each document before you enter your first command or key any of the material because the clock starts when you strike the first key or click the mouse. Also, be sure to check each document to

Session 2

Right Shift, H, E
Correcting Errors, Backspace, Insert, Delete

Session Goals

**Right Shift,
H, E, Backspace,
Insert, Delete**

**Correcting errors with
Backspace, Overtype,
and Delete**

**2.1-
2.5** ***ON-SCREEN EXERCISES: GETTING STARTED***

If you exited Snap Paradigm Keyboarding at the end of Session 1, proceed as follows:

1 At the Windows desktop, double-click the *Internet Explorer* 🖉 icon.
2 At the Internet Explorer screen, click on the entry in the Address text box.
3 Key **www.keyboarding.emcp.com** and click *GO*.
4 At the Paradigm Keyboarding with Snap page, enter your login name in the Login Name text box (lower right corner of the screen). Enter the password from your User Guide in the Password text box.
5 Click the arrow in the red box [→].
6 Your Paradigm Keyboarding with Snap Welcome page appears. Go to Exercise 2.1 and click <u>Warmup</u>.
7 The Launch Keyboarding dialog box appears; click the Launch button. Follow the instructions on the screens to complete Exercises 2.1 through 2.5.
8 When you complete Exercise 2.5, Locational Reinforcement, there will be a message on the screen to return to page 6 in the text to complete Exercise 2.6, which is a review of what has been presented in the software.

2.6 ***TEXTBOOK EXERCISES: REINFORCEMENT***

With a clear editing window displayed, you will now key drill lines you keyed earlier along with some new ones. This activity will be a reinforcement and review of the key reaches presented in Exercises 2.2–2.5. In addition, you will learn several ways to correct errors.

Correcting Errors

Here are three ways to correct any keying errors you might make as you complete Reinforcement activities:

Backspace: deletes characters as you backspace over them.

Overtype: replaces text letter by letter at the insertion point position. This feature is turned on and off when you press ***Insert***. (This is referred to as a toggle key.)

Delete: deletes character at the insertion point position.

Session

60

MEDICAL DOCUMENT PREPARATION PRODUCTIVITY CHECK

Session Goals

3-Minute: 40 WAM/1 error
5-Minute: 35 WAM/1 error

Using selected features presented in Sessions 34–58

Writing an assessment of the Keyboarding course

60.1-
60.2

ON-SCREEN: GETTING STARTED

If you are continuing immediately from Session 59, go to the three-minute timing. If you exited the program at the end of Session 59, access the Session 60 menu and double-click Warm-Up.

60.3

THREE-MINUTE TIMING

Goal: 40 WAM/1 error

SI: 1.50

Take one 3-minute timing.

1   Nature lovers cannot find words that describe the strange beauty of a coral reef. These fragile and dainty aquatic kingdoms have been compared to colorful gardens; the sea animals are the flowers of this classic garden. The strangely eerie sights beneath the waters of the seas have made scientists gasp at the exquisite coral reef beauty.

      Some reefs contain hundreds of varieties of coral. The warm and clear water is ideal for the continued healthy existence of all those small stony coral polyps. They are the architects of the coral reef. Others who live in this ocean world are countless invertebrates and a number of different species of fish. The creatures are beautiful and sometimes bizarre in appearance and can be seen in almost every shape and color to be imagined.

      Each of the tiny creatures has a different and unique form of protective gear. The sea urchin is well fortified with an arsenal of rock-like, blunt spines. The lionfish exudes some of the most powerful and poisonous venom in the world. The stonefish is a near-perfect replica of a rock; but when an unsuspecting fish is nearby, it is quickly captured by the stonefish.

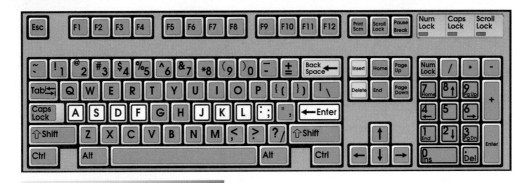

Correcting with Backspace

Move the insertion point to the right of the letter you want to correct. Press the Backspace key to delete the letter, then key the correct letter. To practice correcting with the Backspace key, do the following:

1 Key **saf**.
2 Press the Backspace key to delete f.
3 Key the letter **d**.
4 Press the space bar, then key **lasd**.
5 Press the Backspace key to delete the d.
6 Key the letter **s**.
7 Press the space bar, then key **flasd**.
8 Press the Backspace key to delete d.
9 Key the letter **k**. Press **Enter**.

Your line should now look like this:

sad lass flask

Correcting with Overtype

By default, Overtype is off. This means that anything you key is inserted in the text rather than keyed over existing text. If you want to insert or add text, leave Overtype off. If, however, you want to key over something, turn Overtype on by pressing the **Insert** key. Overtype stays in effect until you press the **Insert** key again.

To practice correcting with the Overtype feature, do the following:

1 Key the following line:

Sad All Asks Dads Fads Alas Flask Falls

2 Press the **Insert** key.
3 Change the uppercase S in Sad to a lowercase s. To do this, move the insertion point with either the mouse or the left arrow key immediately left of the S and key **s**.
4 Change the remaining uppercase letters to lowercase.
5 Turn Overtype off by pressing the **Insert** key.

Your line should now look like this:

sad all asks dads fads alas flask falls

12

PRODUCTIVITY CHECK

Correcting with Delete

When correcting with the Delete key, simply position the insertion point on or just to the left of the character to be deleted. Press the **Delete** key to remove the character, then key the correct letter.

To practice correcting with the Delete key, do the following:

1 Key the following line:

Fall Alas Sad Asksv

2 Position the insertion point on or just to left of a in Fall.
3 Press the **Delete** key.
4 Key **e**.
5 Position the insertion point on or just to left of the last s in Asks.
6 Press **Delete**.

Your line should now look like this:

Fell Alas Sad Ask

Reviewing the Right Shift, H, and E Keys

Remember: The right Shift key is used to make capital letters that are keyed with the left hand.

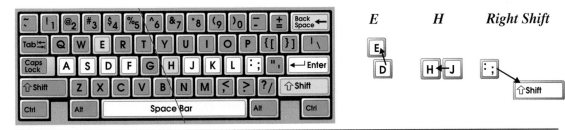

Drill Instructions

- Key each line once; keep your eyes on the copy.
- Press **Enter** at the end of each line.
- Key the appropriate group of lines again if you need more practice. Do not try to correct errors.

Right Shift Drill

1 Ad All Asks Adds Alas All Ask As Add Ad
2 Fad fad Falls falls Fall fall Fads fads
3 Sad All Asks Dads Fads Alas Flask Falls

¶ Ovarian cancer screening tests are usually conducted only when medically indicated. Prostate *BF*

¶ Digital rectal examination: the doctor inserts a gloved finger into the rectum and feels the prostate gland through the rectum wall for bumps or abnormal areas.

¶ Transrectal ultrasonography: high frequency sound waves are sent out by a probe. The sound waves bounce off the prostate gland and produce echoes used to creat a ~~pricute~~ *e / picture* called a sonogram.

¶ PSA: a blood test used to *de* ~~tect~~ the levels of prostate specific antigen (PSA). High levels of PSA are also found in men with noncancerous prostate conditions.

¶ Prostate examinations are generally conducted during an individual's annual physical exam.

] Summary [*BF*
Every prson, regardless of his or her personal risk level or the presence or absence of symptoms, should have reguilar cancer screening.

59.8
Document C

Improving Readability

Open Document **059proa**. You are to improve the readability of this document by inserting paragraphs and adding first-, second-, and/or third-level headings. Read the whole document before deciding where to insert headings. When finished, reread the document to see if your headings are, in fact, helpful to the reader. The headings are to help the reader focus on the content of the paragraph(s) that follow. Proofread and correct any errors made. Save, name (**059wprc**), print, and close the document.

ENDING THE SESSION

As noted earlier, deleting documents no longer needed is a good habit to develop. This gives you more space to store new information and reduces the list of files that you must go through to open documents. Delete all wpr documents for Unit 9, Sessions 39–44, print any files from Session 59 not printed earlier, then continue with the next session or exit the program. (If necessary, review procedures for any of the above activities found on page 300 of Session 54.)

Students in Online Classes

If you do not reach 25 WAM on Documents A and/or B, go to the word processor, activate the timing feature, and repeat the Document(s). Push for 25 WAM. Name and save the document(s) 059wpra and/or 059wprb.

Ergonomic Tip
Keep wrists in nonbent position. This helps reduce repetitive stress injuries.

H Drill

1 jh hall hall hall sash sash has sash hash
2 half half half lash lash lash half lash
3 Dads sash Falls Shall Shall Flash Flash

E Drill

Key lines 1–2 once for speed; try to make your fingers go faster.

1 deal dead deaf fade seat led lead lease lake
2 she she ale ale elf elf elk elk heat heat fake fake

Key lines 3–5 once for control; slow down and concentrate on control.

3 deal deal ease ease else else desk desk fell fell
4 fade fade feel feel dead dead head head heal heal
5 Elk Elk Else Ease Ed Elf Else Ease Ed Ed

Additional Drill

Key the following drill. Press **Enter** after each line.

1 half half
2 flash flash shall shall
3 fall hall alas dash half
4 lad lad lads lads Flak Flak Flask Flask

5 Sad Dad Add Ask Fad Salad Flak Dads All
6 Dads Ask lad Ask dad lads lass lass Add
7 jh has had has had has had has had lash
8 ha has ash Ash Ash had ash ash hall Flash

9 eel deed eel she see she see ale elf ale fee
10 ease deal ease deal else desk else desk fell
11 fade feel fade feel dead head dead head heal
12 Else Elk Ease Ed Elf Else Ease Ed Elf Ed

5 To correct errors, click View Original. Make any necessary changes, then recheck the document.

6 Click Next Exercise.

Document B

] Screening for Cancer [BF all caps   Underline 4th level headings

] Introduction [BF

¶ There is no way to know for sure if a person will or will not get cancer. However, there are some thngs you can do to reduce your risk of getting cancer.

] Screening guidelines [BF

¶ Following <u>screening guidelines</u> can lower your likelihood of getting cancer. Screening tests check people for the development of cancer even if they have no symptoms. Scientists have studied patterns of cancer in the population to learn which people are more likely to get certain types of cancer (Cancer Institute 4).

<u>Breast</u> BF

¶ Breast self examination: a monthly self-exam helps to detect changes in breast tissue.

¶ Clinicical breast examination: during your routine annual physical examination, your doctor will check your breasts and under your arms for lumps or other unusual changes.

¶ Mamography: a special x-ray is used to find tumors too small for you or your doctor to feel. The National Cancer Institute (National Cancer Institute Newsletter 7) recommends that women in their forties and older have mammograms on a regular basis, every one to two years.

<u>Cervix</u> BF

¶ Pap smears: a wooden scraper and/or small brush are used at a woman's annual doctor's visit to collect a sample of cells from the cervix and upper vagina.

<u>Colon and rectum</u> BF

¶ Fecal/occult blood test: detects hidden blood in the stool.

¶ Sigmoidoscopy: an examination of the rectum and lower colon with a lighted instrument.

¶ Colonoscopy: an examination of the recturm and entire colon with a lighted instrument.

¶ Double contrast barium enema: a series of x-rays of the colon and rectum. The x-rays are taken after the patient is given an enema with a white, chalky solution that contains barium to outline the colon and rectum on the x-rays.

¶ Digital rectal exam: the doctor inserts a lubricated gloved finger into the rectum to feel for abnormal areas.

¶ Frequency of colorectal screening depends on an individual's personal cancer risk.

<u>Oral Cavity</u> BF

¶ During a physical examination, your dentist or doctor may inspect the mouth, the floor of the mouth, the front and sides of the tongue, and the soft palate.

<u>Ovarian</u> BF

¶ Pelvic examination: the doctor feels the vagina, recturm, and lower abdomen for masses or growths.

¶ Transvaginal ultrasonography: high-frequency sound waves are sent out by a probe. The sound waves bounce off the ovaries and produce echoes used to create a ~~pieutc~~ called a sonogram.   *picture*

¶ CA125: a blood test used to detect levels of CA 125, which is sometimes present in the blood of women with ovarian cancer.

¶ Culdocentesis: a needle is inserted through the vaginal wall. Fluid is removed and tested for abnormal cells.

Continued on next page

At the end of each session, you have three options:

- Print any documents you have created.
- Continue with the next session.
- Exit Paradigm Keyboarding with Snap.

Print

To print Exercises 2.1–2.6 proceed as follows:

1   Click the Close ⊠ button in the top right corner of the screen.
2   At your Paradigm Keyboarding with Snap Welcome page, point to Reports on the Snap menu bar, and click View Submissions Report.
3   At the View Submissions Report Wizard, click Show session files.
4   Click Show Report.
5   Click 002ses.rtf.
6   At the Word Processor dialog box, click Launch.
7   Click File, and then click Print.
8   At the Print dialog box, click OK.
9   Click the Close button to close the Paradigm Word Processor.
10 Click Home on the Snap menu bar to return to the Welcome page.

Continue

To continue on the next session, click the Next Exercise ➡ button **twice**. This will take you to Exercise 3.2. (You will bypass Exercise 3.1 Warmup since you are already warmed up.)

Exit

To exit, do the following:

1   Click the Close ⊠ button in the top right corner of the screen.
2   At your Paradigm Keyboarding with Snap Welcome page, click Logout.

Ergonomic Tip

Press keys lightly and do not use pressure when keying.

59.6

Document A

Edited Unbound Manuscript

1 At the *Session 59 Document A* screen, key document A as a multiple-page unbound manuscript.
   a Use double-line spacing.
   b Place page numbers in the upper-right corner.
   c Key the body of the document as a single paragraph.
2 Proofread and correct any errors.
3 Click Check to automatically name (**059proa**), save, and check the document.
4 To print with errors highlighted, click the Print button.
5 Correct errors, then recheck the document.
6 Click Next Exercise.

Document A

WHAT IS CANCER? Cancer is really a group of diseases characterized by uncontrolled growth and spread of abnormal cells. There are more that 100 different types of cancer. The type of cancer is determined by the organ in which the cancer starts, the kind of cell from which it is derived, as well as the appearce of the cancer cells. Healthy cells that make up the body's tissues grow, divide, and replace themselves in a systematic way. This process keeps the body in good repair. Sometimes, however, normal cells lose their ability to limit and direct their growth. They divide too rapidly and grow out of control. Too much tissue is jproduced, and a tumor begins to form. They body normally has a built-in mechanism that causes abnormal cells to die and not reproduce (apoptosis). For reasons not yet well understood, apoptosis does not take place in cancer. As a result, a tumor is formed. The initial tumor is called the "primary" tumor. Cells from the primary tkurmor can break off and form "secondary" tumors in other parts of the body. When cancer spreads, the type of cancer remains the same as the primary tumor. For example, breast cancer that has spread to the bone is not "bone cancer." It is called *metastatic* breast cancer. Doctors use the term *metastatic* to refer to tumors that have spread to distant organs. Tumors can be either *benign* or *malignant*. Benign tkumors are not cancerous. They do not spread to other parts of the body and they are seldom a threat to life. Often, benign tumors can be removed by surgery and are not likely to return. Malignant tumors are cancerous. They can invade and destroy nearby tissue and organs. Malignant tumors are caable of metastasis. By entering the bloodstream or the lymph syste, cancerous cells are able to travel to other parts of the body and form new turmors. Because cancer can spread, it is important to find out as early as possible if a tumor is present and if it is cancerous.

59.7

Document B

Edited Bound Manuscript

1 At the *Session 59 Document B* screen, key Document B as a bound manuscript with the following specifications:
   a Change the left margin to 1.5 inches.
   b Use double line spacing.
   c After keying the text, number the pages in the upper-right corner.
2 Proofread and correct any errors in the document.
3 Click Check to automatically name (**059prob**), save, and check the document.
4 Print the document.

3

PERIOD, T, COMMA, CAPS LOCK

Session Goals

   Period, T, Comma, Caps Lock

Descriptive Words

3.1- 3.6   ON-SCREEN EXERCISES: GETTING STARTED

If you exited Snap Paradigm Keyboarding at the end of Session 2, proceed as follows:

1   At the Windows desktop, double-click the *Internet Explorer* icon.
2   At the Internet Explorer screen, click on the entry in the Address text box.
3   Key **www.keyboarding.emcp.com** and click *GO*.
4   At the Paradigm Keyboarding with Snap page, enter your login name in the Login Name text box (lower right corner of the screen). Enter your password in the Password text box.
5   Click the arrow in the red box.
6   Your Paradigm Keyboarding with Snap Welcome page appears. Go to Exercise 3.1 and click <u>Warmup</u>.
7   The Launch Keyboarding dialog box appears; click the Launch button. Follow the instructions on the screens to complete Exercises 3.1 through 3.6.
8   When you complete Exercise 3.6, Locational Reinforcement, there will be a message on the screen to return to page 11 in the text to complete Exercise 3.7, which is a review of what has been presented in the software.

3.7   TEXTBOOK EXERCISES: REINFORCEMENT

In this activity, you will review the key reaches and activities presented in Exercises 3.2–3.6.

Reviewing the Period, T, Comma, and Caps Lock Keys

Caps Lock   *T*   *Comma*   *Period*

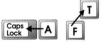

The bark disease, or chestnut blight, was first discovered on an eastern site in the early nineteen hundreds. Within but a few years, the parasites had spread throughout the entire eastern coastal states and damaged trees. The Dutch elm disease was brought into our nation in the nineteen thirties. Within a period of 45 years, great numbers of mature elm trees have been destroyed throughout the entire nation. Although the two blights are quite similar, there is a major difference. The chestnut disease can be spread by airborne spores; a bird, insect, or animal can also carry the parasite. The elm disease is spread by spores also but is only carried by a species of beetle.

A major hope for both types of trees remains in chemical prevention and biological strains. On test plots, the use of chemicals has been quite successful; however, when tested in the major forest areas of our land, chemicals have not been so successful. At this time, control of the diseases seems to offer the best answer to the problem.

For the long term, homeowners should think about preventing mass tree loss by planting a variety of tree types. Certain diseases affect only some species. Thus, if you grow a wide range of trees, your landscape will not have huge holes if an illness invades one species. Pick trees that are hardy in the city as well as on the land.

TEXTBOOK EXERCISES: PROGRESS CHECK

Now that you have completed the manuscripts unit, it is time to determine how quickly you can key new examples of these documents.

Key the following documents as quickly as possible, correcting all errors. You want the document to be "mailable." In other words, when you finish the document, it will be completely correct.

Your goal is to key each document in mailable form at 25 WAM or higher. The timing starts as you begin keying the first line of the manuscript or activating a word processing feature and ends when you click the Check icon.

It is your responsibility to review each document before it is keyed. Before keying the edited documents, do the following:

1   Read the document to be sure you understand the proofreader's marks and that all errors have been found.
2   Check for proper formatting.
3   Note the word processing features to be used so that they can be reviewed if necessary.

If you key any documents at a rate below 25 WAM and/or are missing errors that should have been corrected, your instructor may ask you to repeat those specific documents using the PWP Timing Feature.

Drill Instructions

- Key each line once.
- If you are not comfortable with a reach, repeat the appropriate group of two lines.

Period Drill

Important: Tap the space bar once after the period at the end of a sentence. Only one space is required when you use a proportionally spaced font such as the PKB default, Times New Roman. (Proportionally spaced means each character is designed relative to the other letters. The i, for example, is narrower than the t or the m. On the other hand, characters in monospaced fonts such as Courier each take up the same amount of space.)

For this text, unless instructed otherwise, enter one space after a period or other sentence-ending punctuation.

Note: If a period ends a line, press **Enter** immediately. There is no need to tap the space bar.

1 All lads shall dash. A lad shall fall.
2 Ask a sad lad. Sad lads fall. Ask Al.

T Drill

1 ft at hat hats sat sat tall tall data data
2 fast fast slat slat halt halt last last fat fat

Comma Drill

Remember: Do not space before a comma, but always space once after a comma (except when keying numbers).

1 That tall, fat, fast lad shall ask dad.
2 A flat, half lath falls; all lads halt.

Caps Lock Drill

Note: The little finger on the left hand reaches to press *Caps Lock*.

1 STALK A FAST LAD; A SAD LAD HAS A FALL.
2 DAD HALTS A TALL LAD. A SAD LAD HALTS.

Note: Tap the Caps Lock key to return to lower case.

59.4 THREE-MINUTE TIMING

Goal: 40 WAM/1 error

SI: 1.51

Take one 3-minute timing.

1   When using binoculars, try to rest the elbows on a firm surface to steady the glasses. A telescope is fairly simple to learn to use. Many telescopes are equipped with a finder. The finder will assist you in focusing on the portions of the sky that you wish to study. Adjusting a finder is a quite simple maneuver. With little practice, you can become an expert at using all types of optical equipment. An image will sometimes seem to shimmer. Any shimmering effect could be due to the fact that you jarred the telescope tube or binoculars; the effect may also be due to a turbulence or an atmospheric disturbance. You will soon discover that the best nights for viewing and observing the stars are those nights when the temperatures have remained fairly steady for several nights.

    Within our own galaxy, you can observe many beautiful sights. A lovely domain that you can admire is the satiny stars. It is easy to see all sorts of patterns in the heavens if you simply relax and turn your imagination loose. You can obtain diagrams with which to study, observe, and chart the various star patterns. If you have the equipment to look beyond our own galaxy, you will be able to observe stars and galaxies far out into space. An observatory is a marvelous place to observe the heavens. The starry displays and changing seasons are not to be missed by an astronomer. You can develop a very fine hobby through stargazing if you care to take the time.

59.5 FIVE-MINUTE TIMING

Goal: 35 WAM/1 error

SI: 1.52

Take one 5-minute timing on the paragraphs that follow. If you finish the four paragraphs before time is up, start over.

1   Many of the beautiful and stately elm trees that have covered our huge nation for several decades are in trouble. Spreading chestnut trees, common a few years ago, no longer populate the forests of our nation. Both magnificent species have been the victims of fungal parasites that have invaded our lands. At first, halting the diseases seemed to be quite impossible, but now the prospects are excellent that the ravaging and destructive blight can be arrested. The future of both species seems to look very much brighter.

Continued on next page

Building Speed

Your mind controls your fingers, so think **speed.** After you practice setting your "mind" goal several times, you should find that your mind eventually controls your fingers automatically.

Key lines 1–3 once. Key lines 1–3 again as fast as you can.

Students in Online Classes

Key each group of three lines twice; push for speed while keeping your eyes on the copy. Do not correct errors.

1 Stalk a fast lad; a sad lad has a hat.
2 A lad talks; the dad talks; a dad talks.
3 Dad halts the sad lad. A sad lad halts.

Additional Drill

Key the following drill. Key each line once. If you find yourself hesitating, repeat the line. Press *Enter* after each line.

1 The lads dash. A dad asks the lads.
2 Feds dash. Dads dash. Dads ask the sad lads.
3 Ask Al. Sad lads halt. Ask a sad lad.

4 data data data slat slat slat jet jet jet
5 that that that task task talk talk talk
6 salt salt salt flat flat flat lath lath lath

7 A flat atlas; a flat hat; a flat flask.
8 A half a flask; a half lath; half a slat.
9 A sad lad halts. Dad halts a fat lad.

10 A sad lad has a hat. Stalk a fast lad.
11 A half lath; half a flask; half a slat.
12 The fat lads talked fast. A dad talks fast.

13 Dash, Al, Flat, half, lath, head, heat,
14 A fat, sad, flat, hall shaft has the lead.
15 Dale asked Al. Dad asked the lads.

ENDING THE SESSION

At the end of each session, you have three options:
- Print any documents you have created.
- Continue with the next session.
- Exit Paradigm Keyboarding with Snap.

Session 59

PRODUCTION PROGRESS CHECK— MEDICAL MANUSCRIPTS

Session Goals

1-Minute: 45 WAM/1 error
3-Minute: 40 WAM/1 error
5-Minute: 35 WAM/1 error

Reinforce improving readability

Use selected features presented in Sessions 34–58

59.1-59.2   ON-SCREEN EXERCISES: GETTING STARTED

If you exited the program at the end of the previous session, refer to page 11 in Session 3 to review how to open the next session. If you are continuing immediately from Session 58, start with Exercise 59.2. Click the Next Exercise or Previous Exercise button if you are not at the correct exercise.

59.3   ONE-MINUTE TIMING

Goal: 45 WAM/1 error

SI: 1.52

- Take a 1-minute timing on the following material.
- Use your most recent timing to set a speed or accuracy goal.

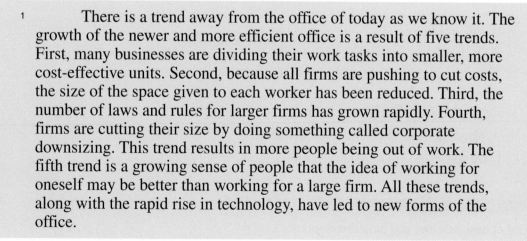

1   There is a trend away from the office of today as we know it. The growth of the newer and more efficient office is a result of five trends. First, many businesses are dividing their work tasks into smaller, more cost-effective units. Second, because all firms are pushing to cut costs, the size of the space given to each worker has been reduced. Third, the number of laws and rules for larger firms has grown rapidly. Fourth, firms are cutting their size by doing something called corporate downsizing. This trend results in more people being out of work. The fifth trend is a growing sense of people that the idea of working for oneself may be better than working for a large firm. All these trends, along with the rapid rise in technology, have led to new forms of the office.

Print

To print Exercises 3.1–3.7 proceed as follows:

1. Click the Close ☒ button in the top right corner of the screen.
2. At your Paradigm Keyboarding with Snap Welcome page, point to Reports on the Snap menu bar, and click View Submissions Report.
3. At the View Submissions Report Wizard, click Show session files.
4. Click Show Report.
5. Click 003ses.rtf.
6. At the Word Processor dialog box, click Launch.
7. Click File, and then click Print.
8. At the Print dialog box, click OK.
9. Click the Close button to close the Paradigm Word Processor.
10. Click Home on the Snap menu bar to return to the Welcome page.

Continue

To continue on the next session, click the Next Exercise ➡ button twice. This will take you to Exercise 4.2. (You will bypass Exercise 4.1 Warmup since you are already warmed up.)

Exit

To exit, do the following:

1. Click the Close ☒ button in the top right corner of the screen.
2. At your Paradigm Keyboarding with Snap Welcome page, click Logout.

Ergonomic Tip

Keep the keyboard positioned with the front edge lower than the back so that the forearms are slightly raised and wrists straight.

Quoting directly or indirectly from sources referenced in your manuscript lends credence to the thesis (main point) of your manuscript or research paper. These references to your sources also indicate the extent of your research.

Quotations, especially direct quotations, can be over-used. Including more than five or six per page may give the impression that you have merely gathered information and have not analyzed it or presented any new ideas. Instead, use direct quotations occasionally for effect or when the direct quote is a powerfully written statement that would lose its impact if summarized.

Paraphrased or summarized statements (quotations or statements of others expressed in your own words) help maintain a consistency of tone and writing style and also give the impression that you have understood the material and can combine the various pieces of information to produce perhaps new or different ideas.

58.8 **Document** Summarizing
D

To practice your summarizing (paraphrasing) skills, open document 056proa and read the information carefully. Then key a one-page summary of the main ideas. Title the document **Summary of the "Our Bodies are Made to Move" Article** (center and bold the title). Then save the summary as **058wprd**. Print and close the document.

ENDING THE SESSION

To end this session, print any files from Session 58 not printed earlier, then continue with the next session or exit the program. If necessary, review the procedures found on page 300 of Session 54.

Ergonomic Tip
While sitting, straighten and stiffen each leg to the front and push the heel away so the back of the leg is stretched. This will help relax leg muscles and joints.

N, LEFT SHIFT, COLON
Review of Correcting Errors

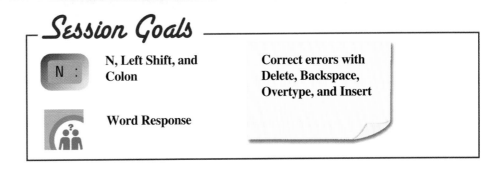

Session Goals

| N : | N, Left Shift, and Colon | Correct errors with Delete, Backspace, Overtype, and Insert |
| | Word Response | |

4.1- 4.8

ON-SCREEN EXERCISES: GETTING STARTED

If you are continuing immediately from Session 3, you are already warmed up and are looking at Exercise 4.2. Click the Next Exercise ➡ or Previous Exercise ⬅ button if you are not at the correct exercise.

If you exited the program at the end of the previous session, refer to page 11 of Session 3 for instructions on entering the program.

4.9

TEXTBOOK EXERCISES: REINFORCEMENT

Some of the drills you completed in Exercises 4.2–4.8 are repeated here, along with some new ones, to reinforce your keyboarding skills. You will also review error correction methods. When you have finished the Exercises in Session 4, click Print (if desired), click Next Exercise twice to continue with Exercise 5.2, or click the Close button ✕ to exit the program.

Building Keyboarding Speed

To increase your keyboarding skills, you must key without watching your fingers. Concentrate on keeping your eyes on the copy whether from the screen or text. When asked to key at a controlled rate or for accuracy, concentrate on making the correct reaches. When pushing for speed, concentrate on making your fingers move faster.

Reviewing the N, Left Shift, and Colon Keys

Left Shift   *N*

MEMORY: LOSING IT, KEEPING IT, IMPROVING IT

(Center in the top third of the page)

Submitted to

(ds)

Insert your Instructor's name and title
School Name
City, State

(Center in the middle third of the page)

Keyed by

(ds)

Insert your name
Name of the class
School Name
City, State

(ds)

Current date

(Center in the bottom third of the page)

N Drill

Key lines 1–2 once; push for speed.

Think speed as you key each line once— keep your eyes on the copy. Do not correct errors.

1 an an and and land land sand sand tanks
2 slant slant thank thank and and ant ant

Key lines 3–5 once for control. If you make more than two errors on a line, repeat it.

3 Jan shall hand a sad lad an atlas fast.
4 Hal shall thank that tall and lank lad.
5 Hats and sandals shall stand as a fad.

Left Shift and Colon Drill

• Shift of semi (;) key produces a colon (:)
• When keying documents, press the space bar once after keying a colon.

1 jJ kK lL ;: Jj Kk Ll ;: JL; jK lL ::;:; KL: hH:
2 Had; Lad; Has; Lass; Half: Lads: Hall: Jade:
3 Lass Lad Lads Head: Halt: Lead: Lads: Jet:

Additional Drill

Key the following drill. Press **Enter** after each line. If you find yourself hesitating when keying a line, repeat it.

1 land land than than flank flank tan tan slant slant
2 thank thank nasal nasal and Fan Fan Stand Stand
3 A tan shaft lands and halts that task.

4 As a fad, hats and sandals shall stand the sand.
5 Sal and Dana shall stand and talk last.
6 flash: flash: half: half: nail: nail: hand: hand:

7 Jean shall sell the saddle, jeans, and seashells.
8 Handle the kettle that leaks; taste the lean tea.
9 She landed at a nest. The fat hen left the lake.
10 He felt tense. The ten lads and dad halted a theft.

58.6

Document
B

1 At the *Session 58 Document B* screen, open document 058proa.
2 Using PWP's Cut and Paste feature, move the section entitled "A Good Night's Rest Can Help Your Memory" (including the paragraph and bulleted items) so that it follows the section on "Tips for Keeping your Mind Active" with its paragraph and bulleted items.
3 In the section "Tips to Improve Your Memory," replace the bulleted items with numbered paragraphs.
4 After making the changes, check the document to see that the format is intact.
5 Name (**058wprb**), save, and print the document.
6 Click Next Exercise.

TITLE PAGES FOR MANUSCRIPTS

The title page for a manuscript consists of three sections as follows:

The title is presented in all capitals and centered vertically and horizontally in the top third of the page. One of the critical elements of the title is that it clearly identifies what the content is about.

The name of each individual who is to receive the manuscript, his or her title, and affiliation are centered vertically and horizontally in the center third of the page.

The names of each individual who prepared the manuscript, his or her title, and affiliation, and the date of the manuscript (a double space below) are centered vertically and horizontally in the bottom third of the page.

There are 66 vertical lines on a page. There is a top and bottom default margin of one inch at the top and bottom of the page (6 lines to the inch). Thus, when the page is divided into three sections, each section has 22 vertical lines. The first line of the top section is line 7 (the default top margin took up 6 lines). The centering feature of the software adjusts the center point between the left and right margin that also has a 1-inch default.

58.7

Document
C

Title Page

1 At the *Session 58 Document C* screen, key Document C as the title page for the manuscript 058proa, "Memory: Losing It, Keeping It, Improving It." See page 178 in Session 39, to review vertical centering.
2 Proofread and correct any errors in the document.
3 Click Check to automatically name (**058proc**), save, and check the document.
4 Print the document.
4 To correct errors, click View Original. Make any necessary changes, then recheck the document.
5 Click Next Exercise.

Correcting Errors: Review

There are four ways to correct any keyboarding errors you make:

Backspace   When you backspace over a character on the screen, the character is deleted.

Delete   Press the **Delete** key to erase the character immediately right of the insertion point position.

Overtype   This function allows you to replace, or *type over,* existing text. To use Overtype, press the **Insert** key. The Overtype mode stays in effect until you press **Insert** again.

Insert   When you want to insert letters that were left out of a word, move the insertion point to the location where the first character will be added. Key the characters to be added.

To practice the correction methods, go to line 3 in the previous N drill (page 16) and change *Jan* to *Dan.* In line 4 insert *At last* at the beginning of the sentence and delete *and lank lad,* replacing it with *lass.*

ENDING THE SESSION

At this point, you may print this session's files, continue to the next session, or exit the program. See page 13 of Session 3 if you need to review procedures.

Ergonomic Tip
Use only finger, not wrist, movements to strike keys.

Tips to Improve Your Memory

There are a number of things you can do to improve your memory. The following are examples of what you can do (Haddock 12):

- Use an organizer (such as a daytimer or digital palm pilot).
- Talk aloud to yourself (for example, "I am getting up to go get my address book"). You might carry a small tape recorder to record things you want to remember.
- Post notes in your house, car, and office reminding you to do things.
- Keeping things in the same place so you can find them easily (keys on a key rack).
- Lessen distractions by doing one thing at a time. For example, don't try to listen to the television while talking to someone.
- Take care of yourself. Poor sleep, stress, and a poor diet can affect your memory.
- Use bulletin boards and wall charts.
- Use a telephone answering machine.
- Use a beeping key chain—find a key by clapping hands or whistling.
- Bundle tasks from your to-do list. (While at the sink, clean your glasses after you brush your teeth.)
- Use memory tricks such as rhymes, acronyms (for example, remember your phone when you leave home).
- Understand how you learn best.
  - Do you remember best by <u>hearing</u>? Try talking out loud or using a tape recorder.
  - By <u>doing</u>? Try writing things down or acting them out.
  - By <u>seeing</u>? Try using signs and an organizer.

By using all three learning techniques, you stand a better chance of improving your memory.

Summary

Losing one's memory affects not only the individual but the caregivers who must work with the individual. As noted throughout this manuscript, there are many things we can do to keep and improve our memories. Reducing cardiovascular risk factors, keeping your mind active, getting a good night's sleep, and applying the techniques presented for improving your memory represent ways to keep our brains healthy and strong.

Session 5

I, G
Using Tab Defaults and Word Wrap

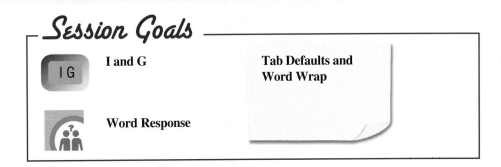

Session Goals

I G	I and G		Tab Defaults and Word Wrap
	Word Response		

5.1-
5.8

ON-SCREEN EXERCISES: GETTING STARTED

If you are continuing immediately from Session 4, you are already warmed up and are looking at Exercise 5.2. Click the Next Exercise 🔜 or Previous Exercise 🔙 button if you are not at the correct exercise.

If you exited the program at the end of the previous session, refer to page 11 of Session 3 for instructions on entering the program.

5.9

TEXTBOOK EXERCISES: REINFORCEMENT

Now you will review the key reaches and activities completed in Exercises 5.2–5.8 The new material includes practice with using word wrap and tab defaults. When you have finished this exercise, click Print (if desired), click Next Exercise twice to continue with Exercise 6.2, or click the Close button ✖ to exit the program.

Reviewing the I and G Keys

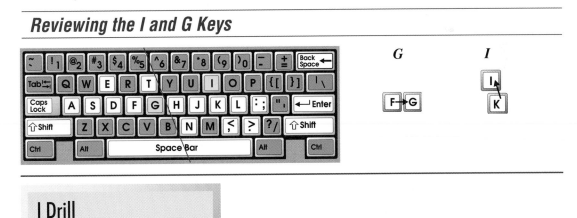

I Drill

Key lines 1–2 once; push for speed.

1 if if in in it it kid kid his fail fine file find
2 The kid thinks I had the idea that he did finish.

Preventing Memory Loss Is Easier Than Correcting It

The most common diseases that cause dementia (severe memory loss) are Alzheimer's and vascular dementia. Vascular dementia can be prevented. And even if a person does get Alzheimer's disease, taking steps to protect the brain's blood by decreasing cardiovascular risk may lessen the impact of the disease (Harvard's Men's Health Watch 4).

Here are examples of important things you can do to lessen your cardiovascular risk factors:
- Do not smoke.
- Maintain normal blood pressure.
- Maintain healthy cholesterol levels (less than 200).
- Maintain normal or near-normal blood sugar.
- Follow a healthy diet.
- Exercise regularly.
- Avoid obesity.
- Reduce stress.
- If you drink alcohol, limit it to one drink a day for women, and two for men.

A Good Night's Rest Can Help Your Memory

Research tell us that getting 6 to 8 hours of sleep a night is ideal (Gilbert c 87). That is perhaps easier said than done. Insomnia becomes more common as we get older. But the following tips may help:
- Try to go to sleep at the same time time each night and wake up at the same time each morning.
- Do not exercise right before your bedtime. Try to exercise earlier in the day or at least several hours before bedtime.
- Do not drink coffee or other drinks with caffeine after mid-morning.
- If you are not tired, don't try to sleep. If you have been lying in bed tossing and turning for 20 minutes or more try getting up and reading.

Tips for Keeping Your Mind Active

Keeping our minds active contributes to maintaining a healthy brain. The following are examples of how to keep your mind active (Arizona Medical Newsletter 6):

Continue to Learn:
- Take up a new hobby.
- Sign up for a course.
- Do anything NEW that is interesting and stimulating.

Exercise Your Brain:
- Play board games, chess, computer games, or Scrabble.
- Try crossword or jigsaw puzzles.

Try Activities That Require Both Mental and Physical Skills:
- Folk or square dancing.
- Painting, ceramics, sculpture.

Continued on next page

Key lines 3–5 once at a controlled rate. If you make more than two errors on a line, repeat it.

3 Ill Inside Indeed If Illness Island Indeed Inside
4 She is a skilled athlete and likes little detail.
5 He did ski that hill. That is indeed a sad test.

G Drill

Key lines 1–2 once; push for speed.

1 gal gal gas gas get get sag sag egg egg gal gal
2 Dennis and Gene nailed a lath in the fallen gate.

Key lines 3–5 once; concentrate on control—try not to make errors.

3 Giant Giggle Glide Gentle Gene Gain Gift Glad Get
4 The endless agenda had eight legal details added
5 Al tested his stiff leg. He gnashed his big teeth.

Additional Drill

Key the following drill. Press *Enter* after each line.

1 His skin is thin; he is ill; he feels faint; see, he is ill.
2 He thinks it is a fad. I dislike that snide kid.
3 The kitten is a little lifeless and is an infant.

4 She shall indeed need that inside aid as enlisted.
5 His knife slid inside as the ill thief listened.
6 As the sled glides, the infant giggles in delight.

7 She disliked it. The kitten tangled that tinsel.
8 Tina, the gentle giant, giggled at Gina, the elf.
9 As she dashed ahead in glee, Leslie sang a jingle.
10 If he skis at night, Dad needs a light flashlight.

> **Think control** as you key each line. If you make more than two errors on a line, repeat it. Keep your eyes on the copy in the text as you key.

Introducing the Tab Key and Word Wrap

Tab Key

The first line of a paragraph is usually indented approximately one-half inch. In PKB, there is a preset tab every 0.5 inches.

58.5

Document A

Edited Bound Manuscript with Text Notes

1 At the *Session 58 Document A* screen, key Document A by completing the following steps:

  a Read the document before keying to make sure all errors have been corrected in the editing process.

  b Follow the formatting guidelines presented in Session 55.

  c Change to double spacing.

  d Enter the title in all caps and bolded on Line 7.

  e Change the left and right margins to 1.25.

  f Number the pages in the upper right corner except for page 1.

  g Enter hard page breaks where appropriate.

Students in Online Classes

Be sure to check Session 55 for proper formatting of the four levels of headings.

2 After keying Document A, proofread and correct any errors.

3 Click the Check icon to automatically name (**058proa**), save, and check the document.

4 Print the document.

5 To correct errors, click View Original. Make any necessary changes, then recheck the document.

6 Click Next Exercise.

Document A

MEMORY: LOSING IT, KEEPING IT, IMPROVING IT

Introduction

Many of us joke about "senior moments" as we forget where we left our keys or our glasses, or we can't remember the name of someone we know. People who are sharp enough to worry about when they left their keys probably have little reason to be concered. However, when these "senior moments" start happening a lot, we tend to worry about what they might mean.

Some Memory Loss Is Normal

In a special report from Harvard Medical School (Gilbert a 54), researchers tell us that some memory loss is normal with aging. It is often not a result of illness or disease, but due to normal age-related changes in the brain. The good news is that we do not necessarily lose a lot of our brain functioning as we age. In fact, new research shows that we can "grow new brain cells and make new connections between brain cells well into well into old age" (Gilbert b 67). We now have strong evidence that the brain acts something like a muscle. The more we use our brains, the stronger they become, and the loger they remain strong.

Pay Attention When Learning

If you are slower at learning new things and having trouble remembering due to normal aging, it will help to pay more attention when you are learning something new. Also concentrate on the new information by repeating it several times in your mind. If possible, repeat what you have learned with the person who presented the instruction. Or, if appropriate, apply what has been presented.

Continued on next page

To see how the preset tabs work, press the **Tab** key once, key the first word in the first column, press the **Tab** key twice, and key the first word in the second column. Press **Enter** to move to the next line of the first column. Repeat the process for the remaining lines.

→	lane	→	→	Feat
→	tie	→	→	Tease
→	aid	→	→	That
→	nail	→	→	Giant
→	leaf	→	→	Fate

Word Wrap

When you key paragraphs of text (for example, in a letter), you do not need to press **Enter** at the end of each line. Word wrap is a feature that automatically wraps a word to the next line once that word exceeds the right margin. With word wrap, you need to press **Enter** only to end a paragraph, create a blank line, or end a short line (for example, a person's name in an envelope address).

Key the two paragraphs that follow. Use the **Tab** key to indent the first line of each paragraph and let word wrap move the insertion point to the next line. Press **Enter** twice at the end of each paragraph to leave a blank line between paragraphs.

→ An idle lad finishes last. He is shiftless as he sits and tells his tales. He needs an insight in the elegant things in life. An idle lad finishes last. He is shiftless as he sits and tells his tales.

→ Allan is attaining a skill in legal defense. The giant task is thankless. He insists that all the details heighten his thinking. Allan is attaining a skill in legal defense.

ENDING THE SESSION

Now you may print this session's files, continue to the next session, or exit the program. See page 13 of Session 3 if you need to review procedures.

Ergonomic Tip
Don't choke the mouse; hold it lightly and click without using force.

1   If you work with a computer, you should have the habit of backing up your computer system. Few computer users, however, understand and use system backup. When a backup for a computer system is done, the files and data from the computer's hard drive are transferred to a storage unit that is separate from the main computer. The data stored on the secondary system is called the system backup. If your machine should "crash" or lose data from the hard drive, the backup system can restore the data to the computer's hard drive in no time.

Most people don't know how important a good system backup is to the user. Just think of losing a week's (or even a day's) data due to operator error, a fire, an earthquake, or a flood that causes water damage. You can see why you should back up your files.

Loss of data is costly in terms of money and time. Studies have shown that a large data loss may cost a business the use of the data for 18 to 20 days. The dollar cost to restore sales data and marketing facts can climb into the thousands of dollars. It is true that the data can be recovered, but there may be a loss of customers due to loss of sales.

The most common backup method for small businesses and home users is to copy the data to floppy disks. To make the backup task easy, most computer stores have many backup software programs from which to choose. Not only is the backup task quicker and easier, but some of these programs use data compression (shrinking the space needed to save data). The one problem with this backup method is that it takes a lot of disks and the user must be on hand to change disks when needed.

The latest backup tool, which is not lower in cost at this time, is the optical disk. These disks hold a quite large amount of information that can be read by laser technology. The problem with some optical disks is that they can be used (written to) one time only.

Users should keep one rule in mind when using a backup. Follow a routine for backup and do it daily or weekly. Some users back up their data each hour.

TEXTBOOK EXERCISES: BOUND MANUSCRIPT WITH TEXT NOTES AND TITLE PAGE

In Session 58 you will have an opportunity to prepare a bound manuscript that has been edited. Many of the word processing features that have been introduced in earlier sessions will be used. Following the completion of Document A, several changes will be made to include rearranging the text using PWP's Cut and Paste feature and changing bulleted items to numbered items.

In Document C, you will be introduced to the steps for preparing a title page for manuscripts and then prepare a title page for Document A. The final activity in Session 58, Document D, is to apply the technique of summarizing the content of a manuscript.

Session Goals

Review Review keys from Sessions 1–5

25 WAM/2 errors

6.1 ON-SCREEN EXERCISES: GETTING STARTED

If you are continuing immediately from Session 5, you are already warmed up and are looking at Exercise 6.2. Click the Next Exercise or Previous Exercise button if you are not at the correct exercise. The copy for Exercises 6.2–6.4 is in your text. Exercise 6.2 consists of two 1-minute timings.

If you exited the program at the end of the previous session, refer to page 11 of Session 3 for instructions on entering the program.

6.2 CHECKING YOUR SKILL: ONE-MINUTE TIMINGS

The next activity in Session 6 is a timing to assess your keyboarding speed. You will see a message on the screen directing you to take two 1-minute timings on the paragraph that follows. If you finish the paragraph before time is up, strike **Enter** and start over. The program's "clock" begins when you strike the first key. When the time is up, the keyboard will "freeze," and the program calculates your words a minute (WAM) plus errors. Your goal is to key at least 25 words a minute (25 WAM) with no more than 2 errors. Be sure to use word wrap and indent the paragraph.

1   That gallant knight led the detail. A tall, thin lad assisted at the flank. The knight failed the task and feels the defeat. A sadness sifts in as his shield falls.

6.3 TEXTBOOK EXERCISES: REINFORCEMENT

The Special Drills that follow provide additional practice on the keys that you have learned in Sessions 1–5. However, if you are already keying over 25 WAM with no more than 2 errors and do not hesitate when keying, Click the Next Exercise button three times. This will take you to Session 7, Exercise 2.

If you are not at the 25 WAM level, and/or are making more than 2 errors, proceed with the Special Drills to build speed and/or accuracy. Here are guidelines for choosing drills:

1 If you have not mastered a key reach (you hesitate before striking the key), key the speed-building lines.
2 If you are not keying at least 25 WAM, key the speed-building lines.
3 If you are making more than 2 errors per minute, key the accuracy-building lines. If you make more than two errors on a line, key it again.

Session 58
BOUND MEDICAL MANUSCRIPTS WITH TEXT NOTES AND TITLE PAGE

Session Goals

1-Minute: 45 WAM/1 error
5-Minute: 35 WAM/1 error

Summarizing information

Title page

**58.1-
58.2**

ON-SCREEN EXERCISES: GETTING STARTED

If you exited the program at the end of the previous session, refer to page 11 in Session 3 to review how to open the next session. If you are continuing immediately from Session 57, start with Exercise 58.2. Click the Next Exercise or Previous Exercise button if you are not at the correct exercise.

58.3 ## ONE-MINUTE TIMINGS

Goal: 45 WAM/1 error

SI: 1.50

- Take two 1-minute timings.
- Use your most recent timing speed to set a speed or accuracy goal.

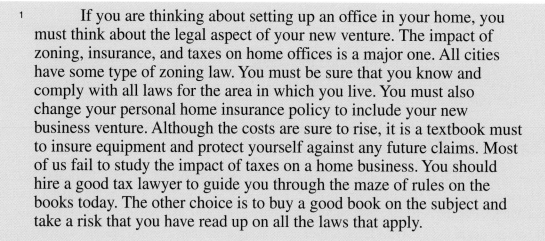

1   If you are thinking about setting up an office in your home, you must think about the legal aspect of your new venture. The impact of zoning, insurance, and taxes on home offices is a major one. All cities have some type of zoning law. You must be sure that you know and comply with all laws for the area in which you live. You must also change your personal home insurance policy to include your new business venture. Although the costs are sure to rise, it is a textbook must to insure equipment and protect yourself against any future claims. Most of us fail to study the impact of taxes on a home business. You should hire a good tax lawyer to guide you through the maze of rules on the books today. The other choice is to buy a good book on the subject and take a risk that you have read up on all the laws that apply.

58.4 ## FIVE-MINUTE TIMINGS

Goal: 35 WAM/1 error

SI: 1.51

Take two 5-minute timings. If you finish the six paragraphs before time is up, start over.

Once you have completed the drills, click Print (if desired), then click the Next Exercise button. The program will then direct you to take two more 1-minute timings.

Special Drills

- Key each line once.
- If you need more practice, key the group of lines again.

Balanced-Hand Words (Speed)

1 and the ant sit ale elf end hen she end sigh sign
2 aid fit sit did tie die dig fig and the hang then
3 halt than hand lens lake lane then than sign fish

4 idle lens lane sigh then dish disk sign half lake
5 shake snake title aisle angle fight handle island
6 angle sight digit gland eight slant height sleigh
7 signal giant tight an he if it and elf the and he

Letter Combinations (Speed)

1 de den dead deal desk denial dense deft dental
2 di dig dish dial digest dislike dine dike disk
3 I dislike the heat dial that fits the dental fan.

4 fi fish final fine finish fight find fig field finale
5 ga gal gas gag gale gait gallant gasket gadget
6 Gal, finished the gasket and the gas gadget gate.

7 ha hate halt half hash hang handle hand hat had
8 ki kite kindle kilt kiln king kink kit kind
9 That hanging kite tail has halted the hail.

10 le lest left lead lend ledge least leaf lean lease
11 li lid lie lied lien link linking linkage like
12 At least link the left lid and let the length stand.

13 sa sad sat safe sake sale said sang Sal saline
14 si sit site sitting signal sighted sill silken siding
15 Sad Sal sang a signal as she sighted a safe site.

Proofread and make corrections where needed. Save and name the table (**057wprd**), then print and close the document.

ENDING THE SESSION

Now you can print this session's files, continue to the next session, or exit the program. See page 300 of Session 54 if you need to review procedures.

Ergonomic Tip

Instead of a mouse, try a trackball or touch pad. Individuals working with laptop computers generally have this option.

16 st stead steal steadiness stateside stag state
17 ta tag talk take tale taste task tan tall tail
18 Steadfast Stell stands and talks and then sits.

19 Te tea test tenth tend tenant tease teak tent
20 th then that than thing this theft thin thesis
21 Then that tested tenant, Ted, did a tenth tea test.

Double-Letter Words (Accuracy)

1 see glee needs indeed feeling needless teens seed
2 egg sell sniff haggle falling eggshell stall eggs
3 eel keen sheen needle fiddles seedling sleek deed

4 add kiss stiff assist endless lifeless still hill
5 fee need sheet seeing dissent likeness steed heel
6 add fell skill allied skilled settling shell tell

7 see feel teeth indeed gallant sledding sleet knee
8 all hall shall little install knitting stall tall
9 Sadness is a feeling I assess as an alleged need.

10 Assist the skiing attendant and lessen all falls.
11 The sleek kitten shall flee the illegal attendants.
12 Haggling is a senseless dissent that is needless.
13 Flatten the stiff fiddle and install the tassels.

Longer Words (Accuracy)

1 endless athlete flatten inflated install disliked
2 lenient distant delighted heading inkling digital
3 A lenient athlete has inflated the flattened keg.

4 Hesitating likeness indefinite alkaline initiated
5 heightened stealing gaslight lengthened delegates
6 The hesitating delegate is stealing the gaslight.

7 Landslide skinflint stateside essential legislate
8 negligent lightness sightless delighted attendant
9 tasteless steadfast defendant thankless seashells
10 Seashells in the landslide delighted a skinflint.

BIBLIOGRAPHY

Armes, Jane, E. J. James, and Betty Jane Onis. *Applied Anatomy and Psychology.* Cincinnati, OH: Poston, Inc., 2006, pp. 286-288.

Dane, Deobrah. "The Rising Cost of Medical Records Storage," *American Medical Association Review.* April 2007, p. 52.

Holbreck, Judy L., and Vincent T. Marcus. *Problems in Medical Records Storage.* Dayton, OH: Western Publishing Company, 2008, p. 2.

Liescke, Connie. *The Language of Medicine.* Chicago, IL: A-Z Publishing Company, 2008, p. 194.

Schuster, Teri. *Pharmacy Calculations.* Dallas, TX: Med Tech Publishers, 2007, pp 134-136.

"Speed and Quality in Handling Patients," *Sun Health Systems,* Vol. 29, No. 3, January 2007, p. 4.

White, Ben, and Vera Riles. *Filing, Retrieving, and Safekeeping.* Denver, CO: Mountain Medical Storage Printing Company, 2008, pp. 1–3.

Wilson, James. *Using Your Medical Skills.* New York: Creative Enterprises, 2007, p. 4.

REINFORCING WRITING SKILLS

Line, bar, and pie graphs provide a visual image of relationships that exist between sets of data. The reader has a picture of what is taking place. Tables on the other hand provide details that are not always evident in graphs so that the reader sees the actual alphabetic/numeric values. A table can be used effectively where a series of items are compared. For example, assume that a group of individuals were being compared by age, sex, height, weight, neck size, and shoe size. This information can be effectively displayed for each individual.

A table can be used to reinforce information that appears in text where conclusions have been made. The table, which is proceeded by some type of introduction, can be followed with text that contains the conclusions drawn. The reader can refer to the table to verify the conclusion.

57.8 **Document D** Preparing a Table

Students in Online Classes

Use the PWP table feature to compare the physical features of six individuals you know. Provide an appropriate title for the table. The features to compare include age, sex, height, weight, and shoe size (guess if you don't know the actual numbers). Do not use names; use a 3-digit code for each person. Include column headings with your table and center the title within the table. Refer to Session 45 if you need to review the steps for creating tables.

Throughout the unit on Medical Reports you created tables for definitions of terms to include shading. To increase the readability of your table for Doc D, use the shading feature.

Now that you have completed the drills, take two 1-minute timings on the following paragraph. Compare the rates with your first attempts. Has your speed improved? Do you have fewer errors? If you are not reaching 25 WAM with 2 or fewer errors, repeat Sessions 1–5.

1   That gallant knight led the detail. A tall, thin lad assisted at the flank. The knight failed the task and feels the defeat. A sadness sifts in as his shield falls.

ENDING THE SESSION

At the end of each session, you have three options:

- Print any documents you have created.
- Continue with the next session.
- Exit Snap Paradigm Keyboarding.

Print

To print Exercises 6.1 and 6.3, follow the directions found on page 14.

To print the timed writings for this session (Exercises 6.2 and 6.4), take the following steps:

1   Click the Close ☒ button in the top right corner of the screen.
2   At your Paradigm Keyboarding with Snap Welcome page, point to Reports on the Snap menu bar, and click View Submissions Report.
3   At the View Submissions Report Wizard, click Show timings files to see the timings text (Exercises 6.2 and 6.4).
4   Click Show Report.
5   Click 006tim.
6   At the Word Processor dialog box, click Launch.
7   Click File, and then click Print.
8   At the Print dialog box, click OK.
9   Click the Close button to close the Paradigm Word Processor.
10   Click Home on the Snap menu bar to return to the Welcome page.

Continue

To continue on the next session, click the Next Exercise ⊡ button **twice**. This will take you to Exercise 7.2. (You will bypass Exercise 7.1 Warmup since you are already warmed up.)

Exit

To exit, do the following:

1   Click the Close ☒ button in the top right corner of the screen.
2   At your Paradigm Keyboarding with Snap Welcome page, click Logout.

Ergonomic Tip
Keep your mouse at the same height and distance as your keyboard.

1 Citation for an Electronic Database Service

Materials from online databases are cited in a manner similar to printed materials except that the usual information is followed by the name of the service provider and the identifying numbers within the service. Here is an example:

> Flax, Rosabel, et al. 2007. *Guidelines for Teaching Healthcare Subjects K -12*. Topeka: Kansas State Department of Education, Topeka Division of Education Services, June 2006, DIALOG, ERIC, ED 178312.

2 Citation of a Software Program

Citations for software programs are to include the following: version, level, release number or date; short name or acronym, if applicable, in parentheses; the location and name of the organization holding the rights to the software; and if applicable, the author of the material. Here is an example:

> *Net Effect, A Simulation for the Medical Office*, Version 1.1, 2008 (NEF), Paradigm Publishing, Inc., St. Paul, MN.

3 Citation of a Document from a Network or the Internet

In addition to the usual information (author's name; title of document; name of the text, periodical, newspaper; and who, where, and when published), the location of the information by category, when cited, the address of the reference, and the network name are included. Here is an example:

> Kulikowski, Stan, "Readability Formula" In *NL-KR* (Digest Vol. 5, No. 10) [electronic bulletin board]. Rochester, NY, 2007 [cited June 2003] Available from *al-kr@emcp.rochester.com*; INTERNET.

Creating Hanging Paragraphs

The first line of a bibliographic entry is keyed at the left margin while second and subsequent lines are wrapped to the first tab stop. This is referred to as a hanging paragraph.

Most commercial word processing packages have a *Hanging Indent* feature that automatically indents the second and succeeding lines of a bibliography entry. As you find yourself using other word processing packages, be aware that this feature may be available. For now, press the tab key once for the second and succeeding lines of each reference to provide the "hanging indent" format.

57.7

Document C

Bibliography

1 Create the bibliography shown in Document C by completing the following steps:
   a Press **Enter** enough times to move the insertion point to line 7.
   b Center and bold the title, **BIBLIOGRAPHY**.
   c Press **Enter** two times. Be sure to return the alignment back to left.
   d Key the bibliographic entries shown in Document C.
2 Click Check to automatically name (**057proc**), save, and check the document.
3 Print and then close **057proc**.

Session 7

P, R, QUESTION MARK

Session Goals

 P, R, and Question Mark

 -ed and -ing word endings

 25 WAM/2 errors

**7.1-
7.7** ## ON-SCREEN EXERCISES: GETTING STARTED

If you exited the program at the end of the previous session, refer to page 11 of Session 3 to review how to open the next session or to continue from where you left off.

7.8 ## TEXTBOOK EXERCISES: REINFORCEMENT

Some of the drills presented earlier in Session 7 are repeated here, along with some new drills, to give you Reinforcement practice. After completing the Reinforcement activities, click the Print button (if desired), then click the Next Exercise button.

Reviewing the P, R, and Question Mark Keys

	R Key	*P Key*	*Question Mark Key*

P Drill

Key lines 1–3 once, pushing for speed.

1 ;p pan pat pea peg pen pep pet pie pig pin pit pails
2 ;p ship tape pink skip slap taps gaps pest sap paste
3 Peasant Pennant Pitfall Patient Pheasant Pleasant Philadelphia

TEXTBOOK EXERCISES: PREPARING A BIBLIOGRAPHY

A bibliography is a formalized listing of all the books, magazines, and other sources used in your report. The listing is placed at the end of the paper. Each bibliographical entry contains the author's name, title, publication facts, and specific page numbers (if appropriate), as follows:

> Joynter, Louise R. *Living Values.* Denver, Colorado: Marchant Press, 2002, pp. 64-67.

Formatting Considerations

- List author's last name first followed by a comma, then first name followed by a period.
- Space only once after periods, question marks, and colons.
- Indent the second and succeeding lines with one tab space.
- Separate the place of publication from publisher's name with a colon (:).
- Include page numbers in the footnote bibliography entry.
- End all entries with a period.
- Single-space each entry. Double-space between entries.

The format for bibliographical entries used in this text is one of the more common styles. Other authors, institutions, and individuals may require a slightly different format. Consult your instructor or a style reference manual for further details.

Guidelines for Preparing a Bibliography

1 The title "Bibliography" is centered on line 7 (approximately 2 inches from the top of the page). Double-space after the title.
2 Entries in the bibliography are listed alphabetically, according to the author's last name. If there is no author information (such as for a magazine article or newspaper article), key the entry as follows:

> "Time Marches On." *The Los Angeles Flyer.* March 10, 2007, p. 38.

Use the word *Time* in alphabetizing.

Guidelines for Bibliographic References from Electronic Sources

More and more research is now being done using electronic publication resources, such as educational software, CD-ROM/DVD products, online database services, and the Internet. Below is a summary of guidelines and some examples of basic bibliographic entries for electronic publications. Keep in mind that these rules are subject to change with the constantly changing technology of electronic information.

Key lines 4–6 once, focusing on either speed or control. If you are focusing on control and you make more than two errors on a line, repeat it.

4 A tall, split, peeling aspen sapling is diseased.
5 Pat speaks and pleads and defends the plaintiffs.
6 Did Jane tape that splint and dispense the pills?

R Drill

Key lines 1–3 twice: first key line 1 for speed, then key line 1 for control. If you make more than 2 errors on line 1 when keying for control, repeat it. Follow the same procedure for lines 2 and 3.

1 fr rain rare real rink rake rage rear ripe rip rage rigid
2 stare there their after pride tired far her press jar tear
3 Refrain Repress Release Retreat Resident Register Reap

Question Mark Drill

Important: Tap the space bar **once** after the question mark at the end of the sentence. This rule applies to all end-of-sentence punctuation when you are using a proportional font such as Times New Roman. When a question mark ends a line in the drill, press *Enter* immediately— do not tap the space bar.

Key lines 1–3 once, keeping your eyes on the copy.

1 Is Jennie ahead? Is Dennis safe? Is Allen late?
2 Is Ken late? Is Dale fit? Is Neil in his teens?
3 Did she dine? Did the leaf fall? Did Jane flee?

Additional Drill

Key the following drill. Press *Enter* after each line.

Students in Online Classes

Think control as you key each line. If you make more than two errors on a line, repeat it. Keep your eyes on the copy in the text as you key.

1 In the sleet, a sheep passed the pines and plants.
2 In his pastel sedan, Jake passed that fast jeep.
3 His left thigh is gashed; the patient is in pain.

4 rest tree trip hire ring fire earn hard dirt fair
5 range ridge raise reign rinse art jar rinse right
6 eager fir ran after heart large dress greed green

7 Shall I still slide in the infield if Jake faints?
8 Has she hit? Has the thief left? Has he landed?
9 Is Dale fit? Is Neil in his teens? Is Ken late?

Document B Remember to key a correct text note entry.

1. Twenty-Nine Ways to Make Patients Feel at Ease – *Mayo Medical Review* (magazine) by Ms. Tracy Fuqua. Appeared in the March 2007 issue on page 29.
2. Book – *Medical Transcription* by Blanche and Alice Ettinger. Published by EMCParadigm in St. Paul, Minnesota in 2004. Taken from page 14.
3. Book by Warren, Eason, Burch, and Ewens. Title: *Medical Assisting: Administrative and Clinical Competencies*. Published in 2007 by Symtalk Publishing Company, Chicago, Illinois. Quoted information from pp 6–10.
4. Quoted from the September 19, 2007, issue of the *San Jose Independent* newspaper, page 17, column 3.
5. *Medical Terminology* (Book) – edited by Deborah Westervelt, published by Ralsten Publishers, Inc., in 2008 – location, Des Moines, Iowa. Material quoted from p. 397.
6. Used quote from p. 86 in March 2007 issue of *Sun Health* magazine in an article entitled "Understanding Your Blood Test Results" – no author given.
7. Report by Stephanie Cox, "Herbal Medicines, put out by the Arizona Colon Cancer Research Group, Phoenix, in 2008, page 46.

The Footnote System

Footnotes are used to tell your reader the exact source of your quoted material and where additional information can be found. The formats for keying footnotes can differ slightly, depending on which reference book is used. Choose one method and be consistent throughout the entire manuscript. One of the most accepted formats is used in this text. Generally, a footnote must include the following: author, title, facts of publication within parentheses (place, publisher, date), and page on which you found the information. Look at this example:

[1]James L. Johnson, *All You Wanted to Know About the Moon* (Tucson, Arizona: Minute Publishing Company, 2006), p. 117.

Footnotes are numbered to prevent confusion about sources. Notice that the number is raised from the rest of the line as a **superior** or **superscript** number. PWP has both superscript and subscript capabilities. Also note that there is only one space after the colon following the publisher's city and state.

Remember: Titles of poems, short stories, chapters, essays, and articles in magazines are enclosed in quotation marks. Titles of books, newspapers, and magazines are keyed in italics (underlining is also acceptable, but only as a second alternative).

Also remember: While commercial word processing software packages have automated features for setting up traditional footnotes, it's faster to use text notes for the person keying the manuscript—there is much less to key, and word processing commands are not needed. In addition, it's easier for the reader to note the source of the information presented since the author's name is next to the quoted information as opposed to being at the bottom of the page. If you have a choice as to which method of source notes to use, text notes are the most efficient.

What Is a Keyboarding Error?

Some errors affect only the appearance of a document. On the other hand, certain keyboarding errors can have a drastic effect on the message being communicated. Consider the result of transposing two numbers in a customer's invoice; for example, keying $19 instead of $91. Following is a list of some common keyboarding mistakes. You will find reviewing the list helpful to ensure that you are aware of possible errors as you complete timings and later as you prepare letters and other documents.

Common Keyboarding Errors

- Keying wrong words
- Transposing numbers
- Placing extra spaces between words or numbers
- Placing a space before a punctuation mark
- Not capitalizing a proper noun or the first word of a sentence
- Capitalizing a word in a sentence that should not be capitalized
- Placing too many spaces after a punctuation mark or between paragraphs
- Using improper left, right, top, or bottom margins
- Not indenting properly
- Being inconsistent in vertical spacing
- Using incorrect punctuation

CHECKING YOUR SKILL

In Session 6 you completed a 1-minute timing. The goals for the timing under the Timings Check that follows are based on your performance in Session 6. If you don't remember your scores, you can review them by accessing the Timings Performance Report from your Paradigm Keyboarding Snap home page, as explained below.

Viewing the Report

You can check your timings scores in the Timings Performance Report by taking the following steps:

1 Exit your current session.
2 Go to your Paradigm Keyboarding with Snap Welcome page.
3 Point to Reports and click Timings Performance Report.
4 At the Timings Performance Report wizard, click Show Report.
5 A table appears showing each timing you have attempted, along with your WAM and number of errors.
6 Click the Show Graph button to see this information in graph form.
7 To return to a keyboarding session, click Home on your Snap menu bar, and then click the name of the next exercise you wish to do.

Dayton, Ohio, by the Western Publishing Company in 2007. The first example shows the text note style. The second example shows the traditional footnote style (see pages 318–319).

The Text Note System

The text note system for referencing notes places the complete source information in a bibliography or works-cited list at the back of the paper. The abbreviated note that is placed in the text refers the reader to the bibliography or works-cited list if more information is desired. This system is easy to key. ***Remember:*** Before keying a paper, always determine which style of referencing is required.

Use the following procedure to key the text note method of referencing:

1 Space once following the quoted material and key the author's last name and page number enclosed in parentheses.
Example:
…and equipment" (Dane 52).

2 Do not put any source note information at the bottom of the page; continue keying the text material.

3 If you have more than one publication by the same author(s) with the same publication date, use **a**, **b**, **c**, and so on to let the reader know which publication in the bibliography is being referenced.
Example:

   (Holbreck and Marcus a 2)   (listed first in bibliography)
   (Holbreck and Marcus b 16)   (listed second in bibliography)
   (Holbreck and Marcus c 118) (listed third in bibliography)

4 If a publication has no author, use the title instead for the text note reference and bibliography.

5 When there are three or more authors, include the last name of the author listed first followed by "et al."

57.6   **Document B**

Text Notes

1 At the *Session 58 Document B* screen, key a correct text note entry for each information source listed in Document B. Key each reference as a numbered paragraph using the *Bullets and Numbering* dialog box. (See Session 42.)

2 Click Check to automatically name (**057prob**), save, and check the document.

3 To print the document with errors highlighted, click the Print button.

4 To correct errors, click View Original. Make changes, then recheck the document.

5 Click Next Exercise.

Students in Online Classes

Reminder: When there are three or more authors, list the last name of the first author followed by "et al." The names of all the authors can be listed in the bibliography.

Take a 1-minute timing on each paragraph; if you finish before time is up, start over. If you did not reach at least 25 WAM on your most recent timing, push for speed. If you are keying at least 25 WAM but are making more than 2 errors per minute, concentrate on accuracy. If you are above 25 WAM and are making 2 or fewer errors, push for speed.

1 Jane prepares legal papers and letters. She prefers reading ledgers and graphs. It is tiring and drains her. If she falters at the start, Jane is risking a defeat. The stern leader sees her stress and praises her spirit.

2 Print the paragraph in large letters. Raise the title and delete the digraphs. Insert three fresh phrases at the end. It is all right if Dane deletes that first phrase. It is a danger and a threat. Perhaps the ending is right.

ENDING THE SESSION

Now you may print this session's files, continue to the next session, or exit the program. See page 24 of Session 6 if you need to review procedures.

Ergonomic Tip
Your hands should float or glide above the keyboard, not rest.

Document A

Quotation Marks

1 Key each of the statements shown in Document A. Concentrate on keying the quotation marks and other punctuation marks in the proper position.
2 Click Check to automatically name (**057proa**), save, and check the document.
3 Print and correct the document, then click Next Exercise.

Document A

In his text *2020 Vision: In the 21st Century*, Lincoln Chen states, "America's health in the 21st Century must wrestle successfully with equity among the young and the aged and among social and ethnic groups."

Ettinger and Ettinger have said, "Voice/Speech recognition software is a rapidly evolving technology that has the potential to change a medical transcriptionist's role."

Warren and Eason define acupressure as "A method of relieving pain or altering the function of a system of the body by applying gentle, firm pressure with the fingers and hands."

According to the latest information, Medical Assistants are multiskilled healthcare practitioners able to perform a wide variety of distinct tasks.

Burch stated that "Vitamins are organic molecules that are critical for the proper functioning of the body."

Ewens emphasized that Diagnostic Imaging provides a detailed view of structures beneath the skin only accessible previously through surgical approaches. . . .

According to recent sources, the quad-sparing method for knee replacement surgery reduces recuperation time by three to four weeks.

The National Heart, Lung, and Blood Institute recommends that an individual's cholesterol be less than 200.

"An ulcer is like a crater or a pit, similar to a pothole on a highway," as noted in layman's terms by the Arizona Colon Cancer Research Group.

Source Note Style—Text Notes or Footnotes?

In recent years, there has been a growing trend to use **text notes** rather than **footnotes** to cite information sources. Text notes are easier and faster to key, and they provide immediate identification. Readers do not need to switch their attention to the bottom of the page to find the publication name or the name of the author. Since both footnotes and text notes may be used to cite sources, be sure to find out which style your organization prefers and use that style consistently throughout your document.

In the following examples of the sample manuscript "Our Paper Highway," the writer quotes material from an article written by Deborah Dane entitled "The Rising Cost of Record Storage" from the April 2007 edition of the magazine *Management and Money*, page 52, and from a book written by Judy L. Holbreck and Vincent T. Marcus, *Problems in Record Storage*, published in

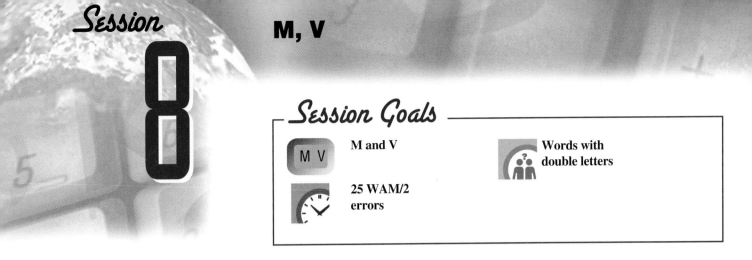

Session Goals

M V **M and V**

Words with double letters

25 WAM/2 errors

8.1- 8.8 ## ON-SCREEN EXERCISES: GETTING STARTED

If you exited the program at the end of the previous session, refer to page 11 of Session 3 to review how to open the next session or to continue from where you left off.

8.9 ## TEXTBOOK EXERCISES: REINFORCEMENT

Some of the drills you completed during the first portion of Session 8 are presented here, along with some new drills, to reinforce your skills with the new key reaches. When you are finished keying the drills, click Print (if desired), then click Next Exercise.

Reviewing the M and V Keys

V Key

M Key

M Drill

Key lines 1–3 once, pushing for speed.

1 jm am am him him man man mad mad jam jam me me mean
2 might might metal metal dream dream ram ram made made
3 Mashed Mean Mailed Minted Melted Makes Melt Might Mild

If you quote directly or indirectly from another source, you can identify the quote by using source notes in the form of text notes, footnotes, or endnotes.

Text notes are brief parenthetical references to the source of an indirect or direct quotation. A text note includes the author's last name and a page number from the work cited, for example, (Updike 25). The works cited are then listed in a more complete form at the end of the report as a *works-cited list* or a *bibliography*.

Footnotes are numbered references that appear at the foot (bottom) of the page. A footnote includes the author's last name, publication title, place of publication, publisher, date of publication, and the page numbers of the information cited. The information cited is coded with a superscript number (a small-size number that appears at the upper-right of a word in the text), and the information source, identified with the same number, is listed at the foot of the page.

Endnotes are another kind of note that is often confused with a footnote. Endnotes offer additional explanation of material cited in the text of a report. Endnotes are numbered with superscripts. Unlike footnotes, however, endnotes all appear at the end of a report and offer additional information rather than the source of a direct or indirect quotation.

Citing Sources

1 *Direct Quotation:* Use quotation marks to enclose the exact words or ideas of another person whom you are quoting directly. *Note:* The source note information in the following examples is shown in the **text note** format.

> Dane stated, "If current trends continue, the cost of filing just one document could rise to ninety-five cents" (Dane 52).
>
> "If current trends continue," stated Dane, "the cost of filing just one document could rise to ninety-five cents" (Dane 52).

2 *Paraphrased Quotation:* In formal writing, material that has been directly quoted is enclosed in quotation marks as shown. If you paraphrased (did not quote the words exactly), you would not need the quotation marks, but you must still give credit for the idea by using a source note. *Note:* The source note information in the following example is shown in the **footnote** format. A superscript number is placed after the quote in the text of your written report; this same number is also placed at the beginning of the corresponding footnote at the bottom of the page.

> One expert indicated that if trends continue, the cost of storing just one document could rise to ninety-five cents.[1]

3 *Ellipsis:* In some printed materials, you will notice a series of three evenly spaced periods (…), called an **ellipsis**. The ellipsis indicates that some words have been omitted from quoted material. When an ellipsis appears at the end of a statement, four periods are used.

Key lines 4–6 twice, concentrating on control.

4 Mike is making a frame; he needs ample sandpaper.
5 Did Mamie transmit the message after amending it?
6 Did Sammie eliminate all mistakes in the message?

V Drill

Key lines 1–3 once, focusing on speed.

1 fv dive dive five five give give grieve grieve drive
2 private private deliver deliver veteran even even vein
3 Negative Negative Seven Seven Advertising Advertising

Key lines 4–6 twice; concentrate on control.

4 Did Van ever deliver the varnish and the shelves?
5 It is evident; the vital lever reverses the vent at five.
6 Marvia served vanilla malts at the private event in Vail.

Additional Drill

Students in Online Classes

Key the following drill. Press *Enter* after each line.

1 The malt that Pam made had milk and mint in it.
2 The fine farm animal, Sandman, had a marked limp.
3 Mail the letter at midnight and add ample stamps.

4 Is that smashed metal mass a damaged helmet, Jim?
5 As her mind dimmed, Minne missed the main message.
6 In a lavish, private plane, the traveler arrived.

7 At the evening event, seven silver vases vanished.
8 Give him a vitamin, the driver has a grave fever.
9 Five vigilant servants evaded the starved vandal.
10 Did Val deliver that vast velvet divan this evening?

> Key lines 1–3 for speed; key lines 4–6 for control, repeat the lines if you have more than two errors; key lines 7–10 for speed. Remember to keep your eyes on the text as you key.

8.10 ONE-MINUTE TIMINGS

Goal: 25 WAM with no more than 2 errors

- Take a 1-minute timing on each paragraph.
- If you finish a paragraph before time is up, start over.

1   In early days of development, computers were quite large. The early computer users were quite pleased with their room-sized computer. Miles of cables were needed for the operation of the computer. By today's standards, those early computers were also very slow to process the instructions and send data. Today, computers are not only faster, but they are being produced in smaller and smaller sizes. The user of today has many sizes from which to choose.

One common model is the one known as the desktop computer. As the name implies, this machine is designed to sit on a desk. Each year, however, the amount of desk space needed grows smaller and smaller. The desktop computer is made to stay in one place, on your desk.

Portable computers are machines designed to be moved from place to place with little effort. Most machines of this type have some sort of battery power and are made to take all the small bumps and jolts to which a unit might be subjected when it is moved from place to place. Some models have strong cases in which to keep the machine while it is being moved.

Notebook computers are one type of portable computer. A notebook model is in a class that weighs less than ten pounds. The keyboard of the notebook, like the desktop keyboard, has all the keys and all the user features. The size of the notebook keyboard is somewhat smaller. Some people find it hard to type on a small keyboard and harder to read the text on the screen.

Subnotebook systems are in a class by themselves. These units are smaller than the notebook type. The weight of this class of machine is less than five pounds. One issue you might have to face when you use this model is typing on the small keyboard. The keys are quite small. Some users feel that the size of the screen is too small to get a good look at the text.

An even smaller model can be found in stores. The palm or handheld type of computer is one that can be held in the palm of your hand. These small machines can be used to make schedules, reminders, and some other limited tasks. The user should not plan to do a lot of tasks on a palm-sized unit. One reason for this limited use is that both the keyboard and the screen are quite small and are hard to use for most people.

TEXTBOOK EXERCISES: PREPARING RESEARCH SOURCE NOTES

An important part of the manuscript writing process is creating the research source notes, which are a means for crediting the source of ideas or information you have used in your manuscript. To use another writer's words or ideas without giving credit is called *plagiarism*, which in some cases is against the law and in all cases is unethical. You **must** give credit to another author if you use his or her ideas.

1   Marna smelled the simmering meat. The steam permeated the air. She managed a small taste and smiled. The meat and milk might help that little girl and ease her pain.

2   As he firmed the damp earth at the tree, the miser imagined he heard a small sigh. Mirages in the misted marsh alarmed him. Grim fears emerged as his mindless tramping faltered.

3   Make that simple diagram first. Then send a message in the mail. Tell that salesman that his latest remarks made the manager mad. The meeting impaired the imminent merger.

4   Traveling in this vast native land is a near marvel. The savage rivers and varied paved miles are impressive. Vivid sights revive the mind and lift spirits. Villages reveal veiled vestiges; a dividend is derived.

5   Even if Gavin is vain, she has avid fans and attentive friends. Her singing is sensitive; she reveals her vast talent. She deserves lavish and vivid praise. Her versatile verses are a massive advantage and elevate her fevered fans.

6   Navigate the even trail in life. Derive all things that are pleasant and reap the advantages. Preserve the vital past and evade vile evils. An avid, aggressive striving is needed in all lives. A varied and diverse path prevents grief.

ENDING THE SESSION

Now you may print this session's files, continue to the next session, or exit the program. See page 24 of Session 6 if you need to review procedures.

Ergonomic Tip
Position your monitor so that the top of the screen is no higher than your eye level.

Session 57

RESEARCH SOURCE NOTES USED WITH MANUSCRIPTS

Session Goals

1-Minute: 45 WAM/1 error
5-Minute: 35 WAM/1 error

Using tables to reinforce conclusions

Hanging indent

57.1-57.2 ON-SCREEN EXERCISES: GETTING STARTED

If you exited the program at the end of the previous session, refer to page 11 in Session 3 to review how to open the next session. If you are continuing immediately from Session 56, start with Exercise 57.2. Click the Next Exercise or Previous Exercise button if you are not at the correct exercise.

57.3 ONE-MINUTE TIMINGS

Goal: 45 WAM/1 error

SI: 1.50

- Take two 1-minute timings.
- Use your most recent timing score to set a speed or accuracy goal.

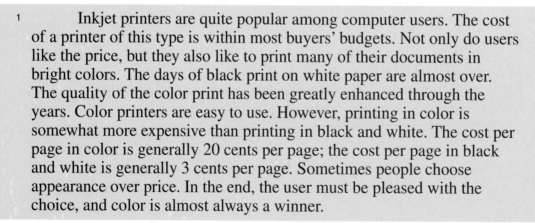

1   Inkjet printers are quite popular among computer users. The cost of a printer of this type is within most buyers' budgets. Not only do users like the price, but they also like to print many of their documents in bright colors. The days of black print on white paper are almost over. The quality of the color print has been greatly enhanced through the years. Color printers are easy to use. However, printing in color is somewhat more expensive than printing in black and white. The cost per page in color is generally 20 cents per page; the cost per page in black and white is generally 3 cents per page. Sometimes people choose appearance over price. In the end, the user must be pleased with the choice, and color is almost always a winner.

57.4 FIVE-MINUTE TIMINGS

Goal: 35 WAM/1 error

SI: 1.50

- Take two 5-minute timings.
- On your second attempt, try to increase speed while keeping errors at 1 per minute.

Session 9

O, B, W

Session Goals

OBW	O, B, W		"W" and "B" Compound words
	25 WAM/2 errors		

9.1-9.10 | ## ON-SCREEN EXERCISES: GETTING STARTED

If you exited the program at the end of the previous session, refer to page 11 of Session 3 to review how to open the next session or to continue from where you left off.

9.11 | ## TEXTBOOK EXERCISES: REINFORCEMENT

Some of the drills you completed during the first portion of Session 9 are repeated here, along with some new ones, to reinforce your learning of the O, B, and W keys. A Thinking Drill exercise then follows. When you have finished these exercises, click Print (if desired), then click Next Exercise.

Reviewing the O, B, and W Keys

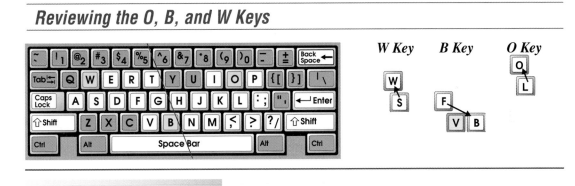

O Drill

Key lines 1–3, pushing for speed.

1 lo do for hop log one old not off pot son golf long
2 along avoid drove prior other toast option oppose some
3 Endorse Diamond Another Visitor Develop Insertion Potato

Share your document with a fellow student. Ask him or her to read it and provide feedback. Did this person get sufficient detail to accomplish the purpose of your document? Ask the student to write her or his comments on your printed copy of the manuscript and sign it. Hand in to your instructor both the outline and the manuscript.

Students in Online Classes

If you do not have access to a class-mate, ask a relative or friend to review the manuscript.

ENDING THE SESSION

Now you may print this session's files, continue to the next session, or exit the program. See page 300 in Session 54 to review the procedure.

Ergonomic Tip

Recline when you can and sit back while you are talking on the phone or with people. This will help you to relax and think better.

Key lines 4–6 once for control. If you make more than two errors on a line, repeat it.

4 Ora ordered the onions and olives from the store.
5 The soft fog floated aloft over the lone trooper.
6 Did the florist remove the thorns from the roses?

B Drill

Key lines 1–3 once; push for speed.

1 fb bad bag ban bar bat bed beg Ben bet bid big bit
2 barter member harbor banker ballot border benefit brake
3 Alphabet Basement Neighbor Remember Remarkable Be

Key lines 4–6 twice: Key line 4 for speed, then key line 4 for control. Follow the same procedure for lines 5 and 6.

4 I grabbed a dab of bread and biked to the harbor.
5 Babe is baffled; the beverage bottles are broken.
6 Barni, the beagle, barks and begs for a big bone.

W Drill

Key lines 1–3 once, pushing for speed.

1 sw jaw wag raw two war wet saw hew how new sew snow
2 review warmer bowler wiring inward wisdom preview
3 Hardware Workable Weakness Endowment Two Window

Key lines 4–6 twice: first for speed, then for control. Follow the same procedures as lines 4–6 in the B drill above.

4 Wear a warm gown if it snows; the weather is raw.
5 The new lawn will grow when watered well at dawn.
6 It is wise to wire the news to the waiting woman.

Additional Drill

Students in Online Classes

Key the following drill. Press **Enter** after each line.

1 He is not an honest senator; he does not fool me.
2 At the rodeo, Jo dropped the looped rope and lost.
3 In the gloom, the senior pilot spotted an airport.

Think control as you key each line. If you make more than two errors on a line, repeat it. Keep your eyes on the copy in the text as you key.

Aerobic Training

Aerobic exercise is any activity that raises the heart rate for more than a few minutes. The genral guideline for aerobic exercise is a minimum of 30 minutes of *e* activity three to five days per week. Aerobic exercise can include activities such as walking, hiking, biking, swimming, dancing, or ridden a stationary bike. *riding*

Strength Training

Strength training is important for building strength, balance, and good posture. Strength training doesn't have to be done at a gym. You can achieve the same results at home using hand weights, bottles of water or sand, or even books.

Flexibility Training

Stretching should be incorporated into any fitness program. Cobined with aerobic *m* activity, it can prevent muscle soreness and can also be done on its own.

Learn More about Physical Activity

To learn more about physical activities *and exercises*, contact your local gyms, recreational centers, wellness programs sponsored by hospitals and physical therapy clinics, YMCAs or YWCAs to find activities or fitness programs suited to your needs. Also, many post secondary schools offer fitness programs and/or can provide you with the names, addresses, telephone numbers, and Internet addresses of other national organizations that can help with questions related to physical activities and exercises.

REINFORCING WRITING SKILLS

A shortcoming of many documents such as manuscripts is that the material is so general that it is of little value to the reader. Open Document 056proa and read it. The reader is given concrete examples of how to develop a fitness program and exercises to use. Ask yourself whether the document provides the necessary facts and examples to convey the intended message to the reader. If the reader has to ask questions for clarification or more details, then the document didn't do the job. Close the document and go to a clear editing window for Document B.

56.6

Document
B

Outline for a Manuscript

You are to prepare an outline that will be used in developing an unbound manuscript. The topic of the manuscript is what you can do to prepare yourself for a successful career in the field of medicine. The outline is to assist you in the development of the manuscript. Be sure to incorporate sufficient details so that the reader "has the facts."
Refer to Session 54 if you need help in formatting your outline. Proofread the outline and correct any errors. Save and name the outline **056wprb**. Print the outline and close the file.

56.7

Document
C

Unbound Manuscript

Now prepare an unbound manuscript using the heading, spacing, and page numbering guidelines used throughout this unit on manuscripts. Time your work so that your WAM rate is calculated. The manuscript is to be at least one-and-a-half pages long.
When composing your manuscript from the outline, be sure to use headings to improve readability. Proofread your manuscript and correct any errors. Save, name (**056wprc**), and print your document.

4 Beneath the bridge in the brook, the bears bathed.

5 He is bitter and bleak; the dark banjo is broken.

6 A nimble rabbit blinks and nibbles bean blossoms.

7 Will Marlow wash in warm water that wool sweater?

8 With a white towel, Warren wiped the jeweled bowl.

9 If Win washes the new window, is he wasting water?

THINKING DRILL

Using the list below, key as many words as you can think of that begin with the letters given.

bo   wo

bi   wh

Key the words in a list. Key all the "bo" words first. Then go to the next set of letters. Try to think of at least 10. If you can think of 20 to 30 words, that's great.

9.12 ONE-MINUTE TIMINGS

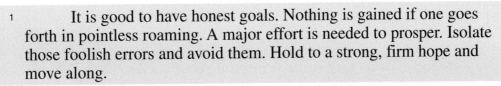

Goal: 25 WAM with no more than 2 errors

- Take a 1-minute timing on each paragraph.
- If you finish a paragraph before time is up, start over.

1   It is good to have honest goals. Nothing is gained if one goes forth in pointless roaming. A major effort is needed to prosper. Isolate those foolish errors and avoid them. Hold to a strong, firm hope and move along.

2   Floss shook in terror as the tornado stormed along the shore. The radio droned on foretelling doom and gloom. The phone popped in her ear as a torrent of rain fell. Alone in the old mansion, her fear overtook her for a moment.

3   Bif booked a berth on the battered boat. As he bragged to his somber brother, the boom of the harbor bells vibrated. Beneath the boasting, Bif began to babble. A belated bolt of disbelief and brooding stabbed at him.

4   Labor to do a noble job. Bosses like brains and ambition. A blend of both brings a desirable habit that boosts a beginner. A babbling boaster absorbs a bore. The absent laborer blemishes his possible bankroll boost.

5   We will await the word of warning in the new tower. The wise, stalwart leader wants to preview the writings of men of worth. He frowns on wrong narrow views. We will follow wise wishes and win a wearisome war and bestow a renewed foothold.

- Listen to your body and heed what it says. Learn to tell the difference between mild discomfort and pain. If it hurts, don't don't do it.
- Include stretching in your exercise program. Stretching can help maintain your range of motion and prevent muscle soreness.
- Be patient. Don't expect too much from yourself too soon. Give yourself time to adjust to your new activities.

Fitting Exercise into Your Life

If you're like many people, finding time to exercise is difficult. Try some of these tips to help you fit more exercise into your daily routine:

1. Make exercise a priority.
2. Ride a stationary bicycle while watching television, or take a ride around the block on your bicycle.
3. Listen to music as you exercise to make it more enjoyable.
4. Rather than meeting a friend for lunch, consider meeting for a walk at a nearby park.
5. Park at least a block away from your destination and walk the remaining distance.
6. Take the stairs instead of the elevator or escalator.
7. Take a walk during your lunch break.
8. Walk or ride your bicycle for short errands.

A Word of Caution

You should always be able to catch your breath and speak comfortably while exercising. It is normal to feel a little discomfort with increased effort, but exercise should never feel painful. Always remember to warm up slowly and to cool down gradually.

It is always important to check with your doctor before increasing your physical activity. This is especially true if you have any of the following:
- A chronic disease or are at high risk for getting one (for example, if you smoke, are overweight, or have a family history of a chronic disease)
- Any new undiagnosed symptom
- Chest pain
- Shortness of breath
- Skipping, racing, or fluttering heart beats
- Infections or fever
- Joint swelling
- Pain or an irregular walking gait after you have fallen

Creating Your Exercise Program

The American College of Sports Medicine suggests using a combination of aerobic, strength, and flexibility training to produce a well-rounded training program.

Continued on next page

6   Will reviewed the written words. He did not wish to show that witless newsman how shallow his words were. However, he wanted to warn the world of the wasted wealth in the wages of the man. He showed the network the handwriting on the wall.

ENDING THE SESSION

Now you may print this session's files, continue to the next session, or exit the program. See page 24 of Session 6 if you need to review procedures.

Ergonomic Tip

Experiment with your foreground and background screen colors to find the combination that is most comfortable for you. Avoid using light-colored characters on the screen. Use dark characters on a light-colored background.

Changing Top and Bottom Margins

By default, the top and bottom margins of the PWP software are 1 inch. There are times when these margins are adjusted. For example, if a manuscript is bound at the top, additional space may be needed for the binding. Also for appearance purposes to give the impression that there is not too much text on the page, the top and bottom margins can be increased to 1.5 inches.

To change top and bottom margins in PWP, choose <u>F</u>ile→Page Set<u>u</u>p. At the *Document Format* dialog box, press ***Tab*** four times and enter the new top margin. Then press ***Tab*** twice and enter the new bottom margin. Then click OK.

56.5

Document A

Edited Top Bound Manuscript

1   At the *Session 56 Document A* screen, key Document A by completing the following steps:
    a   Set the top and bottom margins for 1.5 inches.
    b   Press ***Enter*** until you are at line 7, then center the main heading in all caps.
    c   Set the line spacing for double-spacing.
    d   Number the pages in the top right corner of the page except the first page, which is not numbered.
    e   Key the text and insert hard page breaks at appropriate locations.
2   Proofread and correct any errors in the document.
3   Click Check to automatically name (**056proa**), save, and check the document.
4   Print the document.
5   To correct errors, click View Original. Make any necessary changes, then recheck the document.
6   Click Next Exercise.

Students in Online Classes

Be sure to review steps 1a–1e before starting step 1a. Make sure you know how to activate the features used.

Document A

OUR BODIES ARE MADE TO MOVE!

Getting Fit Doesn't Have to Hurt

Many people avoid exercise in fear of the discomfort that it may bring. But getting fit can actually make you feel better, give you more energy and improve your mood. With gradual steps and an exercise program that fits your lifestyle, exercise can be an enjoyable as well as beneficial addition to your life. No matter what your current level of a fitness is, the first few steps toward health and fitness don't have to be the hardest. Making simple changes to your activity level can help start you on your way to regular fitness.

Keep the following suggestion in mind as you begin an exercise program. s
• Find an exercise activity that you enjoy. You will be more likely to continue exercising if you are having fun as you exercise.
• Start slowly and build up gradually. This is true whether you are beginning an exercise program for the first time or are returning after an extended time away from exercising.
• Cross Train! Vary your activities from day to day. Try doing some type of weight-bearing activity twice a week and aerobic activity on the other days.

- Key each line once.
- If you need more work on speed or accuracy, key the appropriate group of lines again.

Keys Review (Speed)

1 asdf jkl; ;p; frf jmj fvf lol fbf sws pr mv db wm
2 p pad pan peg pen pin pit pie plan phase pledge plane
3 r rap ran red rip rent rests real repels refers roam rope

4 m ham hem men him mate mind mesh manage mandate
5 v vat vim vet vise vent vane vigil valid veneer voter rigor
6 o oh or odd old one oaf opens omit ogle oval of oblong

7 b bad beg bid bop brag blend board brake better bowl
8 w was wed who win woe were when went where with
9 Shanon Olan Bronson George Janet Kent Martin John

Balanced-Hand Words (Speed)

1 lamb blend bland blame amble emblem problem bible
2 lap nap pen paid pane flap span pale spent dispel
3 air pan sir risks lair heir pair hair flair widow

4 map maid mane melt sham lame mend firm make flame
5 vie via pair vivid pelvis disown pens laps disown visit
6 fog sod oak rod foam fork form foam odor soak rod

7 bow wig wow vow down gown wisp with wish when wit
8 Did the lame lamb amble down to the big pale oak?
9 The pale widow paid for the vivid gown and a wig.
10 When did Vivian mend the pair of problem emblems?

Two-Letter Combinations (Speed)

1 pe peg pen pest pets pert peso petite petition
2 pi pin pie piles pipes pink pine pig piston pivot
3 That petite person with pets had piles of pinkish pills.

Session Goals

1-Minute: 45 WAM/1 error
5-Minute: 35 WAM/1 error

Changing top and bottom margins, review of other PWP features

Providing the reader with concrete information

56.1–56.2 ON-SCREEN EXERCISES: GETTING STARTED

If you exited the program at the end of the previous session, refer to page 11 in Session 3 to review how to open the next session. If you are continuing immediately from Session 55, start with Exercise 56.2. Click the Next Exercise or Previous Exercise button if you are not at the correct exercise.

56.3 ONE-MINUTE TIMINGS

Goal: 45 WAM/1 error

SI: 1.49

- Take two 1-minute timings. If you finish before time is up, start over.
- Use your most recent timing speed to set a speed or accuracy goal.

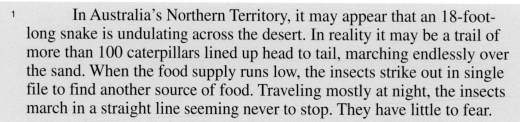

1   In Australia's Northern Territory, it may appear that an 18-foot-long snake is undulating across the desert. In reality it may be a trail of more than 100 caterpillars lined up head to tail, marching endlessly over the sand. When the food supply runs low, the insects strike out in single file to find another source of food. Traveling mostly at night, the insects march in a straight line seeming never to stop. They have little to fear.

56.4 FIVE-MINUTE TIMINGS

Goal: 35 WAM/1 error

SI: 1.51

Take two 5-minute timings.

Session Goals

Review keys from Sessions 1–9

25 WAM/2 errors

10.1 ON-SCREEN EXERCISES: GETTING STARTED

If you are continuing immediately from Session 9, you are already warmed up and are looking at Exercise 10.2. Click the Next Exercise or Previous Exercise button if you are not at the correct exercise. The copy for Exercises 10.2–10.4 is in your text. Exercise 10.2 consists of two 1-minute timings. Instructions to complete the timings and page number are shown on your screen.

If you exited the program at the end of the previous session, refer to page 11 of Session 3 for instructions on entering the program.

10.2 CHECKING YOUR SKILL: ONE-MINUTE TIMING

In Sessions 7–9 you completed a series of 1-minute timings. Before you take the 1-minute timing that follows, check your scores on the Student Report. See page 27 of Session 7 to review the instructions for viewing your report.

Goal: 25 WAM with 2 or fewer errors

> 1   When the winter snow thaws, warm rain washes the world. Wild flowers begin to weave in a slow swing with the wind. Whiffs of a meadow awakened swirl down at the dawn. The dew is a rainbow and twinkles as a jewel. Winter has blown onward.

10.3 TEXTBOOK EXERCISES: REINFORCEMENT

The Special Drills that follow provide additional practice on the keys that you have learned in Sessions 1–9. However, if you are already keying over 25 WAM with no more than 2 errors and do not hesitate when keying, click the Next Exercise button three times. This will take you to Session 11, Exercise 2. If you are not at the 25 WAM with 2 or fewer errors level, proceed with the Special Drills to build speed and/or accuracy. When you have finished the drills, click Print (if desired), then click Next Exercise.

Here are guidelines for choosing drills:

1. If you have not mastered a key reach (you hesitate before striking the key), key the speed-building lines.
2. If you are not keying at least 25 WAM, key the speed-building lines.
3. If you are making more than 2 errors per minute, key the accuracy-building lines. If you make more than two errors on a line, key it again.

1 When computer monitors were first sold, users had a big problem. If the monitor was turned on and sat idle for a long time, the result would be burn-in. The burn-in of a monitor could be seen the next time a user turned on the system. The user would see a faint image of the text that was on the idle screen for a long time. This faint image could never be removed, and the monitor was damaged forever. Before long, developers had solved this problem with screen savers. The screen savers were special software programs that featured some type of moving graphic that would start after a few moments of idle time. Most monitors sold today have been designed to avoid burn-in.

Screen savers are still used today, however. Users have found that some screen savers can be used for security of data. Sometimes, a person has to leave his or her desk for a few minutes or even for a few hours. Perhaps this person has to go to a meeting, to lunch, or to another office for a moment or two. While the person is gone, the screen saver keeps others from seeing the data on the screen. It is not unusual to see moving objects or words on a screen at a desk.

Some screen savers go a step further. After the screen saver has started, the user cannot access the application program without a password. The image just keeps moving on the screen. The one problem with passwords is that most people choose a word that is easily detected by others. Passwords should be unique and hard for others to guess. When the user comes back to the desk to go back to work, he or she enters the password and the computer is up and running once more.

In addition to personalized screen savers, some users have added one more personal item to their systems. This item is a cardboard frame that is placed around the outside edge of the computer. Frames come in all sizes and shapes and descriptions. Computers can be decorated with almost any motif or theme depending on the user's personal choices. Frames are also available in brilliant colors, thus adding a touch of bright color to an otherwise dull office.

You, too, can have a screen saver that fits your personality. Just take a walk through the aisles of a software dealer and you will see all the choices available today. However, you may be like many other people who prefer to keep their desk space clean and uncluttered.

TEXTBOOK EXERCISES: BOUND MANUSCRIPTS

Bound manuscripts are typically longer (more than four pages) than unbound manuscripts and have additional space at the left or top margin for binding purposes. Bound manuscripts frequently include tables, quotations, paraphrasing (quoting what someone has said but in your own words), information sources, and a bibliography. Manuscripts, both bound and unbound, are used primarily in the academic, publishing, and research environments. The next three sessions are devoted to the preparation of bound manuscripts and their components.

4 ra ran rap ranks rake rates raised range rapid random

5 ri rid rip rises ripe right ridges rigid rinse rigs rim

6 Rapid Red ran to the raised ridges on that range.

7 ma man mat math make mail marsh manager margin

8 mi mid mild mind mint midst might misting mire mite

9 The manager might mail the mild mints to the man.

10 va van vat vane vases vast valid varied vanish valve

11 vi vie vim vise vile vine visits vital vintage vision

12 The vital vintage vases vanished from a vast van.

13 oa oak oats oath oatmeal load toad roast float oasis

14 The oath at the oak tree oasis was about oats.

15 ba bad bag bail balk bath badge barks bandages bald

16 bl blade bleak blast blank blight blind blinks blow

17 The bat blinked at a baboon blinded in bandages.

18 wa was war wag wade wait wane wash waste waves wave

19 wi win wit wig wide wipe will wise wield wiper window

20 Winna washed and wiped her window; she wasted water.

Double-Letter Words (Accuracy)

1 slipping sipping happen flipping appease shipping

2 terriers irritates terrains follow all narratives

3 dimmer dinners hammering manners immense immerges

4 moon roof pool hood hook loot took mood root door

5 gobble rabble hobble babble pebble nibbles rabbit

6 of off offers offends offset offense offensive offering off shore

7 Janell slipped the irritated terrier in the door.

8 That immense rabbit followed and nibbled a bottle.

9 She will be shipping the poor winter winner soon.

b   Move the last paragraph in the manuscript beginning with "Even though there . . ." ahead of the paragraph just above it being with "There is much yet to . . ."

3   Name (**055wprc**) and save the document.

4   Print and close the document.

5   Click Next Exercise.

REINFORCING WRITING SKILLS

Have you noticed how headings have been used in Documents A and B of this session? To improve the "readability" of your documents, especially those that require multiple pages, create first-, second-, and third-level headings to help the reader focus on the content. Information that can be shown in logical groups is easier to digest and will be retained for longer periods of time.

55.8

Document D

Creating Headings within a Manuscript

Open 054prob, an unbound manuscript you keyed in Session 54. Read the document carefully, then think of appropriate headings (first, second, third, or combinations of them) and insert them in the proper locations. Format them according to the guidelines you used in this session. Save the new document as **055wprd**, then print and close the file.

ENDING THE SESSION

Now you may print this session's files, continue to the next session, or exit the program. See page 300 in Session 54 to review the procedures.

Ergonomic Tip

Keep the angle between your calf and thigh greater than 60 degrees when seated. This relieves build-up of pressure and cramping in your legs.

Longer Words (Accuracy)

1   elephant dependent safekeeping plaintiff pipeline
2   standard registrar parenthesis telegrams resident
3   That resident registrar sends standard telegrams.

4   familiar eliminate sentimental dependent estimate
5   retrieve primitive advertising privilege negative
6   Eliminate that sentimental, familiar advertising.

7   rational tradition imagination negotiate renovate
8   ambition elaborate observation establish possible
9   stalwart knowledge handwriting wholesale whenever
10   Establish rational imagination whenever possible.

10.4   ONE-MINUTE TIMINGS

Now that you have completed the drills, you are to take two 1-minute timings on the following paragraph. Compare the rates with your first attempt. Has your speed improved? Do you have fewer errors? If you are not reaching 25 WAM with 2 or fewer errors on one of the 1-minute timings, repeat Sessions 7–9.

1   When the winter snow thaws, warm rain washes the world. Wild flowers begin to weave in a slow swing with the wind. Whiffs of a meadow awakened swirl down at the dawn. The dew is a rainbow and twinkles as a jewel. Winter has blown onward.

Ending the Session

Now you may print this session's files, continue to the next session, or exit the program. See page 24 of Session 6 if you need to review procedures.

Students in Online Classes

As noted, repeat Session 7–9 if you didn't reach 25 wam with 2 or fewer errors. Without these skills, it will take you longer to master keyboarding.

Ergonomic Tip

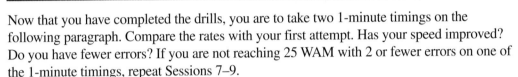

Place paper copy on a copyholder rather than flat on the work surface so you are focusing directly on the copy.

Basal Cell Cancer

Basal cell cancer begins in the lowest layer of the skin, called the basal cell layer. About 75 percent of all skin cancers are basal cell cancers. They usually develop on sun-exposed areas, especially the head and neck. If a basal cell cancer is left untreated, it can grow into nearby areas and invade the bone or other tissues beneath the skin.

Over 95 percent of all non-melanoma skin cancers can be cured. When detected at an early stage, nearly 100 percent are cured.

Early Detection of Skin Cancer

Protection from Sun's Rays

Most skin cancer can be prevented. The incidence of new skin cancers is estimated to be about one million cases annually. At least 3/4 of all skin cancers can be prevented by protection from the sun's rays. Most skin cancers can be treated successfully and cured when detected and treated early.

Early Detection

Early detection of cancer or precancerous conditions can be the key to successful treatment and cure. Screening helps physicians detect and treat growths before they develop into melanoma. A sudden or progressive change in a mole's appearance should be checked by a physician. A simple **ABCD** rule outlines the warning signals of melanoma.

Rule A. **A** is for asymmetry: one half of the mole does not match the other half.

Rule B. **B** is for border irregularity: the edges are ragged, notched, or blurred.

Rule C. **C** is for color, the pigmentation is not uniform.

Rule D. **D** is for diameter greater than 6 millimeters. Any sudden or progressive increase in size should be of special concern.

There is much yet to learn about what causes cancer and how it might be prevented. Our understanding of skin cancer is increasing, and with each new piece of knowledge gained, we have reason to believe that fewer people will develop this disease, and more will be treated successfully.

Even though there have been great advances in cancer diagnosis and treatment, the chances of survival in the late stages of the disease are not good. The best way to control the skin cancer is by early detection, treatment, and prevention. Early detection is critical. Recognition of changes in skin growths or the appearance of new growths is the best way to find early skin cancer. Adults should practice skin self-examination once a month, and suspicious findings should be evaluated promptly by a physician.

55.7

Document C

Using Cut and Paste in a Manuscript

1 Open **055prob**.
2 Use the PWP Cut and Paste feature (if needed, see Session 47 for a review) to make the following changes:
   a Move the heading **Basal Cell Cancer** and the paragraph just below it before the heading **Squamous Cell Cancers**.

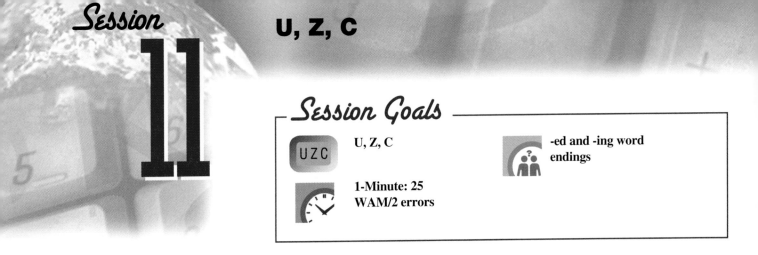

Session 11

U, Z, C

Session Goals

U Z C	U, Z, C

-ed and -ing word endings

1-Minute: 25 WAM/2 errors

11.1-11.10 ON-SCREEN EXERCISES: GETTING STARTED

11.1-11.10 ON-SCREEN EXERCISES: GETTING STARTED

If you exited the program at the end of the previous session, refer to page 11 of Session 3 to review how to open the next session or to continue from where you left off.

11.11 TEXTBOOK EXERCISES: REINFORCEMENT

Some of the drills presented earlier on the computer screen are repeated here to reinforce your keyboarding skills, along with some new drills. When you have finished keying them, click Print (if desired), then Next Exercise.

Reviewing the U, Z, and C Keys

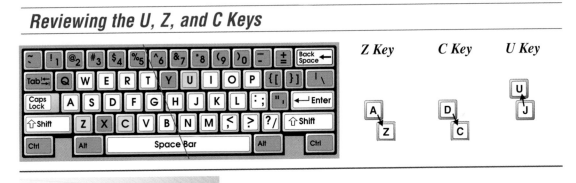

U Drill

Key lines 1–3 once, pushing for speed.

1 ju put put sun sun fun sun mud mud gum gum sum sum
2 vault audit rumor truth about nurse sprung refund blunt
3 Fusion Lawful Nature Urgent Plural Module Suppose

Key lines 4–6 twice: first for speed, then for accuracy.

4 Just be sure to return that blouse to the bureau.
5 That auto bumper is a hunk of junk; it is ruined.
6 A stout runner shouted and slumped to the ground.

55.6

Document   **Unbound Manuscript**

B

1   At the *Session 55 Document B* screen, key Document B by completing the following steps:

    a   Use the default left and right margins (1 inch).

    b   Move the insertion point to line 7.

    c   Change the line spacing to double.

    d   Use the heading format guidelines presented in this session.

    e   Use the widow/orphan guidelines presented in Session 49 for inserting hard page breaks.

    f   Number the pages in the upper-right-hand corner.

    g   Key the text.

2   Proofread and correct any errors in the document.

3   Click Check to automatically name (**055prob**), save, and check the document.

4   Print the document.

5   To correct errors, click View Original. Make any necessary changes, then recheck the document.

6   Click Next Exercise.

Students in Online Classes

Be sure to review the features to be activated before completing step 1a.

Document B

ABOUT SKIN CANCER

Melanoma and Non-melanoma Skin Cancers

Skin cancer (including melanoma and non-melanoma skin cancers, such as basal and squamous cell) is the most common of all cancers. There are more cases of skin cancer than of all other cancers combined. One in every five Americans will develop skin cancer in his/her lifetime.

Melanoma

Melanoma accounts for about 4 percent of all the skin cancer cases but causes about 79 percent of skin cancer deaths, and its rate is increasing. It is called melanoma because it originates from skin cells called melanocytes. Melanoma is more dangerous than either basal or squamous cell skin cancer because it is more likely to spread to other parts of the body. Most melanoma that has spread to distant parts of the body cannot be cured. However, when melanoma is diagnosed at an early stage, it is almost always curable.

Squamous Cell Cancers

Squamous cell cancers begin in the higher levels of the epidermis and account for about 20 percent of all skin cancers. They commonly appear on sun-exposed areas of the body. They can also develop within scars or skin ulcers elsewhere. Squamous cell cancers tend to be more aggressive than basal cell cancers and often invade tissues beneath the skin. They are also likely to spread to distant parts of the body.

Continued on next page

Z Drill

Key lines 1–3 once, pushing for speed. Don't stop to correct errors unless directed by your instructor.

1 az maze maze doze doze raze raze zip zebra zest
2 seize breeze amaze razor hazel zombies wizard zing zane
3 Trapeze Zealous Pretzel Horizon Zealous Zenith

Key lines 4–6 twice: first for speed, then for control.

4 Liz seized that sizzling pizza and ate with zeal.
5 Minimize the hazard and stabilize that bulldozer.
6 Zeb baked a dozen pretzels in the sizzling blaze.

C Drill

Key lines 1–3 once, pushing for speed.

1 ca calk cane case calf camp carp cave cede cad came
2 camera notice impact circle decide zinc clock corner
3 Compare Produce Consult Service Council Enclosure Carl

Key lines 4–6 twice: first for speed, then for control.

4 Carlton, the cat, curled in comfort in the chair.
5 Chris decided to purchase a record and a picture.
6 Cecelia consumed a rich chocolate ice cream cone.

Additional Drill

Students in Online Classes

Key the following drill. Press **Enter** after each line.

1 On the shrub in the puddle, Buff found a huge bug.
2 Sue slurps the sour soup as she slumps and sulks.
3 During the stunt, the group hummed a rousing tune.

4 Hazel won the prize as Buzz gazed with amazement.
5 The freezing drizzle glazed the bronze zinnias.
6 Hal has been penalized after embezzling a zillion.

7 With tonic and citric acid, can Carrie cure colds?
8 Could the clever client conceal crucial evidence?
9 A crow circled the cottage as Carol watched with caution.

> **Key each line for control; if you make more than two errors, repeat the line. Be sure to keep your eyes on the copy in the text as you key.**

 c Change the line spacing to double (Session 54).

 d Use the heading format guidelines presented in this session.

 e Number the pages in the upper-right-hand corner using the Header/Footer feature (Session 45).

 f Key the text.

2 Proofread and correct any errors in the document.

3 Click Check to automatically name (**055proa**), save, and check the document.

4 Print the document.

5 To correct errors, click View Original. Make any necessary changes, then recheck the document.

6 Click Next Exercise.

Students in Online Classes

Be sure to review steps 1a–1f before completing step 1a. Make sure you know how to activate the features used.

Document A

WHAT IS SKIN?
The Value of Skin

Skin is the largest organ of the body. It covers the internal organs and protects them from injury and bacteria and controls the loss of too much water or other fluids. The skin regulates body temperature, helps rid the body of excess water and salts; and provides for pain, temperature, and touch sensation.

The Three Layers of Skin

The skin has three layers: the epidermis, dermis, and subcutaneous.

The Epidermis

The epidermis is the top layer. It is extremely thin (averaging 0.2 mm) and has several parts.

<u>Stratum corneum</u>. The outermost part is called the stratum corneum or horny layer. It is composed of dead cells that are continually shed.

<u>Keratinocytes or squamous cells</u>. Below the stratum corneum are layers of living cells called keratinocytes or squamous cells.

<u>Basal cells</u>. The lowest part of the epidermis is the basal layer. It is made up of basal cells, which continually divide to form new keratinocytes. These replace the older keratinocytes that wear off the skin surface. The basement membrane separates the epidermis from the deeper layers of skin.

The Dermis

The middle layer of the skin is called the dermis. It contains hair follicles, sweat glands, blood vessels, and nerves, which are held in place by a protein called collagen. Collagen gives skin its resilience and strength.

The Subcutaneous

The last and deepest layer of skin is called the subcutaneous. It conserves heat and has a shock-absorbing effect, which helps protect the body's organs from injury. The cells of the subcutaneous produce melanin, which makes skin darker. Melanin is actually an energy sponge. It absorbs damage to prevent further injury from UV rays. So, to get a tan, you have to be injured.

ONE-MINUTE TIMINGS

Goal: 25 WAM with no more than 2 errors

Take a 1-minute timing on each paragraph.

1   The blunt auditor suggested to Duke that the business returns were a fraud. The usual routine of minimum turnovers of funds had been sound, but that fortune of thousands paid to a juror had not been inserted in the annual input. Duke presumed he was ruined and flushed with guilt.

2   Ruth sulked as her aunt poured a dose of the awful blue fluid. The sour stuff was supposed to be used for fatigue from the flu. She paused for a minute and gulped it down. Her aunt found four lumps of sugar for a bonus. Sullen disgust would turn into a laugh as a result.

3   Zeb zipped to that zoo with zest and nuzzled the zebras. He sneezed in the breeze and went to see the lizards. He wants to be a zoologist when he gets older. He knows a zillion things and his dazed and puzzled parents are amazed.

4   Zelda gazed in amazement as Zip, the wizard, seized a wand. It was ablaze with a maze of fire and lights. He did dozens of hazardous feats and puzzled all at the bazaar. He also was a trapeze whiz and dazzled folks.

5   A cookout on the beach could include cheese, carrots, meat sandwiches, and cold juice. If the chill of the ocean is too much, hot chocolate and hot coffee can chase the cold chills. The decent lunch and a chat with chums can enrich affection.

6   An office clerk who lacks basic ethics could become the subject of scorn. Those persisting in cruel and careless attacks on certain new workers can cause havoc. It is logical to follow strict, concise rules concerning office tact. Choose the right track and be sincere.

ENDING THE SESSION

Now you may print this session's files, continue to the next session, or exit the program. See page 24 of Session 6 if you need to review procedures.

Ergonomic Tip

Position your copyholder about the same distance from your eyes as the monitor so that your eyes don't have to refocus with different distances.

Manuscript Headings

The main purpose of headings is to call the reader's attention to the important ideas and sections in the manuscript. Various heading formats are acceptable. The rules for headings, page numbering, and line spacing used throughout the Manuscript Unit follow:

Major title:	Key on approximately line 7 on the first page; center and bold the title; capitalize all letters; double-space to the first-level heading (if used) or to the first line of the body.
First-level heading:	Center; bold and capitalize the first letter of each major word; double-space above and below.
Second-level heading:	Place it flush with the left margin on a separate line; capitalize the first letter of each major word; bold the heading; double-space above and below.
Third-level heading:	Indent with paragraph; capitalize the first letter of first word and any proper names, followed by a colon or period; underscore; double-space before. Note that some manuscript sections have second-level headings only, while others may have second-level headings followed by third-level headings.
Page numbering:	Place page numbers in the upper-right corner beginning with page 2 and leave a double space between the number and the body.
Spacing:	Use double spacing throughout.

PROPER TELEPHONE TECHNIQUES

(ds)

The Business Image

(ds)

It is widely accepted that proper use of the telephone as a business tool is one important quality of an outstanding employee. Most office workers spend two or more hours each day in telephone contact with clients and customers.

(ds)

Caller's Response

(ds)

A prompt answer. Answering the telephone promptly will give the caller a favorable impression of the company. Use a lively, pleasant voice that creates a welcoming atmosphere.

Figure 55.1 Heading format for manuscripts

55.5

**Document
A**

Unbound Manuscript

1 At the *Session 55 Document A* screen, key Document A by completing the following steps:

    a Change the left and right margins to 1.25 inches. (See Session 41 to review changing margins.)

    b Move the insertion point to line 7.

Session Goals

Y X Q   **Y, X, Q**

1-Minute: 25 WAM/2 errors

Y and Q words

12.1- 12.10

ON-SCREEN EXERCISES: GETTING STARTED

If you exited the program at the end of the previous session, refer to page 11 of Session 3 to review how to open the next session or to continue from where you left off.

12.11

TEXTBOOK EXERCISES: REINFORCEMENT

Earlier in the session you completed new-key drills presented on the screen. Now you will repeat some of those drills, along with some new ones, to reinforce your keyboarding skills. When you have finished the drills, click Print (if desired), then Next Exercise.

Reviewing the Y, X, and Q Keys

Y Drill

Key lines 1–3 once, pushing for speed.

1 jy yard play yowl very yolk away lazy sly yield yam
2 spray dairy entry handy lucky staying yonder young
3 Yearn Decay Empty Forty Hurry Lousy Playing Yale Taylor

Key lines 4–6 twice: first for speed, then for control.

4 The kitty and the puppy may not enjoy happy play.
5 It is only your duty to obey every law of safety.
6 Billy is ready to carry the heavy load Wednesday.

1   All machines are made up of parts that work together to perform functions or accomplish tasks for the user. If a machine is to work correctly, all those parts must be in top working condition. One way to make sure that the parts all work correctly is to maintain a regular schedule of cleaning the parts.

A computer is a machine. Therefore, if you want your computer system to work efficiently and have a long life, you need to pay close attention to keeping its parts clean. The parts of a computer system are the mouse, the mouse pad, the monitor, the keyboard, and the central processing unit.

Always turn off the computer before you begin your cleaning routine. The first step in computer cleaning is to use a soft brush or a soft brush attachment for the vacuum cleaner. Carefully brush or vacuum all the cracks and crevices on your monitor, keyboard, and central processing unit. Be sure to brush between the keys on your keyboard and any other hard-to-reach places. While you are brushing, don't forget to brush your mouse pad. In fact, you should brush your mouse pad once a day.

When you have brushed the surface dust and particles away, you can then use liquid cleaners to get rid of the grime that is in the air. Isopropyl alcohol (70%) is one of the most often recommended cleaning agents. You can also use a commercial window cleaner diluted. If you use the alcohol solution, be very careful not to use it directly on the keys, logos, or printed labels, as alcohol will remove some printing. Never pour alcohol directly onto your computer's parts.

Monitors, like windows, pick up particles from the air. The dust and grime that adhere to windows and mirrors also stick to monitor screens. You may even find the words on your screen hard to read through all the dust and fingerprints. Each week, you should clean your screen. You will need a soft brush (or soft vacuum brush), a soft, lint-free cloth or tissue, and a commercial window cleaner or isopropyl alcohol. When you are ready to clean the screen or other external parts, pour a little alcohol or window cleaner onto a lint-free cloth or tissue. Wipe the screen or other part and discard the cloth or tissue. Then, pour a little more cleaning solution onto the tissue and wipe the same area again. Be sure to get the corners clean. You can use small cotton swabs for the corners. Once your computer is clean and working well, set aside a day each week for routine cleaning.

TEXTBOOK EXERCISES: UNBOUND MANUSCRIPTS

Unbound manuscripts are typically one to four pages long. In this session, you will create several versions of unbound manuscripts and learn about creating headings for manuscripts.

X Drill

Key lines 1–3 once, pushing for speed.

1 sx axle next exam flex text hoax apex expedite fix fox
2 deluxe excise expand export prefix excite example
3 Explode Exhaust Examine Anxiety Exporting X ray Expert

Key lines 4–6 twice: first for speed, then for control.

4 Did excess oxygen explode during that experiment?
5 Explain the context and expedite that experiment.
6 Fix the exhaust and examine the axle of the taxi.

Q Drill

Key lines 1–3, pushing for speed.

1 aq quote quire squid quiet squaw query qualify quite
2 quench equate squeak equity squelching quit quartz
3 Squire Quarry Quaver Quorum Quartering Requesting

Key lines 4–6 twice: first for speed, then for control.

4 Do that quotient; it is a frequent quiz question.
5 Ducks squirmed and quacked in the squalid quarry.
6 Does the quitter frequently squabble and quibble?

Additional Drill

Key the following drill. Press **Enter** after each line.

1 In a sunny yard, the sassy gray puppy plays daily.
2 The friendly young boy, Gary, annoys Silly Sally.
3 A hungry baby in the subway was eyed by a sentry.

4 Examine her next; Maxine was exposed to smallpox.
5 The new relaxing exercise was explained in the textbook.
6 Is the lynx a vexing jinx or is it an exotic pet?

Students in Online Classes

Think control as you key the sentence on each line. If you make more than two errors on a line, rekey the sentence. Remember to keep your eyes on the text as you key.

Session Goals

🕐	**1-Minute: 45 WAM/1 error** **5-Minute: 35 WAM/1 error**
✏️	**Improving manuscript readability**

Review word processing features and applications

55.1-
55.2

ON-SCREEN EXERCISES: GETTING STARTED

If you exited the program at the end of the previous session, refer to page 11 in Session 3 to review how to open the next session. If you are continuing immediately from Session 54, start with Exercise 55.2. Click the Next Exercise or Previous Exercise button if you are not at the correct exercise.

55.3 | **ONE-MINUTE TIMINGS**

Goal: 45 WAM/1 error

SI: 1.47

- Take two 1-minute timings on the following material.
- Use your most recent timing speed to set a speed or accuracy goal.

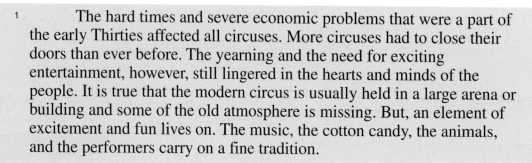

1   The hard times and severe economic problems that were a part of the early Thirties affected all circuses. More circuses had to close their doors than ever before. The yearning and the need for exciting entertainment, however, still lingered in the hearts and minds of the people. It is true that the modern circus is usually held in a large arena or building and some of the old atmosphere is missing. But, an element of excitement and fun lives on. The music, the cotton candy, the animals, and the performers carry on a fine tradition.

55.4 | **FIVE-MINUTE TIMINGS**

Goal: 35 WAM/1 error

SI: 1.49

Take two 5-minute timings.

7 The unique antique aquarium had a thick lacquer on it.

8 In the old square, the quake left queer quagmires.

9 The queasy squirrel was quarantined in the square box.

12.12 ONE-MINUTE TIMINGS

Goal: 25 WAM with no more than 2 errors

Take a 1-minute timing on each paragraph.

1 Basically, employers like a loyal employee. Honesty and courtesy always pay off in any job or duty. Apathy and sloppy typing are always likely to be very costly to a company. Any employee who displays a steady style will be properly rewarded and enjoy a fairly large salary.

2 There is simply no key to easy money. A bad agency may say that you are lucky and a legacy of wealthy glory is yours. Yet, if you try fancy or phony schemes, you will be mighty sorry. Steady, weekly saving is the thrifty means to easy money. Lay a penny away a day and be happy.

3 An extra exercise to help your mind relax is inhaling and exhaling deeply. It extends all the oxygen capacity before it is expelled. Choose an exact time each day to expedite an extra relaxing exertion. Your anxieties and vexations disappear and you relax. Try this exciting experience.

4 Exercise an extreme caution before investing in an old duplex. Have an expert examine all the existing details and explain them to you. It may be easier to buy a luxurious and deluxe apartment house. An experienced land expert knows if it is an expensive venture.

5 The quick squad conquered the unique quintet without question. The quarterback squelched most questions about technique or quality of the team. If they qualify for the trophy, will they quietly squash the next team or will the coach require an extra practice session?

6 Angelique might request a price quotation on an exquisite antique quilt. She acquired it from a queen in a quaint town near the equator. Quiet inquiries have arisen from qualified buyers. The question is, should she keep the quality quilt or sell it quickly as requested?

ENDING THE SESSION

Now you may print this session's files, continue to the next session, or exit the program. See page 24 of Session 6 if you need to review procedures.

> **Ergonomic Tip**
> To sharpen the image, adjust the brightness/contrast controls on your computer screen.

Now you can print any files you have created, continue with the next session, or exit Paradigm Keyboarding with Snap.

Print

To print Exercises 54.1–54.8 proceed as follows:

1   Click the Close ☒ button in the top right corner of the screen.
2   At your Paradigm Keyboarding with Snap Welcome page, point to Reports on the Snap menu bar, and click View Submissions Report.
3   At the View Submissions Report Wizard, click Show session files to see the drill lines text (Exercises 54.1–54.2), Show timings files to see the timings text (Exercises 54.3–54.4), and Show production files or Show unchecked production files to see the production documents (Exercises 54.5–54.8).
4   Click Show Report.
5   Click the name of the file you want to print.
6   At the Word Processor dialog box, click Launch.
7   Click File, and then click Print.
8   At the Print dialog box, click OK.
9   Click the Close button to close the Paradigm Word Processor.
10 Click Home on the Snap menu bar to return to the Welcome page.

Continue

To continue on to the next session, click the Next Exercise button twice to take you to Exercise 55.2.

Exit

To exit, do the following:

1   Click the Close ☒ button in the top right corner of the screen.
2   At your Paradigm Keyboarding with Snap Welcome page, click Logout.

Ergonomic Tip

If your desk will not accommodate your keyboard properly, think about using a keyboard tray.

Session Goals

 Review
Review keys from Sessions 1–12

 1-Minute: 25 WAM/2 errors

13.1 ## ON-SCREEN EXERCISES: GETTING STARTED

If you are continuing immediately from Session 12, you are already warmed up and are looking at Exercise 13.2. Click on the Next Exercise or Previous Exercise button if you are not at the correct exercise.

If you exited the program at the end of the previous session, refer to page 11 of Session 3 for instructions on entering the program.

CHECKING YOUR SKILL: ONE-MINUTE TIMING

13.2

In Sessions 7–9 and 11–12 you completed a series of 1-minute timings. The speed and accuracy goals were presented at the beginning of each set of timings. Check your scores now by accessing your Timing Performance Report (See page 27 for instructions on viewing your report.)

Now take a 1-minute timing on the paragraph that follows, using your scores for the timings in Sessions 7–9 and 11–12 as benchmarks. If you didn't reach at least 25 WAM in those previous timings, push for speed. If you reached the 25 WAM goal but had more than 2 errors, work for accuracy. If you achieved both the speed and accuracy goals, push for even greater speed.

> 1   It is good to have honest goals. Nothing is gained if one goes forth
> in pointless roaming. A major effort is needed to prosper. Isolate those
> foolish errors and avoid them. Hold to a strong, firm hope and move along.

13.3 ## TEXTBOOK EXERCISES: REINFORCEMENT

The Special Drills that follow provide additional practice on the keys that you have learned in Sessions 1–12.

Reinforcing the Keying of Alphabetic Characters

At a clear screen, try these drills to improve your general keyboarding skills:

1   For locational security, key the entire alphabet, keying each letter twice (aa bb cc dd ee ff...). Repeat this process once or twice.
2   To develop your thinking-and-keying skills, key the alphabet backwards (z y x...).
3   Key the following sentence three times to practice all the letters of the alphabet:

MANAGING MEDICAL OFFICE PROCEDURES

Workspace and Reception Area
    Administrative workspace
    Reception area
        Keeping the area clean
        Reception area decor

Managing Office Security
    Limiting access
    Office security systems
    Emergency plan

Managing Office Equipment
    Computers
    Transcription equipment
    Printers, copiers, faxes, scanners
    Paper shredders

REINFORCING WRITING SKILLS

Even with a complete outline of the ideas and information to be covered in a manuscript, many writers have a difficult time writing the first paragraph, which introduces the topic and states the main point, or *thesis*. An effective introduction opens with a few sentences that "hook" the reader's interest. It concludes with a statement of the main point of the manuscript. Above all, do not make the mistake of beginning your paper with the words "I am writing this manuscript because…" or "The purpose of this manuscript is to…." Unimaginative statements such as these tend to immediately turn off the reader. Instead, use one of the following "hooks":

- A surprising statistic or unusual fact
- A colorful example
- A quotation
- A question
- A comparison
- A joke or humorous statement

If you cannot think of a good hook to use, beginning with the thesis statement is acceptable. In fact, this straightforward approach is quite common in work-related writing.

54.8   **Document D**   **Manuscript Introduction**

Using a medical subject or topic that has been assigned in another class, or the thesis statement "More and more doctors are using voice recognition systems to dictate medical reports," compose an introductory paragraph for a manuscript on the subject. The introduction is to be a paragraph of 50 to 100 words. When you have finished, edit your document for clear sentences, effective word choices, and correct punctuation, grammar, and capitalization.

Save and name the document **054wprd**. Then print and close the document.

> The quick brown fox jumped over the lazy dogs.

Repeat these drills whenever you can. They will help you master the alphabetic keys.

Assessing Your Skills

The drills that follow provide additional practice on the keys that you have learned. However, if you are keying over 25 WAM with no more than 2 errors and do not hesitate when keying, you may skip the drills and go to the next session by clicking the Next Exercise button three times. This will take you to Session 14, Exercise 2. If you have not achieved the 25 WAM or fewer than 2 errors level, proceed with the Special Drills to build speed and/or accuracy. When you have finished the drills, click Print (if desired), then Next Exercise.

Use the following guidelines to choose drills:

1 If you cannot key as rapidly as you would like (at least 25 WAM), key each line once of the Balanced-Hand Words drill.
2 If you have not mastered the reach to a key(s) (you hesitate before striking the key), key each line once of the Balanced-Hand Words, Letter Combinations, and Sentences with Letter Combination drills.
3 If you are making more than 2 errors per minute, key each line once of the Double-Letter Words and the Longer Words drills.

Balanced-Hand Words (Speed)

1 sign and the sigh ant sit ale elf hen end she and
2 then hang the and fig dig die tie did sit fit aid
3 fish sign than then lane lake lens hand than halt

4 lake idle half lens lane sign dish sign then disk
5 aisle island handle fight angle title shake snake
6 gland sleigh height fight slant digit angle eight

7 he and the elf and it if he an tight giant signal
8 amble bible problem blame bland blend lamb emblem
9 gown wig bow wow vow down wit when wish with wisp

10 flap pane paid pale spent dispel lap nap pen paid
11 foam fork form foal odor soak rod fog sod oak rod
12 heir lair risks sir pan air widow flair hair pair

13 pelvis disown pens laps vie via pair vivid flames
14 map mane maid melt sham lame mend firm make disks
15 The pale maid paid for the vivid title and a wig.

16 Did the pale lamb amble down to the big bland pen?
17 When did Bob sign the pair of problem emblems?

Home care has grown in recent years. In 1990, there were about 4,275 home-health agencies meeting Medicare standards. Today there are more than 20,000. Only about 750,000 people were served by home-care programs ten years ago. The current figures exceed three million for the elderly alone.

Medicare and Medical Assistance expenditures for home care grew from $90 million in 1988 to nearly $4 billion in fiscal 1994. But that $4 billion is minor compared with the $70 billion spent for institutional care the same year.

Skyrocketing hospital costs and the continued graying of America will place stiffer demands on the health-care system and on the public and private agencies that help pay for that care. By the year 2050, more than 22 percent of our population is expected to be older than 65. The so-called Medicare Trust Fund could be bankrupt by then. Home care's cost-effectiveness could help reduce this fiscal pressure.

During Home-Care Week, we should applaud the work of the thousands of nurses, doctors, therapists, and aides who make home care the thoughtful, humane, and effective program that it is. But we also should use this time to look to the future and address some of the needs on the horizon. It will be up to us and to our elected officials to effect further reforms in the health-care system. Reforms must reduce costs and maintain quality care for citizens of all age groups and socio-economic backgrounds and with varying needs. Home care is now and must continue to be an important part of that education and transformation.

54.7

**Document
C**

Manuscript Outline

1 At the *Session 54 Document C* screen, key the outline shown in Document C by completing the following steps:
  a Click the Center button on the style bar.
  b Key **MANAGING MEDICAL OFFICE PROCEDURES** in bold.
  c Press *Enter* three times.
  d Click the Align Left button on the style bar.
  e Key the text in the outline as shown in Document A.
   1) Set 2 tab stops .25 inch apart from the left margin.
   2) Start first-level entries with Roman numerals (right justified), second-level entries with capital letters, and third-level entries with numbers.
   3) Press *Enter* twice before a new first-level entry.
2 Proofread and correct any errors in the document.
3 Click Check to automatically name (**054proc**), save, and check the document.
4 Print the document.
5 To correct errors, click View Original. Make any necessary changes, then recheck the document.
6 Click Next Exercise.

Be sure to review steps 1a–1e3 before completing step 1a. Make sure you know how to activate the features included.

Letter Combinations (Speed)

1 ta tall tan task taste tale take talk tag talent
2 th thesis thin theft this think than that then throw
3 te tenant tend tell tenth test tea tenor team

4 st stead steal steadiness stateside stag steam
5 sa sad saline Sal sang said sale sake safe sat sake
6 si since simple sinker sit single sift sip sin siphon

7 pe pets pest pen peg pea peat penguin pension
8 pi pine pink pipes piles pie pin pious pint
9 li like linkage linking link lien lied lie lid lime

10 le leaf least ledge lend lead left lest leap legacy
11 bl blade bleak blast blank blinds blind blight blow
12 ba bandages barks badge bath balk bail bag bad band

13 mi mire misting might midst mint mind milk mid
14 ma margin manager marsh mail make math mat man
15 oa float roast toad load oatmeal oath oats oak boat

16 ri rinse rigid ridges right ripe rises rip rid rice
17 ra rapid range raised rates rake ranks rap ran rayon
18 vi vintage vital visits vine vile vise vim vie viable

19 va vanish varied valid vast vases vane vat van varnish
20 wa waves waste wane wait wade wag war was wash wand
21 wi wiper wield wise will wipe wide wig wit win window

Sentences with Letter Combinations (Speed)

1 Janie washed and wiped her wig; she wasted water.
2 The boy blinked at a baby bound in bandages.
3 Those offensive oats floated off of that oatmeal.

4 The vital vintage vases vanished from a vast van.
5 The manager might mail the mild mints to the man.
6 Rapid Red ran to the raised ridges on that range.

Changing Line Spacing

If you review the illustration of an unbound manuscript on page 303, you will note that the text is double-spaced. Since the PWP default is single spacing, you will want to change the line spacing. You can do this before you key the text or you can key the text, select it, and then change the line spacing.

The PWP software provides three line spacing alternatives: single, one and a half, and double. To change to double spacing, click the Double Space button ≣ on the style bar.

54.6 Unbound Manuscript

Document B

1 At the *Session 54 Document B* screen, key Document B by completing the following steps:
   a Change the left and right margins to 0.75 inch (see Session 41).
   b Press *Enter* six times. (This moves the insertion point to line 7.)
   c Click the Double Space button on the style bar to change to double spacing.
   d Center the title **HOME-CARE IMPORTANCE GROWS**.
   e Key the text shown in Document B.
   f When the text is keyed, number pages in the upper-right corner using the Header/Footer feature. (See Session 45.)
2 Proofread and correct any errors in the document.
3 Click Check to automatically name (**054prob**), save, and check the document.
4 Print the document.
5 To correct errors, click View Original. Make any necessary changes, then recheck the document.
6 Click Next Exercise.

Document B

HOME-CARE IMPORTANCE GROWS

National Home-Care Week has been set aside to pay tribute to the many care-givers who serve not only the elderly but also the sick, disabled, and terminally ill of all ages in the comfort and security of their own homes.

It is striking how few people are aware of home care. It has been around for more than 100 years. Millions of people are given necessary health-care services at home each year by thousands of dedicated individuals.

If given a choice, most of us would prefer to stay at home rather than go to a hospital or nursing home. Home offers us sanctuary and privacy. Being cared for at home keeps our families together. It preserves the dignity of the individual in need of care, be that person young, old, temporarily or permanently disabled, or even dying. Home care also is less expensive than institutional care. The National Association for Home Care reports that in 1994 the average cost per Medicare beneficiary was about $2,500 for home care, $3,000 for nursing care, and $7,675 for hospital care.

Students in Online Classes

Since the clock starts when you press your first key, review steps 1a–1f before completing step 1a.

Continued on next page

7 That person had piles of pipes for them.

8 Then that steady tenant, Ted, did a tenth strength test.

9 Steadfast Stacy talks a lot and stands as she talks.

10 Sad Sal sang a signal as she sighted a safe date.

11 At least lower the left lid and shorten the length.

12 That hanging kite tail brings the person around.

13 Gal, finish the gasket for the gas gadget game.

14 I dislike the heat dial that fits the dental fan.

Double-Letter Words (Accuracy)

1 seed teens needless feeling indeed needs glee see

2 tall stall knitting install little shall hall all

3 heel steed likeness dissent seeing sheet need fee

4 see feel teeth indeed gallant sledding sleet knee

5 hill still lifeless endless assist stiff kiss add

6 eggs stall eggshell falling haggle sniff sell egg

7 tell shell settling skilled allied skill fell add

8 deed sleek seedling fiddles needle sheen keen eel

9 rabble rabbit gobble nibbles pebble babble hobble

10 narratives all follow terrains irritates terriers

11 door root mood took loot hook hood pool roof moon

12 immerges immense manners hammering dinners dimmer

13 shipping appease flipping happen sipping slipping

14 of offensive offense offset offends offers off of

15 She will be stalling the nice contest winner now.

16 That immense rabbit emerged and nibbled a carrot.

17 Tu Wee slipped the irritated kitten into the house.

Longer Words (Accuracy)

1 negative retrieve primitive privilege advertising

2 estimate familiar eliminate dependent sentimental

3 Eliminate that sentimental, familiar advertising.

Manuscript Outline

Document
A

1 At the *Session 54 Document A* screen, key the outline shown in Document A by completing the following steps:

    a Click the Center button on the style bar.

    b Key **OUR PAPER HIGHWAY**.

    c Press *Enter* three times.

    d Click the Align Left button on the style bar.

    e Key the text in the outline as shown in Document A. Set 4 tab stops .25 inch apart from the left margin. (See Session 45 to review tab setting.) Right justify the Roman numerals.

2 Proofread and correct any errors in the document.

3 Click Check to automatically name (**054proa**), save, and check the document.

4 Print the document.

5 To correct errors, click View Original. Make any necessary changes, then recheck the document.

6 Click Next Exercise.

Document A

Students in Online Classes

Review steps 1a–1e before completing step 1a to make sure you know how to activate the word processing features to be used. This will help increase your WAM rate.

OUR PAPER HIGHWAY

   I. Importance of Records Storage
     A. Usage today
        1. Productivity increase
        2. Correspondence volume
     B. Costs today
        1. Higher salaries
        2. Need for more equipment

  II. Methods of Storage and Retrieval
     A. Alphabetic filing
        1. Characteristics
        2. Specific uses
            a. Telephone books
               (1) Uniform information presentation
               (2) Easy-to-locate format
            b. Libraries
               (1) Combination records storage
               (2) Concise retrieval system
     B. Computer storage
        1. Flash drives
        2. Disk (magnetic and optical)

 III. Additional Problems in Records Storage
     A. Faxed documents
     B. Mistrust of computer data storage

4   resident standard telegrams registrar parenthesis

5   pipeline elephant dependent plaintiff safekeeping

6   That resident registrar sends standard telegrams.

7   initiated hesitating alkaline likeness indefinite

8   delegates heightened lengthened stealing gaslight

9   The hesitating delegate is stealing the gaslight.

10 digital lenient distant inkling heading delighted

11 disliked endless athlete install flatten inflated

12 A lenient athlete has inflated the flattened keg.

13 whenever stalwart wholesale handwriting knowledge

14 renovate negotiate imagination tradition rational

15 possible establish observation elaborate ambition

16 Establish rational imagination whenever possible.

17 seashells tasteless steadfast thankless defendant

18 attendant delighted sightless lightness negligent

19 legislate essential stateside skinflint landslide

20 Seashells in the landslide delighted a skinflint.

13.4 REPEATING THE ONE-MINUTE TIMING

Now that you have finished the Reinforcement section, the next activity is to take two
timings on the following paragraph. (Check your screen for specific information.)

1   It is good to have honest goals. Nothing is gained if one goes
forth in pointless roaming. A major effort is needed to prosper. Isolate
those foolish errors and avoid them. Hold to a strong, firm hope and
move along.

Compare the results with your earlier attempt. Has your speed improved?
Do you have fewer errors? If you are not reaching 25 WAM with 2 or
fewer errors on the 1-minute timings, repeat Sessions 11–12.

ENDING THE SESSION

Now you may print this session's files, continue to the next session, or
exit the program. See page 13 of Session 3 if you need to review procedures.

Ergonomic Tip
To minimize eye strain, align the computer monitor and keyboard directly in front of you.

Preparing an Outline

An outline is helpful to both the person creating the manuscript and the person reading it. Text is minimized so that both parties can concentrate on pertinent information. Keep in mind the guidelines presented in the preceding paragraph for developing an effective manuscript to include an outline.

Some commercial word processing packages include an *Outlining* feature that is helpful in the formatting process by automatically numbering, lettering, spacing, and indenting. The user just enters the text that is to appear on each of the lines. Since this feature is not available in the PWP software, you will be responsible for formatting the outline.

The outline consists of a centered heading, all caps, bolded, and placed on the line approximately 2 inches from the top margin (line 7 in PWP). The body of the outline begins a triple space below the heading. The body of the outline is single-spaced with a double space before first level statements. Review the example shown in Figure 54.2.

This is an example, do not key.

FONT ALTERNATIVES

(ts)

I.   Font
    A. Typeface
        1. Proportional spaced
        2. Monospaced
    B. Type Styles
        1. Times New Roman
        2. Courier

(ds)

II.   Point Sizes
    A. Difference in pitch and point
    B. Point size range
    C. Commonly used point sizes for specific applications

Figure 54.2 Typical outline

Note in the above examples that the Roman numerals are right justified as is done when working with Arabic numbers. This can be done when you are creating your outline by manually adding spaces to the left of Roman numerals consisting of only one or two characters. Automatic outline generators on commercial word processors typically do not right justify Roman numerals. Note that a tab setting of .25 inch creates a more visually pleasing outline structure than does the default setting of .5 inch.

2

NUMERIC KEYS

A manuscript is a multiple-page document that is prepared for publication purposes. It might be published as a magazine or journal article, as a research report, or even as a book. In the academic setting, manuscripts are oftentimes term papers that are completed for a particular course.

Manuscripts can be bound or unbound. Unbound manuscripts are generally short—one to four pages. Bound manuscripts are usually five or more pages long and include a title page, a table of contents, the body of the document with footnotes or text notes, and endnotes plus the bibliography.

The most efficient method of preparing a manuscript is to divide the process into the following steps:

- Identify the topic.
- Research the topic for background information.
- Take notes on cards or in some type of electronic format. Include the source of the information (title, author, publisher, publication date, pages).
- Using your PC, prepare an outline of the major ideas; edit and revise it.
- Using your PC, compose a rough draft of the report; include quotations from source notes or other information obtained from your research sources.
- Revise the writing and edit the document for punctuation, spelling, and capitalization.
- Prepare a bibliography.

Manuscripts are prepared using a specific format. The format must be consistent, with careful attention to details such as spacing, punctuation, and order. Two formats, the traditional and the simplified, are widely used in colleges and in the workplace. The illustration that follows displays the first page of a bound, simplified-style manuscript. Text notes (author's name plus page) are used to reference the research sources. The main difference between the traditional and the simplified style is the spacing before and after titles, subtitles, and headings. The traditional format uses a triple space; the simplified format uses a double space, which saves preparation time. For the manuscripts you prepare in this text's assignments, follow the simplified format. If you are keying a manuscript for a specific medical facility or school, however, be sure to follow their guidelines.

OUR PAPER HIGHWAY

The storing of valuable documents and records has had a place in history almost from the beginning of time. Even then, people tried to find a way to preserve and keep important records of their existence. As buying and selling evolved, the need to keep important records of major business transactions also grew. Throughout history, records storage and retrieval has always been an exciting and interesting career field.

(ds)

Importance of Records Storage

(ds)

Because of added productivity and the increased volume of business correspondence, the amount of paper used by companies has increased beyond human expectations or imagination. Business records, in spite of computerized data storage, take up more space than any other single item (Holbreck and Marcus 56). Space considerations as well as increased expenses for maintaining records storage have elevated the issue of records storage to a top priority.

Figure 54.1 Bound educational manuscript (simplified format)

Session

14

1, 2, 3

INTRODUCTION

Session 14 is the first session on mastering the number row, located just above the alphabetic keys on your keyboard. Since numbers are used so frequently with the alphabetic keys and with many of the symbols (for example, the percent sign), developing equal skills with numbers, symbols, and letters is important.

14.1-14.5 ## ON-SCREEN EXERCISES: GETTING STARTED

If you are continuing immediately from Session 13, you are already warmed up so start with Exercise 14.2. Click on the Next Exercise or Previous Exercise button if you are not at the correct exercise.

If you exited the program at the end of the previous session, refer to page 11 of Session 3 for instructions on entering the program.

14.6 ## TEXTBOOK EXERCISES: REINFORCEMENT

Some of the drills presented earlier on the screen are repeated here to strengthen your keyboarding skills, along with some new drills. When you have finished the drills, click Print (if desired), then Next Exercise.

Keying Numbers

Whether you keyboard for personal or for business use, you will frequently key numbers. Some of the numbers that occur regularly in textual material include social security, telephone, address/ZIP Code/postal zone, age, weight, height, credit card, and driver's license numbers.

Reviewing the 1, 2, and 3 Keys

- Use the home-row method (anchor the left hand on asdf, the right hand on jkl;).
- Whenever possible, think of numbers in units of two and three digits (as you key 11, think eleven).
- When letters and numbers are combined, think of the letter(s) plus a two- or three-digit number (for a111, think ay/one-eleven).

Goal: 35 WAM/1 error

SI: 1.49

Take one 5-minute timing.

1   Each day, many people move all of their belongings from one place to another place. The move may be a short one, just across the street. Or, the move may be a long one, all the way across the country.

One item many people forget until the last minute is the personal computer. Most of us do not know how to pack and move a computer safely. As with all items being moved, a computer is prone to damage if it is not packed and handled properly. There are a few well known tips for you to follow when you are planning a move.

The first thing you should do is to make a backup of your hard disk before you turn off the machine prior to the move. You can back up your files to external diskettes or to a tape backup system. Because the backup will take many external disks, you may want to invest in a tape backup system. This purchase will be of great help to you and is also quite inexpensive. While you are backing up your files, now would be a good time to write down the model and serial numbers. You will have proof and identification of each item if damage or loss should occur en route.

After you have made a complete backup of all your files and system, the next step is to begin taking your computer apart. Before you start this step, be sure to unplug your system. Then you can detach the cables from the peripheral devices such as your mouse, your printer, your keyboard, and any other devices you may be using. It is a good idea to label each cable with a small tag. That way, when you reach your destination, you can attach each cable in exactly the right place. As you unplug each cable or plug, it is also a good idea to put a small tag on each plug or port from which you removed a plug or a cable.

When you have completely detached every cable and plug, you can then begin packing your computer parts for the move. The best packing container is, of course, the original box in which your computer came. However, most of us have either misplaced this box or thrown it away. The next best container is a box that is about two inches larger than your system. Line the bottom of the box with newspapers or several inches of packing material. Foam packing materials work well; popcorn works just as well. Next, place your computer in the box and line the edges with the packing materials. Then, put the mouse and keyboard (each in a plastic bag) in the box with the computer. It would be a good idea to put layers of newspaper around these items. You can then fill the box to the top with more packing material. Seal the box and label it, and you are done.

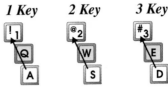

1 Key Drill

Key line 1 for control; key line 2 for speed. (Note that the lines contain the number 1, not the letter l.)

1   al lal alll al al all alll al llall al lal all al

2   all alll lla al lal all llla 111 lla 11 al lla la

2 Key Drill

Key line 1 twice for control; key line 2 twice for speed. Remember: When keying 21, think twenty-one, not two one.

1   1 2 1 21 221 122 121 221 2 1 212 112 1 12 21 21 2

2   al2 2al 112a 12al2 21al 122a all a2a 12a la2a 122

Note: Did you think of 221 as ***two-twenty-one***? Did you think of 112a as ***one-twelve/ay***?

Keying Numbers with Four Digits

When working with groups of numbers having four digits and no natural break, think of the numbers as two pairs.

Key lines 1 and 2; read the numbers in pairs to gain speed. As you key 1221 think twelve/twenty-one.

1   1221 1112 1221 1112 2112 2112 1122 1122 1221 2221

2   a1122 a1221 1112a 1212a a1112 a2112 a1212 a1221a2

Keying Numbers with Five or More Digits

When keying number groups that have more than four digits and no natural breaks such as spaces, commas, or decimals, use a 2-3-2 reading pattern. For the number 21221, think ***twenty-one/two twenty-one***. For the number 2121221, think ***twenty-one/two-twelve/twenty-one***.

Key lines 1–5 once; mentally pronounce the number combinations as they are keyed.

1   21 221 21 221 21 221 a21 212a 12 11a 2121 a121 a2

2   21221 21121 21221 a21112 a12212 a12121 21212 a122

3   a2112121 22 1 21a 2122121 12221 a212a 1221a 12221

54

UNBOUND MEDICAL MANUSCRIPTS

Session Goals

1-Minute: 45 WAM/1 error	**Changing line spacing, preparing outlines, and setting tabs**
5-Minute: 35 WAM/1 error	
Getting the reader's interest	

54.1-54.2 ON-SCREEN EXERCISES: GETTING STARTED

If you are continuing immediately from Session 53, start with Exercise 54.2. Click on the Next Exercise or Previous Exercise button if you are not at the correct exercise.

If you exited the program at the end of the previous session, refer to page 11 in Session 3 for instructions on entering the program.

54.3 ONE-MINUTE TIMING

Goal: 45 WAM/1 error

SI: 1.48

- Take a 1-minute timing on the following material.
- Use your most recent timing speed to set a speed or accuracy goal.

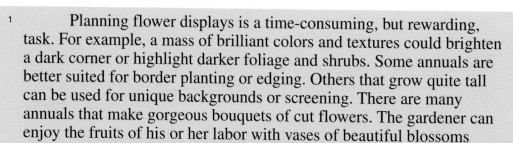

1   Planning flower displays is a time-consuming, but rewarding, task. For example, a mass of brilliant colors and textures could brighten a dark corner or highlight darker foliage and shrubs. Some annuals are better suited for border planting or edging. Others that grow quite tall can be used for unique backgrounds or screening. There are many annuals that make gorgeous bouquets of cut flowers. The gardener can enjoy the fruits of his or her labor with vases of beautiful blossoms placed all around the house. Having your own garden is a benefit you will appreciate time and again. Your friends and relatives will thank you for having a green thumb.

4 12 12 12 12 121 121 121 121 a2a a221 a221 2a211 1
5 212a1 121221a 12122a1 22221a 12212a 221221a 21a22

Remember: Keep your fingers on the home row and reach from that position to key a particular number or several numbers. Return your finger to the home-row position after striking a number.

3 Key Drill

Key lines 1–3. Repeat the lines, keeping your eyes on the copy while mentally reading the numbers as combinations.

1 332 32 213 231 12 1321 231 32 231 2312 232 1213 3
2 a33 a3 a32 a321 a233 a3232 a132 13232 3223212 a23
3 a323 a3212321 a13231a a1 231a a123 232 32 332 a13

Sentences

(Omit if Sessions 1–13 have not been completed.)

Key lines 1–3 once for speed.

1 Jean shall sell the 321 seashells and 212 stones.
2 Taste the lean tea; handle the kettle that leaks.
3 The 11 attendants halted a ring of thieves. They felt proud.

Key lines 4–6 once for control. Key lines 4–6 again. If you make a mistake on a line, start over until you can complete the line without error. Then go to the next line.

4 See, he is ill; his skin is flushed; he feels faint.
5 Enlist the 13 students to help with the many tasks.
6 She is a skilled athlete who strives for perfection.

Additional Drill

Key the following drill. Press ***Enter*** after each line. Remember to mentally read numbers with 2 or more digits in combinations.

Students in Online Classes

Reading numbers in groups will help you gain speed and improve accuracy. This method is sometimes referred to as "syllabizing" numbers.

1 2 21 21 12 1 112 212 1 2 221 121 121 221 21 1 2 1
2 222 222 22 222 2 222 222 22 2 2 222 222 22 22 2 2
3 3 3 3 33 33 33 33 33 333 33 33 3 3 3 33 33 33 3 3 3

4 1231 3323 321 13 33212 323321 233 23 231 13 233 3
5 a22132213 a21321 2331 2a 22312a 231132a 323132112
6 3112 1232 3321 2311 3122 1312 3222 3221 1223 1233

7 23 3231 2231 123 121 233 32 12131 221312 31131 12
8 3123 123212 133132 123 321233 3112 32 132 1132 21
9 32 321 33312 12 3 23222123 1122331 12 1223 311132

11

MEDICAL MANUSCRIPTS

Goal: 30 WAM with no more than 2 errors

Take a 1-minute timing on each paragraph.

1 　　　　When business is weak, there is not a lot of demand for money. So savings are invested in the stock market. The prices of stocks and bonds go up and interest rates go down. When business is strong, the demand for loans goes up to expand production, and consumers buy cars and homes. This pushes interest rates up.

2 　　　　The blunt auditor suggested to Duke that the business returns were a fraud. The usual routine of minimum turnovers of funds had been sound, but that fortune of thousands paid to the 12 jurors had not been inserted in the annual input. Duke presumed he was ruined and flushed with guilt.

ENDING THE SESSION

Now you may print this session's files, continue to the next session, or exit the program.

Print

To print Exercises 14.1–14.7 proceed as follows:

1 Click the Close ☒ button in the top right corner of the screen.
2 At your Paradigm Keyboarding with Snap Welcome page, point to Reports on the Snap menu bar, and click View Submissions Report.
3 At the View Submissions Report Wizard, click <u>Show session files</u> to see the drill lines text (Exercises 14.1–14.6), or <u>Show timings files</u> to see the timings text (Exercise 14.7).
4 Click Show Report.
5 Click the name of the file you want to print.
6 At the Word Processor dialog box, click Launch.
7 Click <u>F</u>ile, and then click <u>P</u>rint.
8 At the Print dialog box, click OK.
9 Click the Close button to close the Paradigm Word Processor.
10 Click Home on the Snap menu bar to return to the Welcome page.

Continue

To continue on the next session, click the Next Exercise ➡ button **twice**. This will take you to Exercise 15.2. (You will bypass Exercise 15.1 <u>Warmup</u> since you are already warmed up.)

Exit

To exit, do the following:

1 Click the Close ☒ button in the top right corner of the screen.
2 At your Paradigm Keyboarding with Snap Welcome page, click <u>Logout</u>.

Ergonomic Tip

Sit in a slightly reclined position with thighs parallel to each other. In other words, do not cross your legs, as it cuts off circulation.

53.10

Document F

E-Mail Message

Compose an e-mail message to your instructor that includes at least two paragraphs. In the first paragraph identify a medical facility where you would like to work, what your position would be, and why you would like to work there. In the second paragraph note the skills, experiences, personality traits, and education that you have that relate to this facility and the job you desire.

Use the same e-mail format that was introduced in Session 36. Provide an appropriate subject line. Calculate your WAM rate for creating the draft of your e-mail message by using the timing feature in PWP. (Click on the WAM Only button at the lower portion of the screen, then click the Stop button 🖳 when finished and your WAM rate will be calculated.) Proofread and correct any errors. Save your e-mail message as **053wprf.** E-mail the message to your instructor.

ENDING THE SESSION

Now you may print this session's files, continue to the next session, or exit the program. See pages 230–231 in Session 45 to review the procedures.

Ergonomic Tip

Keep your phone within easy reach and on the most convenient side. If you hold the phone with your left hand, place your telephone on the left side.

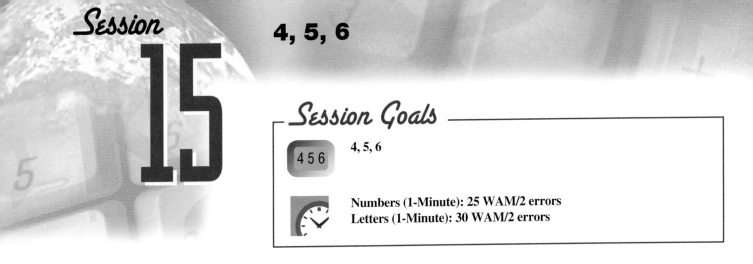

Session 15

4, 5, 6

Session Goals

456   **4, 5, 6**

Numbers (1-Minute): 25 WAM/2 errors
Letters (1-Minute): 30 WAM/2 errors

15.1-
15.6

ON-SCREEN EXERCISES: GETTING STARTED

If you are continuing immediately from Session 14, you are already warmed up so start with Exercise 15.2. Click the Next Exercise or Previous Exercise button if you are not at the correct exercise.

If you exited the program at the end of the previous session, refer to page 11 of Session 3 for instructions on entering the program.

15.7

TEXTBOOK EXERCISES: REINFORCEMENT

Some of the Session 15 drills that were presented on-screen are repeated here, along with some new drills, to reinforce your sense of where keys are located. When you are finished with the drills, click Print (if desired), then Next Exercise.

Reviewing the 4, 5, and 6 Keys

4 Key Drill

Key lines 1–3 twice: first key line 1 for speed, then key the same line for control. Do the same thing for lines 2 and 3. You will key faster if you think of the numbers in groups.

1   14 134 1431 2343 343123 43 334 3 3421 23214 432442

2   al4 a4231 24 4a24 1432a 34 a4321 a4323 a431 a342 a

3   4343213413 34343213311 4323412341 3431233 44342 43

53.9

Document E

Discharge Summary

1. At the *Session 53 Document E* screen, insert Document 050prob. Enter the information for the heading as follows:
   a. NAME: **Lucille Cheng**
   b. MEDICAL RECORD #: **19323**
   c. ADMITTED: **08/06/**Current year
   d. ROOM: **S-430**
   e. PHYSICIAN: **G. P. Munez, M.D.**
   f. DISCHARGED: **08/12/**Current year
2. Key the body of the discharge summary report.
3. Proofread, correct, and print the document and click the Check icon. Your document is automatically saved as **053proe**.
4. Click Next Exercise.

Document E

SUMMARY: The 64-year-old female was brought to the Center with a small bowel obstrukction. She had surgery once in the past for adhesions of her pelvis. A long weighted Anderson tube was placed and the patient continued to pass gas. She had a bowel movement the second day with decreased pain and tenderness. Most of the pain was in the left lower quadrant. She continues to improve. X-rays were repeated every day, and there is still some air in the small bowel, but this is slowly improving. Tenderness switched over to the right side of the abdomen. Bowel movements were present every day. The patient was passing fluids. On the second, third, and fourth days, there was an increase in the size of the loop of one of the small bowels. Still there was gas in the colon. After discussion with the patient, she decided that she wanted to go home. She does not have medical insurance. She was taking fluids. She was not having any tenderness or abdominal pain. She will stay on a clear liquid diet and will be followed as an outpatient.

FINAL DIAGNOSIS: Small bowel obstruction, intermittent.

OPERATION: None.

_____

G. P. MUNEZ, M.D.

GPM/your initials
DD: 08/12/current year
DT: 08/14/current year
DOCUMENT: 6830-DS

5 Key Drill

Key lines 1–3 twice: first for speed, then for control just as you did for the 4 Key Drill. Anchor the "a" or "f" finger on the home row depending on whether you are keying the numbers 3, 4, 5, or 1, 2, and read the numbers in groups.

1 11 55 a55 11 55 a55 11 55 55 11 51 a51 15 15 15 5

2 55 44 a45 54 14 15 24 25 34 35 53 43 52 42 51 41a

3 15115 15115 a55151 a55151 15 5151 151 al55 a51151

6 Key Drill

Key lines 1–3 twice: first for speed, then for control, just as you did in the 5 Key Drill. Anchor the ";" finger on the home row when keying the number 6.

1 11 a66 11 66 11 66 11 66 11 66 a66 11 66 11 66 61

2 166 166 a661 661 161 161 a611 661 661 116 11 a666

3 11666 16661 61 66 66 111 666 661 1166 16661 61 61

Students in Online Classes

> Do not touch the key between the home row and the number key you are entering. This would slow you down; in addition, all keyboards do not have the same alignment.

Additional Drill

Key the following drill. Press **Enter** after each line. Concentrate on reading the number in 2-3 combinations.

1 44 44 444 44 44 44 4 4444 44 4 4 444 444 44 44 4 4

2 334 44 343 22343 3443 23423 3422 4321 343 344 43 4

3 43 44342 3431233 4323412341 34343213311 4343213413

4 151 51 55 51 55 15 51 15 15 15 5 5 5 55 55 55 5 5

5 51 15115 155 151 51511 15 55151 55151 15115 15115

6 123 a15a a15a a321 a321a21515 a21515 15115 15115

7 6 61 61 61 61 61 666 666 6 6 6 6 66 66 66 66 6 6 6

8 a666 111 116 661 661 a611 161 161 661 a661 166 166

9 61 61 16661 1166 661 666 111 66 66 61 16661 11666

Sentences

(Omit if Sessions 1–13 have not been completed.)

Key lines 1–10 twice: first for speed, then for control. Follow the same procedure used in the 6 Key Drill above.

1 Dennis and Gene nailed 16 boards onto the old gate.

2 Helen had seen the 12 lighted signs shining at night.

3 Anne and Bill ate a salad and 15 figs and a big steak.

3 Proofread and correct any errors; click the Check icon and print the document.
4 Your document will be saved automatically as **053proc**.
5 Click Next Exercise.

Document C

OPERATIVE REPORT

PREOPERATIVE DIAGNOSIS: Coronary artery disease.
POSTOPERATIVE DIAGNOSIS: Same.
OPERATIVE PROCEDURE: Pt ay circumflex coronary artery.

This is a 63-year-old white male with coronary artery disease with recently unstable symptoms who underwent coronary arteriography last Friday, revealing a high grade stenosis of the circumflex coronary artery with some associated thrombus. He was continued on medications over the weekend and was stable and was brought back at this time for ay of the lesion.

Informed consent was obtained.

In the postabsorptive state and following 2 mg of Versed given in the laboratory, the patient was prepped and draped in the usual fashion. Two percent Lidocaine anesthesia was administered to the right femoral region. An 8 French introducer sheath was placed into the right femoral artery and 15,000 units of heparin was given intravenously and a heparin drip begun.

A #38 French left guiding catheter was used. The lesion was crossed with an ACS 0.014 high torque floppy guidewire and dilated with a Mansfield slider ST balloon catheter. There was a good ag result. After insuring ag and hemodynamic stability, all guidewires and guiding catheters were withdrqwn from the body. The sheath was sutured in place and the patient returned to his room in good condition.

_____

N. S. MAWE, M.D.

NSM/Your initials
DD: 3/16/Current year
DT: 3/16/Current year
DOCUMENT: 8557-OR

53.8

Document D

Operative Report

1 At a clear screen, open Document 053proc. Using PWP's Search and Replace feature, change the two-letter codes to their full words. Remember to select the <u>W</u>hole words only check box.
2 Name and save the Document as **053wprd**. Print the document.
3 Click Next Exercise.

4 Leslie sang a tiny jingle as she dashed ahead in glee.

5 When Tom tested his stiff ankle, he gnashed his teeth.

6 Please appease that helpless, pleading, pious plaintiff.

7 A tall, split, peeling aspen sapling is plainly diseased.

8 Pat speaks and pleads and defends the three plaintiffs.

9 Did Tim tape that splint and dispense the correct pills?

10 The spaniel has 134 bites and needs some skilled help.

15.8 NUMBER TIMINGS

Goal: 25 WAM with no more than 2 errors

Take a 1-minute timing on each group of numbers.

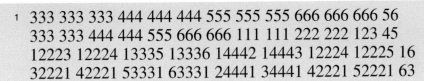

1 333 333 333 444 444 444 555 555 555 666 666 666 56
333 333 444 444 555 666 666 111 111 222 222 123 45
12223 12224 13335 13336 14442 14443 12224 12225 16
32221 42221 53331 63331 24441 34441 42221 52221 63

2 26 35 346 34 45 46 251 2346 235 325 625 463 51616 2
6242 4621 31446 51432 51431 4265 4261 5431 5421 6
16 61 61 31 31 31 3655 66 16 62 5661 6546 665 566 2
16 661 626 365 4466 1263 4565 16 15 1615 26 62 54 3

15.9 LETTER TIMINGS

Goal: 30 WAM with no more than 2 errors

Take a 1-minute timing on each paragraph.

3 Over 25 million pagers have been sold. More than half of all pagers sold are for personal use. Parents have beepers so babysitters can reach them when they go out. Adults give their elderly parents and teenagers their beeper number so they can be reached easily. Construction and factory workers use pagers because they do not have easy access to a telephone.

4 Muffin is a genuine bulldog. Although he weighs 64 pounds, he bounds about with a flourish. It is fun to see him plunge around, indulging in the pure pleasure of running. He huffs and puffs and slumps to the ground. No doubt, he will jump and lunge again after a pause and find trouble.

CONSULTANT'S REPORT

CONSULTATION: Upon n-o examination, the patient's pupils are symmetrically reactive withiout evidence of ptosis. He hnow has complete absence of voitional vertical eye movements, with very slowed horizontal saccade. Doll's-head-eye maneuver shows full em reflexes. The general neurologic examination showed an increased tone involving the ap.

IMPRESSIONS:

1.   Progressive sp (Steele-Richardson-Olzewski syndrome).

RECOMMENDATIONS: In the near future, the patient will likely require a feeding tube placement because of probelms with aspiration. I have discussed with the patient and his son the aggressiveness of future medical care with regard to treatment of aspiration pneumonia and the complications of being totally immobilized. We plan on helping out on a regular basis at this point.

_____

D. V. CROSBY, M.D.

DVC/Your initials
DD: 09/14/Current year
DT: 09/14/Current year
DOCUMENT: 655-CR

53.6

Document B

Consultant's Report

1   At a clear screen, open document 053proa. Using PWP's Search and Replace feature, change the two-letter codes to their full words. Remember to select the <u>W</u>hole words only check box.

2   Name and save the document as **053wprb.** Print the document.

3   Click Next Exercise.

53.7

Document C

Operative Report

1   At the *Session 053 Document C* screen, insert Document 049prob. Enter the information for the heading as follows:

   a   NAME: **Sean J. O'Connell**
   b   MEDICAL RECORD #: **5773**
   c   SURG: **F. J. Schillar, M.D.**
   d   ROOM: **S-322**
   e   ASST: **G. A. Hasart, ORT**
   f   DATE OF BIRTH: **02/22/1943**
   g   ANES: **K. E. Lundigen, M.D.**
   h   PHYSICIAN: **N. S. Mawe, M.D.**
   i   DATE/OPERATION: **03/15/**Current year

2   Key the body of the operative report. Codes for three medical terms have been used. Key the two-letter codes as shown.

      Pt   =   Percutaneous transluminal
      ay   =   angioplasty
      ag   =   angiographic

5   Thomas bought a used car from a dealer at 16532 Halsted Street. Although the bumper and the trunk were ruined, he assumed that it would run. If he would flush the rust from the lumbering hulk of junk, he might be able to use it. His woeful anguish spurred a new thought; perhaps it was useless.

ENDING THE SESSION

Now you may print this session's files, continue to the next session, or exit the program. See page 55 of Session 14 if you need to review procedures.

Ergonomic Tip
Keep both feet flat on the floor or a footrest to minimize fatigue.

Textbook Exercises: Medical Reports and Forms Progress Check

Now that you have completed the Medical Reports and Forms unit, it is time to determine how quickly you can key a variety of medical reports and forms. You will complete three medical reports using templates created in earlier sessions of this unit. The three reports are as follows: Medical Consultant's Report, Operative Report, and a Discharge Summary Report.

Key the following reports as quickly as possible, correcting all errors. When you finish and check the documents, you are indicating that everything is completely correct with no errors.

Your goal is to key each report, correctly formatted, with all errors corrected at 25 WAM or higher. The timing starts as you begin keying and ends when you click the Check icon after the document has been completed and all errors corrected. It is your responsibility to review the report and its instructions before it is keyed.

If you key a report at a rate below 25 WAM and/or are missing errors that should have been corrected, your instructor may ask you to repeat those specific reports.

The final activity of Session 53 is to compose a memo to your instructor that identifies a medical facility where you would like to work plus other supporting information. You are to use the PWP timing feature to check your WAM rate.

Medical Consultant's Report

53.5

Document A

Reminder: Before opening the template for the report, read the instructions and the content of Document A.

1 At the *Session 53 Document A* screen, insert Document 046prob. Enter the information for the heading as follows:
   a NAME: **Alfred J. Marchant**
   b MEDICAL RECORD #: **9035**
   c ROOM: **S-68**
   d DATE OF BIRTH: **10/12/1941**
   e ADMITTED: **09/14**/Current year
   f DATE OF CONSULT: **09/14**/Current year
   g PHYSICIAN: **L. V. Gibbons, M.D.**
   h CONSULTANT: **D. V. Crosby, M.D.**

2 Key the body of the consultant's report. Codes for four medical terms have been used. Key the two-letter codes as shown.

n-o	=	neuro-ophthalmic
em	=	extraocular motility
ap	=	appendicular musculature
sp	=	supranuclear palsy

3 Proofread and correct any errors; click the Check icon and print the document.
4 Your document will be saved automatically as **053proa**.
5 Click Next Exercise.

7, 8, 9, 0, COMMA, DECIMAL

Session Goals

 7, 8, 9, 0, Comma, Decimal

 Numbers (1-Minute): 25 WAM/2 errors
Letters (1-Minute): 30 WAM/2 errors

16.1-16.8 ON-SCREEN EXERCISES: GETTING STARTED

If you exited the program at the end of the previous session, refer to page 56 of Session 15 to review how to open the next session or to continue from where you left off.

16.9 TEXTBOOK EXERCISES: REINFORCEMENT

Earlier in the session you completed new-key drills presented on the screen. Now you will repeat some of those drills, along with some new drills, to reinforce your keyboarding skills. When you have finished the drills, click Print (if desired), then Next Exercise.

Reviewing the 7, 8, 9, and 0 Keys

7 Key Drill

Key lines 1–3 twice: first for control, then for speed. Anchor the ";" finger on the home row.

1 a55 77 66 76 57 57 a76 77 777 677 a555 76 6 a755a a755a
2 767 767 5767 5757 a576 7675a 7675a 77 777 666 555 a75a
3 a576a 76a5a 6675a 6675 5667 777 a65a7 5672 a7765 a575a

We live in an age where technological change is impacting the way we work and live. What technologies will be at our fingertips in the year 2010 that will change how we live from day to day?

Here are two examples of evolving technologies. Information that is being retained has been stored on paper. Other ways of storing data have been introduced that are better than using paper. A paper based system is costly since it is labor intensive. Storage and retrieval are slow compared to other means of storing data such as optical disk systems. Storing paper requires a great deal of space when you consider what is required for storing the same amount of data on other types of media to include film and disks.

Something has to be done to change the way we keep information. Will this change by the year 2010? It must, but what technology will it be that brings about this change? Optical disk technology is one alternative, but nothing is for sure. One point that must be considered is the human factor. It is hard for people to change. Even though there are a number of inefficiencies associated with paper based systems, it is hard to break habits. Microfilm has been around as a substitute for paper for over 50 years; yet, less than three percent of the records kept by businesses are on microfilm.

Another technology that no doubt will change in the future is voice communications. Great strides were made with the advent of cellular phone systems introduced in Chicago in 1983. This technology was accepted faster than any other innovation in our time. While this system has provided the means to stay in touch with others while away from home or workplace, there are some concerns.

Cellular phone service doesn't reach all places. These systems started out by transmitting analog signals. There are limits with this type of signal in terms of speed, distance, and accuracy when compared to sending digital signals. Also, in some mobile systems it is hard to find a person when he or she moves from one place to another. A replacement for these systems is PCS—Personal Communication Systems. The signal is digital, it costs less than cellular systems as smaller antennas are used and the cells are smaller, which adds to the number of channels since there are more cells.

Will 2010 be the year that newborn infants will receive a number or some type of code or method of recognition that will be theirs for life that will serve as their address wherever they are?

See how quickly you can complete the following:

1   Key the numbers 1 through 7 three times. Space once after
    each number. Keep your eyes on the screen.
2   Reverse the order; key from 7 down to 1. Space once after
    each number.

8 Key Drill

Key lines 1–3 twice: first for control, then for speed. Anchor either
the "j" or the ";" finger on the home row.

1   88 11 588 11 88 11 88 11 88 11 688 11 88 11 8 8823 1482
2   8182 81828 2845 6817 71882 6818 2238 885 888 288 388
3   557 8283 38482 78681 11812 8823 28 28 888 321 854 488

Now complete the following drill to develop speed and concentration:

1   Key the numbers 1 through 8 three times. Space once between numbers. Again, keep
    your eyes on the screen. Do not look at your fingers.
2   Reverse the order; key from 8 back to 1 three times. Space once between numbers.

9 Key Drill

Key lines 1–3 twice for control. Anchor the "j" finger at home as the "l" finger keys 9.
Remember to read the numbers as groups.

1   8489 19891 1919 1891 9981 19867 183218 189 19 698 98
2   99 88 589 998 998 888 991 999 498 98 99 88 94 32989 29
3   23 1989 2239 39823 59891 123 698 92919 9812 375 688 9

Here's another drill to develop speed with the 9 key:

1   Key the numbers 1 through 9 three times. Space once between numbers. Remember keep
    your eyes on the screen.
2   Reverse the order; key from 9 back to 1 three times. Again, space once between numbers.

0 (Zero) Key Drill

Key the following line three times for control. Anchor the "j" finger at home as the ";" finger
strikes 0.

Note: Be sure to use the zero key, not the capital O.

10 20 30 40 50 60 70 80 90 a10 a20 a30 240 250 10 115 619 057

Now try this drill to help you focus on the location of each number key:

1   Key the numbers from 1 to 100. Space once after each number. Use word wrap.
2   Key the numbers from 2 to 200 by twos. Space once after each number. Again, use word
    wrap.

Session Goals

1-Minute: 45 WAM/1 error
5-Minute: 35 WAM/1 error

**Search and Replace
and using templates**

Composing an e-mail message

53.1-53.2 ON-SCREEN EXERCISES: GETTING STARTED

If you exited the program at the end of the previous session, refer to page 11 in Session 3 to review how to open the next session. If you are continuing immediately from Session 52, start with Exercise 53.2. Click the Next Exercise or Previous Exercise button if you are not at the correct exercise.

53.3 ONE-MINUTE TIMINGS

Goal: 45 WAM/1 error

SI: 1.48

• Take two 1-minute timings on the following material.

• Remember to set either a speed or accuracy goal. Note that the WAM goal has been increased to 45.

> [1]   There are many sources to tap when searching for that first job. Schools usually employ guidance counselors who will assist you with a search for your first job. Some large schools also have a job referral service, which brings an employer and an employee together. Frequently, the local employment service is an excellent source for employment opportunities. If you are out of school, the Civil Service Office will also make information available to you. The student who is determined to find that first job will learn quite rapidly that there are many kinds of new career choices in the marketplace.

53.4 FIVE-MINUTE TIMINGS

Goal: 35 WAM/1 error

SI: 1.48

Take two 5-minute timings. The 5-minute WAM goal has been increased from 30 to 35.

Number Concentration Drill

Key lines 1–5 twice for control. Concentrate on reading the numbers in groups.

1 11201 1316 14037 22304 3405 4506 35607 6708 78092 1415

2 6816z 62317 73218 2219 32206 8782 19222 90234 1929 3030

3 45317 7932 34332 13476 9535 87369 1370 1743 37744 7645

4 2674 65647 1674 84859 34750 25151 23270 45524 8910 573

5 91524 7853 85426 1927 52938 22304 11201 78092 7753 361

Comma and Decimal Keys

You have now been introduced to all ten digits and are ready to review other areas of the keyboard. There are two symbols used frequently with numbers—the *comma* and the *decimal point* (also used as a period at the end of a sentence). These keys were reviewed in Session 3 but because they are used frequently with numbers, more practice is offered here.

Comma Key   *Decimal Key*

Comma Key Drill

When numbers are separated by commas, decimals, spaces, letters, or other symbols, use those division points as natural breaks between groups of numbers. For example, 5,134 would be read *five/comma/one thirty-four*.

Key lines 1–3 twice: first for control, then for speed. Concentrate on grouping the numbers by division points.

1 1,368 16,434 92,860 58,167 34,511 76,924 6,331 21,468

2 38,107 48,243 1,509 5,114 15,816 6,184,336 98,165,225

3 4,408,452 251,145 12,259 1,259 159,467 43,410 875,243

Decimal Key Drill

Key lines 1–3 for control. Concentrate on reading numbers by division points. If you make a mistake, start over until you complete the line without an error.

1 41,345.51 15,378.78 31,428.27 89,261,500.68 59.63 61.3

2 91,007.23 851,267.18 109.01 13.17 8.43 4.40 596.27 39.8

3 990.85 67,349.34 23,265.08 186.84 4.23 .87 8,582 13.455

- Call a nurse if you need help; a nurse can be reached by pressing the button. You can call a nurse for help by pressing the button.
- The administrative assistant prepared a progress report.

52.11

Document G

Memo on the Subject of Sexist Words

Think of five job titles that are commonly associated with males and five job titles frequently associated with females. Then compose a memo to a school administrator or counselor in which you describe the kinds of sexual stereotyping that occur in written communications about these positions. Give examples of how the sexist words affect attitudes and behavior in the workplace.

Be sure to include a descriptive subject for your memo. If the opportunity presents itself, incorporate the PWP features that have been used so far. Proofread and correct any errors. Save your document as **052wprg**. Print, then close your document.

ENDING THE SESSION

Now you may print this session's files, continue to the next session, or exit the program. See pages 230–231 in Session 45 to review the procedures.

Ergonomic Tip

Room lighting should be bright enough to allow everyone to see but not so bright as to compete with the monitor.

Additional Drill

Key the following drill for speed. Press **Enter** after each line.

1 77 77 7 7777 7777 777 777 77 77 7 7 7777 777 77 7
2 6 76 a555 677 777 77 a76 57 57 76 66 77 a55 75 75
3 4651 1234 3467 461234 3457 56712 62345 5671 71234

4 88 88 88 88 88 888 888 88 88 8 8 8 88 88 88 8 8 8
5 8 11 88 11 688 11 88 11 88 11 88 11 588 11 88 411
6 88 2238 6818 71882 6817 2845 81828 8182 1482 8823

7 91 999 99 9 999 9 99 99 99 91 91 91 99 9 999 9 99
8 19 189 183218 19867 9981 1891 1919 19891 8489 989
9 92919 698 123 59891 39823 2239 1989 2923 32989 94

10 10 20 30 40 50 60 70 80 90 a10 a20 a30 240 250 10
11 6,151 6,719 1,438 4,497 5,313 7,893 38,751 45,134
12 .87 4.23 186.84 23,265.08 67,349.34 990.85 596.27

Sentences

(Omit if Sessions 1–13 have not been completed.)

Key lines 1–10 twice: first for speed, then for control.

1 Of the 15,220 rangers, 170 sprained their ankles last year.
2 Dirk did the drills first and drank the delicious tea later.
3 Take 12 or 13 fresh, green grapes as your dessert treat.

4 He risks great danger if he departs after the dinner.
5 The 14 interns gratefully lingered in the green garden.
6 The meat manager made a simple remark and smirked.

7 Did Mary send the 380 messages after amending them?
8 Pam had made some malts with milk, mint, and mango.
9 The firefighters attempted an immense task and missed.
10 Did Sammie eliminate the 16 mistakes in the message?

16.10 NUMBER TIMINGS

Goal: 25 WAM with no more than 2 errors

- Take a 1-minute timing on each group of numbers.
- Press **Enter** at the end of each line.

two-zero plain and the skin was closed with steel clips. The patient seemed to tolerate the procedure well and was taken to the recovery room in satisfactory condition.

_____

L. R. Orr, M.D.

LRO/xx
DD: 08/31/Current year
DT: 08/31/Current year
DOCUMENT: 5333-OR

52.10

Document F

Changing Operative Report Using Search and Replace

1   At the *Session 52 Document F* screen, open Document E.
2   Using PWP's Search and Replace feature (See pages 207–208 in Session 43, for a review), change the two-letter codes to their full words. Remember to select the <u>W</u>hole words only check box.
    pr = peritoneum
    ir = interlocking
    sb = subcutaneous
3   Proofread the document to make sure that the replacements didn't cause formatting errors.
4   Name, save, and print the document as **052wprf**.

REINFORCING WRITING SKILLS

Avoiding Sexist Words

Sexist words are offensive and unprofessional. However, in many situations, writers may not be aware that they are using such prejudicial words. Note the following examples:

- If a doctor is needed, *he* can be paged. (All doctors aren't males.)
- Call a nurse if you need help; *she* can be reached by pressing the button. (All nurses are not females.)
- The administrative assistant prepared *her* progress report. (Both males and females work as administrative assistants.)

To avoid sexist labels and stereotyping, use plural pronouns (they, their). In situations where that is not possible, refer to both sexes with pronoun phrases such as he or she. Or use words that don't make reference to a person's sex, such as student, person, individual. Here are examples of how to change the above sentences to eliminate sexist expressions:

- If a doctor is needed, he or she can be paged.
  Page a doctor if you need help.
  Doctors are available by page.

Students in Online Classes

Prepare an e-mail rather than a memo for the document 052prog. If you do not know the e-mail address of your school administrator or counselor, send the e-mail to your instructor.

1. .81 85 823 8466 8877 7868 58 45 238 845 866 8143 8 8123
5671 82345 3458 8612348 3467 1238 886 81387 5834278
58743218 11386518 2251386 87 88 8811318 8 5481 8375
18 2368 8 7628 81 61842 8811318 18 8788 5792 6139 144

2. 91 95 923 8466 9977 7898 69 45 239 945 966 9143 9 9123
5671 92345 3458 9612349 3467 12392 996 81389 5934278
59743219 11386519 2251396 973 99 9911319 9 5491 9375
19 2368 9 7629 947 61942 99111319 19 979 7426 5187 239

3. 27 821 59361 40352 89734 92035 64019 9356 693 958 3177
501 6512 96 8742 56034 56832 85923 780 847 91 6409 7483
9467 3520 5945 2635 5705 8932 6485 1956 23670 81251800
165 208125635 69312 9871 6017340 2 716941 8320193 5163
8613 5113818 8542001 88490 6 2361 15432 11621618 11234
19051 3399 668 45441 4091 25937 68465 21893 492 591 783

16.11 LETTER TIMINGS

Goal: 30 WAM with no more than 2 errors

Take a 1-minute timing on each paragraph.

1.   Zeb went to the zoo to see the 179 new animals. He went especially to see the 18 species of lizards. He wants to be a zoologist when he gets older. He knows many things about animals, and his parents are really amazed.

2.   A cookout on the beach could include 6 kinds of cheese, carrots, 3 types of meat sandwiches, and 14 cans of cold juice. If the chill of the ocean is too much, hot chocolate and hot coffee can chase the cold chills. The decent lunch and a chat with friends can enrich affection.

3.   An office clerk who lacks basic ethics could become the subject of scorn. Those who gossip about or verbally abuse new workers can cause problems. It is smart to follow the 13 rules that are printed on the bulletin board about getting along with fellow workers. Do the right thing and be sincere.

ENDING THE SESSION

Now you may print this session's files, continue to the next session, or exit the program. See page 55 of Session 14 if you need to review procedures.

Ergonomic Tip

The human body is made to move. When you stay in one position too long, you will end up stiff, sore, and stressed. After sitting at your workstation for 45-60 minutes, stand up and stretch your arms and legs.

Document E

Operative Report

1. At the *Session 52 Document E* screen, insert Document 049prob. Enter the information for the heading as follows:
   a. NAME: **Jeanine A. Kvinsland**
   b. MEDICAL RECORD #: **3990**
   c. SURG: **L. R. Orr, M.D.**
   d. ROOM: **780**
   e. ASST: **C. H. Pridaux, R.N.**
   f. DATE OF BIRTH: **10/19/1981**
   g. ANES: **F. A. Bresch, M.D.**
   h. PHYSICIAN: **B. E. Stohr, M.D.**
   i. DATE OF OPERATION: **08/29/Current year**
   When entering the Name, Medical Record #, Room, Date of Birth, and Physician information, use your right arrow key to move past the colon, press the space bar once, and enter the data. For the other entries in the heading and in the body of the report press the End key, then press the space bar once.
2. Before keying the radiology report, proof the document to check for errors that may have been overlooked.
3. Key the body of the operative report. Throughout this document, the codes for three medical terms have been used. Key the two-letter codes as shown. These codes will be changed using the Search and Replace feature in the next document.
   pr = peritoneum
   ir = interlocking
   sb = subcutaneous
4. Depending on where the page break falls, insert a hard page break if appropriate.
5. Proofread and correct the document; click the Check icon and print.
6. The document is automatically saved as **052proe**.
7. Click Next Exercise.

Document E

PREOPERATIVE DIAGNOSIS: Attempted vaginal birth after previous cesarean section; failure to progress with premature rupture of membranes.
POSTOPERATIVE DIAGNOSIS: Same.
OPERATIVE PROCEDURE: Repeated low transverse cesarean section. After the induction of satisfactory spinal anesthesia with the patient in the lateral supine position, she was prepped and draped in the usual manner for abdominal procedure. A Foley catheter had been inserted into the bladder and the abdomen was entered through a previous low transverse incision without difficulty. Upon approaching the fascia there was about 2 to 3 centimeter central defect. The parietal pr was then incised and entered. Then the visceral pr was incised and the bladder was pushed downward. The lower uterine segment was entered transversely and the infant was delivered. The placenta was extracted manually and the uterine defect was closed in two layers. The first being a running ir suture of number one chromic followed by an imbricating Lembert suture. Hemostasis was adequate and the visceral pr was closed with number two-zero chromic. The pelvis was evacuated of a blood clot and the anterior pr closed with number zero chromic sponge pad and needle counts were correct. The fascia was dissected off giving a free edge and this was closed with number one Maxon. This sb tissue was closed with

Continued on next page

Session 17

NUMBER PATTERNS; USING PRESET TABS

**17.1-
17.3** ## ON-SCREEN EXERCISES: GETTING STARTED

If you exited the program at the end of the previous session, refer to page 56 of Session 15 to review how to open the next session or to continue from where you left off.

17.4 ## TEXTBOOK EXERCISES: REINFORCEMENT

Some of the drills that were presented on-screen during the first part of Session 17 are repeated here, along with some new drills, to reinforce your keyboarding skills. When you have finished the drills, click Print (if desired), then Next Exercise.

Keying Numbers

Complete these drills to reinforce your number keying skills:

1 Key this line of numbers two times:

11 22 33 44 55 66 77 88 99 00

2 The most frequently used number is 0, followed by 5. To build your skills with these numbers, first key to 500 by tens; then key to 200 by fives.

Example: 10 20 30 40 50 60 etc.
Example: 5 10 15 20 25 30 35 40 45 50 etc.

3 To reinforce your ability to think while keying numbers, start at 100 and key to 0 by threes.

Example: 100 97 94 91 88 85 82 79 etc.

Repeat these drills whenever you can. They will help you master numbers.

Reading Number Groups

Remember, when numbers are grouped naturally by commas, spaces, and decimals, read the number by those groups. For example, 1,676,352.17 is read *one/comma/six seventy-six/comma/three fifty-two/decimal/seventeen*.

Radiology Report

Document C

1. At the *Session 52 Document C* screen, insert Document 048prob. Enter the information for the heading as follows:
   a. NAME: **Sharon A. York**
   b. MEDICAL RECORD #: **2743**
   c. ADMITTED: **05/12**/Current year
   d. ROOM: **S-345**
   e. PHYSICIAN: **B. T. Houston, M.D.**
   f. DATE/PROCEDURE: **05/13**/Current year
2. Before keying the radiology report, proof the document to check for errors that may have been overlooked.
3. Key the body of the radiology report. Codes for three medical terms have been used. Key the two-letter codes as shown.

en	=	endotracheal
pv	=	perihilar vascular
po	=	pneumothorax

4. Proofread and correct any errors you have made; click the Check icon and then print. The document is automatically saved as **052proc**.
5. Click Next Exercise.

Document C

PROCEDURE: Portable chest X-ray.

A single portable view of the chest was taken after open-heart surgery. A comparison was made with an earlier study of the same date. The en tube is now is place as is a Swan-Ganz catheter. Mediastinal drain and right chest tubes are in place. The heart appears to be generous in size and the right border is somewhat indistinct of pv structure. There is no sign of po.

IMPRESSION:

1. Satisfactory postmedian sternotomy chest.

_____
S. E. KING, M.D.

SEK/your initials
DD: 05/13/Current year
DT: 05/14/Current year
DOCUMENT: 8939-RR

Radiology Report

Document D

1. At a clear screen, open Document 052proc. Using PWP's Search and Replace feature, change the two-letter codes to their full words. Remember to select the Whole words only check box.
2. Name and save the document as **052wprd.** Print the document.
3. Click Next Exercise.

Key lines 1–3 twice: first for control, then for speed. Concentrate on reading numbers in groups.

1 1,676,352.17 3,131 2.24 436,342 101.31 166,891 89
2 236,731 831,643 534.67 4,091,867 3,587.13 501,316
3 61,301.04 .36 89,341.76 31,700.73 151,317 416,319

Creating Columns of Numbers

Using the preset tabs every 0.5 inches, create the columns of numbers shown below by keying the first four-digit number and then pressing **Tab** twice to move between columns. Press **Enter** at end of the line.

4901	8702	3303	3904	7205
6106	8307	9408	2709	3710
1511	5712	2613	9114	1515
5716	9117	5618	6619	3820
2621	3122	4523	2324	3125
6726	3528	8528	3529	4130
7731	6932	8533	7434	9935
8836	2337	6138	1639	5840

Students in Online Classes

It is faster to keep groups of numbers in columns by moving across the columns using the tab feature. Keying all the numbers in a column and then moving to the next column is slower.

Numbers Drill

Key lines 1–3 twice: first for control, then for speed. Remember to read the numbers in 2-3-2 combinations.

1 7371130 91368840 1534986003 51673455189 963310931
2 21468159 515113 6873931 438761 223026501 89340013
3 6135910 619822385 3676 1090101 3948131 1788434341

Additional Drill

Key the following drill for control. Press **Enter** after each line.

1 2 34141 38886190 1 5133459 789 386005138 45134157
2 9,586,713 39,913,867 55,565,577 231,464 2,361,731
3 4,131 59.39 13,667 63,485 .98 78,431 40.83 76,924

4 47 681107 741 23 15281 59,602,388 2.95 96175 284 4
5 56451089 904 82 67,832,523.15 571.28 903 84.22 99
6 15 510 67414451 281,401,282.00 61700 29.15 106 80

Note: When entering the Name, Room, Admitted, and Physician information, use your right arrow key to move past the colon, press the space bar once, and enter the data. For the other entries in the heading and in the body of the report, press the End key, and then press the space bar once.

3 Key the body of the consultant's report. Throughout this document, the codes for three medical terms have been used. Key the two-letter codes as shown. These codes will be changed using the Search and Replace feature in the next document.

    ht = hematochezia
    ah = adhesions
    ob = obstruction

4 Read the Document A before keying it; correct any errors in Document A that may have been overlooked.

5 Proofread and correct the document you prepared.

6 Click the Check icon, Document A will be saved automatically as **052proa.**

7 Click Next Exercise.

Document A

> CONSULTATION: Ms. Wambaugh is a 63-year-old female who developed abdominal pain over the past two days. The pain is getting worse and she seems to have a full feeling. The patient says she has had increasing abdominal girth and nausea and vomiting. The patient's stool seems to be normal. She has had some loose stools with no melena or ht. The patient had had abdominal ah and surgery was performed on these in 1988. The ah were the result of a hysterectomy and pelvic surgery. The patient was seen in the emergency room where she was determined to have a small bowel ob. Laboratory data shows a WBC of 7,000 with shift. Abdominal x-rays show some air fluid levels.
> IMPRESSIONS: Small bowel ob.
> RECOMMENDATIONS: The patient has been admitted to the hospital. A conservative management will be tried with a Long Weighted Anderson Tube. The patient had a difficult surgery in 1988 for ah, and it would be better if the bowel ob can be resolved without surgery. She is grossly overweight and is not a good surgical candidate.
>
>   _____
>   Roushani A. Mansoor, M.D.
>
> RAM/xx
> DD:08/30/Current year
> DT: 08/30/Current year
> DOCUMENT: 949-CR

52.6

Document B

Changing Medical Consultant's Report Using Search and Replace

1 At the *Session 52 Document B* screen, open 052proa.

2 Using PWP's Search and Replace feature (See pages 207–208 in Session 43 for a review), change the two-letter codes to their full words. Remember to select the Whole words only check box.

    ht = hematochezia
    ah = adhesions
    ob = obstruction

3 Proofread the document to make sure that the replacements didn't cause formatting errors.

4 Name, save, and print the document as **052wprb.**

7 4559 71.26 8674005 21 4.86 489,753 4605141 50 224
8 531 78911 556 9,454.89 49724301 5,410 8.26 667101
9 2,466 61780 434215 5436 33216 4457004 96.48 82 46

Important: If you have not completed Sessions 1–13 (the alphabetic keys), go to Ending the Session. Otherwise proceed to the General Guidelines for Expressing Numbers and read and key each of the examples.

General Guidelines for Expressing Numbers

Authorities do not always agree on when to spell out numbers and when to use figures. The guidelines illustrated here are those that are widely accepted.

Key the examples for each guideline. Read what you have keyed so that you have a mental image of the applications for the guidelines.

1 Spell out numbers one through ten; use figures for numbers 11 and above.

The computer science class includes six women.
At least 40 men are enrolled in beginning keyboarding.

2 If any of the numbers in a series is above ten, use figures for all the numbers.

We have 16 Compaq computers, 14 Dell computers, and 8 Gateway computers.

3 When a sentence begins with a number, spell it out (or rewrite the sentence).

Three hundred students are majoring in business.
Business majors number 300.

4 If the day of the month precedes the month, express it in words.

We will meet on the sixth of December.

5 If the day of the month follows the month, express it in figures.

We will meet on December 6 at the restaurant.

6 If the date is in the form of month, day, and year, express the day and year in figures. *Note:* Always follow the year with a comma unless it appears at the end of a sentence.

We will meet on December 6, 2007, at the restaurant.

7 Use figures for measurements, percentages, and other mathematical expressions.

We need new carpet for a room that is 11 feet x 12 feet.
The package weighs about 7 pounds.
I will ask for a 6 percent raise.

8 Generally, use figures to express fractions and mixed numbers in technical writing or in physical measurements.

They used 3.5 feet of coaxial cable.

¹ When guests visit our homes, most of us enjoy the experience. The preparation period preceding a visit is not so enjoyable. Usually, a thorough cleaning and polishing is in order, along with planning good meals for the guests. The entire family labors to prepare their home for the expected guests. Excitement mounts as the magic time for the arrival of the guests draws nearer. Sometimes, the waiting will seem like an eternity. After the guests have arrived, there is usually an excited hustle and bustle as the unpacking chores are done. Everyone can then settle down for a friendly chat to catch up on all events at a leisurely pace.

A welcome guest is one who tries not to intrude in established family routines. Guests might assist, whenever possible, with the burden of routine chores such as cooking, cleaning, or other duties. If a visit is lengthy, it is traditional to send a gift or a small token of thanks to the host family after the visit is over. An accompanying personal note is needed to thank the host family.

TEXTBOOK EXERCISES: REVIEW OF THREE MEDICAL REPORTS

In this session, a consultant's report, a radiology report, and an operative report will be completed using the templates created for these reports in Sessions 46, 48, and 49. Two-letter codes will be used for selective medical terms in the three documents. A second copy will be prepared for each document using PWP's Search and Replace feature to insert the full words for the codes used.

Your goal for the three reports is 25 WAM with all errors corrected. Should you not reach 25 WAM on each report, use the PWP timing feature to repeat the documents until you reach at least 25 WAM. The next session (53) is a production progress check for medical reports and forms. Session 52 provides an opportunity to assess your skills and practice in those areas where you need to improve before completing the final session in Unit 10 Medical Reports and Forms.

The Reinforcing Writing Skills section focuses on avoiding sexist words in documents. Students in on-campus classes will prepare a memo to your school administrator or counselor about sexual stereotyping in five job titles associated with men and five job titles associated with women. Students in online classes will prepare an e-mail instead of a memo.

52.5

Document A

Medical Consultant's Report

1　At the Session 52 Document A screen open document 046prob, the Consultant's Report Form prepared in Session 46, and take the following steps:
　a　Choose Insert→File.
　b　At the Insert File dialog box, double click **046prob**.
2　Enter the information for the headings as follows:
　a　NAME: **Clara J. Wambaugh**
　b　MEDICAL RECORD #: **7833**
　c　ROOM: **135**
　d　DATE OF BIRTH: **05/29/1941**
　e　ADMITTED: **08/30/Current year**
　f　DATE OF CONSULT: **08/30/Current year**
　g　PHYSICIAN: **M. T. Flores, M.D.**
　h　CONSULTANT: **Roushani A. Mansoor, M.D.**

If the fraction appears alone or does not express a direct physical measurement, spell out the fraction.

> He makes only half of what she makes.

9   Use figures to express decimals.

> He is 6.5 feet tall.

10   For ages, follow the general guidelines for numbers.

> He is 20 years old.
> She is nine months old.

11   Use figures to express clock time.

> Pack your bags right away so we can make the 5:20 p.m. flight.

12   Key house numbers in figures.

> His address is 13038 N. Westgate Drive.

13   Spell out street names that contain numbers ten or below; if the numbers are above ten, express the names in figures.

> The store is located on First Avenue.
> My address is 17815 N. 13th Avenue.

Sentences

Key lines 1–10 twice: first for speed, then for control.

1   Did Van ever deliver the varnish and the 150 shelves?
2   Vinnie lives in their villa; he enjoys the vast veranda.
3   It is evident; the vital lever reverses the vexing vent.

4   Ron delivered the 18 leather chairs late this evening.
5   Marvel served 286 vanilla shakes at two gala events.
6   The driver developed a fever; give him 13 vitamins.

7   That starving animal evaded 103 vigilant observers.
8   She does not fool them; she is not an honest senator.
9   Opal ordered the onions and olives from the market.
10   Did the florist remove all the thorns from the roses?

17.5   ONE-MINUTE TIMINGS

Goal: 30 WAM with no more than 2 errors

Take a 1-minute timing on each paragraph.

REVIEW REPORTS AND FORMS

Session Goals

1-Minute: 40 WAM/1 error 3-Minute: 35 WAM/1 error		Review Search and Replace
Avoid sexist words		

52.1-52.2 ON-SCREEN EXERCISES: GETTING STARTED

If you exited the program at the end of the previous session, refer to page 11 in Session 3 to review how to open the next session. If you are continuing immediately from Session 51, start with Exercise 52.2. Click the Next Exercise or Previous Exercise button if you are not at the correct exercise.

52.3 ONE-MINUTE TIMINGS

Goal: 40 WAM/1 error

SI: 1.49

- Take two 1-minute timings. If you finish before time is up, start over.
- Be sure to set a goal for each timing you take, whether 1, 3, or 5 minutes. The goal will be either speed or accuracy depending on what your most current WAM rates and accuracy levels are.

> 1   How fast should you exercise? It may surprise you to know that experts say slow and easy may be better for you than fast and hard, especially if you are out of shape. The body burns two types of fuel: glycogen (high-grade) and fat (low-grade). It stands to reason that if you are driving your body as if it were a race car, you are going to consume high-grade fuel. But if you are rolling smoothly along, your body can eat up more of the low-grade stuff, which is the fat.

52.4 THREE-MINUTE TIMINGS

Goal: 35 WAM/1 error

SI: 1.49

Take two 3-minute timings. If you finish the two paragraphs before time is up, start over with the first paragraph.

1   The United States Agency for International Development sponsors a speakers program that provides citizens with an opportunity to learn about the culture of other countries. Educators, business men and women, and school administrators with a need to have firsthand information are eligible. More than 125 countries participate in this program.

2   A career in science involves selecting a path among several options. One could choose to become a doctor in a clinic or a teacher in a medical school. An active search through more than 190 college catalogs will indicate which courses to select. Contact campus finance officers to check cost factors.

3   Mack, a black Scottie, is a champion canine. A constant companion is the yellow cat called Chicco. Crowds laugh and applaud as Mack and Chicco do their tricks to music. Mack can count 15 objects and walk on his hind legs. Chicco jumps over Mack, adding a certain clownish touch to the act.

ENDING THE SESSION

Now you may print this session's files, continue to the next session, or exit the program. See page 55 of Session 14 if you need to review procedures.

Ergonomic Tip

You shouldn't have to reach for your keyboard. Move the keyboard so that you can keep your elbows at your side as you position your fingers over the home-row keys.

Document E

Choosing Information to Graph

To practice deciding what information in a report to chart, review the report completed as Document C. Select areas of information that could be represented in a graph of some kind. Then write a memo to your instructor explaining what information you would graph, the kind of graph you would use, and why this information should be charted. If you can think of other visuals or displays that would help explain the report data, mention those in your memo as well.

Check that your memo is written in complete, clear sentences and that you have used correct punctuation, sentence structure, word choices, and capitalization. Save the memo as **051wpre**. Then print and close the document.

ENDING THE SESSION

Now you may print this session's files, continue to the next session, or exit the program. See pages 230–231 in Session 45 to review the procedures.

Ergonomic Tip

Try standing while you do some of your tasks. Often this will increase your productivity.

3

PUNCTUATION/ SYMBOL KEYS

Changing a Consent Form Using Search and Replace and Cut and Paste

1 At the *Session 51 Document D* screen open document 051proc.

2 Using PWP's Search and Replace feature, change the two-letter codes to their full words (pages 207 and 208 in Session 43 if you need help):

> ae = adenomatous
>
> po = polyps
>
> co = colorectal

3 Using PWP's Cut and Paste feature, move paragraph 3 page 2 Confidentiality so that it follows paragraph 5 page 2 Benefits. Be sure that the appropriate paragraph numbers are correct. (See pages 245–246 in Session 47 if you need help.)

4 Proofread to make sure that the replacements didn't cause formatting problems. No doubt the page breaks will have to change since words that were represented by two-letter codes are now spelled in full. (See page 257 in Session 49 for the guidelines on widow/orphan protection.)

5 Name, save, and print the document as **051wprd**.

REINFORCING WRITING SKILLS

There are a variety of ways to help individuals better understand and retain written information. Charts and graphs, for example, are an excellent choice because they display numerical data and illustrate numerical relationships almost instantly.

The three most common types of graphs are line, bar, and pie. Line graphs show the relationship between two sets of information. One set of data is plotted horizontally; the other set is plotted vertically. A line connects the points where the two sets of data intersect.

Bar graphs also show relationships between sets of data. Instead of a line connecting the points where data sets intersect, however, bars are drawn either vertically or horizontally. An example of data that could be charted in a bar graph is the occupancy rate for a hospital during its first six months of operation, as shown below:

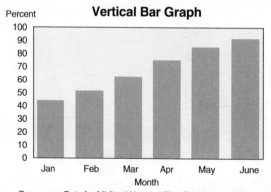

Occupancy Rate for Midland Hospital First Six Months of Operation

Pie graphs represent simple data such as percentages of a total amount. The federal budget, for example, is often represented in newspapers via a pie chart. The total pie represents 100 percent. The expenditures for defense, education, and other items are shown as a slice of the pie. The area in which our government spends the most money is shown as the largest piece of the pie.

Session Goals

Hyphen, Dash, Underscore

1-Minute: 30 WAM/2 errors
3-Minute: 25 WAM/2 errors

Hyphenating words
Using dashes

18.1-18.4 ON-SCREEN EXERCISES: GETTING STARTED

If you are continuing immediately from Session 17, you are already warmed up so start with Exercise 18.2. Click the Next Exercise or Previous Exercise button if you are not at the correct exercise.

If you exited the program at the end of the previous session, refer to page 11 of Session 3 for instructions on entering the program.

18.5 ON-SCREEN EXERCISES: THINKING DRILLS

This section includes three Thinking Drills that provide practice using the hyphen, dash, and underscore/underline punctuation marks. Then you are to apply the punctuation guidelines in response to questions posed in the Thinking Drills. Read the guidelines for each topic before you key the corresponding drills.

General Guidelines for Word Division

A hyphen is a mark of punctuation used to divide words that must be carried over to the next line. Although most word processing programs offer an automatic hyphenation feature, the software sometimes asks the user to make hyphenation decisions during the hyphenating process. The guidelines that follow include the essential rules. However, there are exceptions to the rules. When in doubt, consult a dictionary.

1   The general rule is to leave at least three letters of a word at the end of a line and carry over at least three letters to the next line. The rule has been modified since software packages leave or carry over only two letters of a word when automatic hyphenation is used.

2   Never divide a word that is the last word of a paragraph or a page.

Divide

3   Between syllables according to pronunciation   provoke   *may be divided*   pro-voke

---

Yes_____   No_____   Intial_____

My co tissue, blood, and/or buccal cells may be stored for future genetic rsearch to Ic(Learn more about co po and co cancer prevention.

Yes_____   No_____   Intial_____

A representative of the Colon Cancer Prevention Program may contact me in the future to ask me to take part in more research.

Yes_____   No_____   Intial_____

Please sign your name below after you check and initial your answers.

_____   _____
Subject's Printed Name   Subject's Signature

                                                                              a.m.
_____   _____ p.m.
Date   Time

_____   _____
Witness Signature   Date

Participant's Initials_____

SUBJECT'S CONSENT FORM

Selenium Study-Addendum B

Investigator's Affidavit: I have carefully explained to the subject the nature of the above project. I hereby certify that to the best of my knowledge the person who is signing the consent form understands clearly the nature, demands, benefits and risk involved in his/her participation and his/her signature is legally valid. A medical problem or language or educational barrier has not precluded this understanding.

_____   _____
Investigator's Signature   Date

                                                    Participant's Initials _____

4	Between two consonants	napkin	*may be divided*	nap-kin
	unless a root word would be destroyed	billing	*may be divided*	bill-ing (not bil-ling)
5	Between two vowels that are pronounced separately	continuation	*may be divided*	continu-ation
6	**After** a one-syllable vowel rather than **before** (preferable)	benefactor	*may be divided*	bene-factor
	unless the vowel is a part of a suffix	acceptable	*may be divided*	accept-able
7	Between two parts of a compound word	salesperson	*may be divided*	sales-person

8 Do not key more than two consecutive lines ending with hyphens. ***Note:*** Some software packages allow three lines with automatic hyphenation.

Do not divide

9	Words of one syllable	which	*never*	wh-ich
		storm	*never*	sto-rm
10	Words with a one-letter prefix	along	*not*	a-long
		enough	*not*	e-nough
11	A syllable with a silent vowel sound	yelled	*never*	yel-led
		strained	*never*	strain-ed
12	Proper nouns, abbreviations, contractions, or number combinations	Barbara	*not*	Bar-bara
		FBI	*not*	F-BI
		couldn't	*not*	could-n't
		31 Oak Lane	*not*	3-1 Oak Lane
		March 14	*not*	March 1-4

18.6 ▌ *THINKING DRILL*

Now you will have an opportunity to apply the word-division guidelines in a Thinking Drill. Follow the instructions on the screen. After you have completed the drill, return to the text and review the information that follows on using hyphens in compound words and numbers.

7. <u>Liability</u>: Side effects or harm are possible in any research program despite the use of high standards of care and could occur through no fault of mine or the investigators involved. Known risks have been describred in this consent form. However, unforeseeable harm may also occur and require care. I do not give up any of my legal rights by signing this form. In the event that I require or am billed for medical care that I feel has been caused by the research, I should contact the principal investigator, Martin J. Chosnyk, M.D. at 555/659-2398. If I have questions regarding my rights as a research subject, I may call the University of Colorado Human Subjects Committee Office at 555/645-9922.

Participant's Initials _____

SUBJECT'S CONSENT FORM

Selenium Study-Addendum B

1. <u>Authorization</u>: Before giving my consent by signing this form, the methods, inconveniences, risks, and benefits have been explained to my and my questions have been answered. I may ask questions at any time and I am free to withdraw from the project at any time without causing bad feelings or affecting my medical care. May participation in this project may be ended by the investigator or by the sponsor for reasons that would be explained. New information developed during the course of this study that mayk affect my willingness to continue in the research project will be given to me, as jit becomes available. This consent form will be field in any area designated by the Human Subjects Committee with access restricted to the Principal Investigator, Martin J. Chosnyk, M.D. or authorized representatives of the Colorado Cancer Center. I do not give up my legal rights by signing this form. A copy of this signed consent form will be given to me.

2. After rading each sentence, check "Yes" or "No" and initial.

3. **No matter what I decide, I can change my mind at any time in the future.**

My co tissue, blood, buccal cells, and/or toenails may be kept for future research to learn more about co po, their prevention and treatment.

Continued on next page

General Guidelines for Compound Words and Numbers

A hyphen is used to separate some compound words. It is also used in spelled-out numbers.

1   A hyphen is used as a "combining" mark. Not all authorities agree on which combinations should or should not be hyphenated. If in doubt, consult a reference book or dictionary.

   a   As a general rule, use a hyphen between two or more word combinations used as a unit **before** a noun.

   > a 15-story building
   > the still-active volcano
   > a hard-working person

   b   If the word combinations used as a unit appear **after** a noun, do not hyphenate.

   > a building 15 stories high
   > the volcano that is still active
   > a person who is hard working

   c   Words beginning with **ex**, **self**, and **vice** are usually hyphenated.

   > ex-roommate
   > self-taught
   > vice-principal

2   Hyphenate **spelled-out** fractions and hyphenate **spelled-out** numbers between 21 and 99 if they stand alone or if they are used with numbers over 100. Never hyphenate numerals such as 21 or 66.

   > one and one-third
   > sixty-six
   > one hundred sixty-six

18.7   THINKING DRILL

In the Thinking Drill that appears on your screen, you are to apply the guidelines for hyphenating compound words. Follow the instructions on the screen. After you have completed the drill, return to the text and review the information that follows on using dashes.

General Guidelines for the Dash

The dash is often used (1) in place of quotation marks or parentheses, (2) to avoid the confusion of too many commas, (3) for special emphasis, and (4) to indicate a side comment. Study the following examples:

> There is a flaw in the plan—a fatal one. [special emphasis]
>
> All books—fiction, poetry, and drama—are on sale. [in place of parentheses]
>
> I cooked the meal—but they got the credit for it. [special emphasis]
>
> I said once—and I will say it again—I disagree. [side comment]

Now you have the opportunity to practice using the dash in a special Thinking Drill that displays on your screen. Follow the directions on the screen. After you complete the drill, you will return to the text for additional key review.

have additional co po removed during my participation in the study that will be reviewed by a study pathologist.

6. [Standard Treatment: My decision to participate or not to participate in this part of the study will not affect my medical treatment in any way or my participation in the "Phase III Study of the Effects of Selenium on ae po Recurrence in Person with ae co po."

Participant's Initials _____

SUBJECT'S CONSENT FORM

Selenium Study-Addendum B

1. Procedures: If I agree to participate, the tissue examined by the study pathologist will remane stored at the Colorado Cancer Center, Analytical Laboratory in Denver. Blood samples taken during my regularly scheduled study visits at baseline, months 3 and 12 of the first year, and once per year thereafter will be stored at the Colorado Cancer Center for future research. Toenail clippings taken at the beginning and end of the study will be stored at the Colorado Cancer Center for future research. Buccal cells taken the the beginning of the study, year 1, and end of the study will be sotred at the Colorado Cancer Center for future research.

2. Results related to the research tests will not be made available to me or to my doctor since there will be no donor names or other identifying information attached to these samples. Results will not be put into my health record or have an effect on my care.

3. Confidentiality: Information obtained will be kept confidential and used only for scientific puprposes. The tissue, blood, buccal cells, and toenail samples are labeled with coded identification numbers only. My name and any identifying information will not be used in any presentation or publication of results.

4. Risks: Testing of stored tissue samples, blood, buccal cells, and toenail clippings present no risks to me. The samples will be used for medical research only. No information will ever be made available on individual participants.

5. Benefits: The research done with my tissue samples, blood, buccal cells, and toenail clippings will not help me directly, but it might help people who have co po and/or cancer in the future. My participation will help to establish an under-standing of the factors that influence the development of co po and/or cancer.

6. Participation Costs and Subject Compensation: There will be no costs of monetary compensation for these additional tests on stored tissue samples, blood, buccal cells, and toenail clippings.

In the activities that follow, you will review the Underscore Key and do additional drills. When you are finished with the drills, click Print (if desired), then Next Exercise.

Reviewing the Underscore Key

Use the Underscore key on the keyboard when keying a blank line. Remember to hold down the *Left Shift* key.

Underscore Drill

To practice using the Underscore key, key lines 1–2 twice: first for control, then for speed.

1 The number of persons who will attend _____.
 (Press underscore key 10 times—if you hold the underscore key down, you will get a continuous line until you release the shift key and the underscore key.)

2 Enter the street address here _____. (Press underscore key 10 times.)

Additional Drill (hyphen, dash, underscore)

Key the following drill. Press *Enter* after each line.

1 ;-;- ;-; ;-; ;-; ;-;- ;- ;- -;-; ;-; ;-; ;- ;- ;-
2 ex-roommate, self-taught, vice-principal, one and one-third
3 sixty-six, a self-employed person, a last-minute effort
4 one hundred fifty-six, eight-cylinder engine, twenty-six

5 ;—; ;—; —;—; —;—; ;—; — — ;—; —;—; —
6 There is a flaw in the plan—a fatal one.
7 All books—fiction, poetry, and drama—are on sale.
8 I said once—and I will say it again—I disagree.

9 I cooked the meal—but they got the credit for it.
10 ;-;_ ;- _;_ _;_ — — ;__; ;-_ ; ;-_; ___ ;- ;_;_;_ ;-;_;
11 The book title is_____
12 Enter your name here_____

Students in Online Classes

The dash can be presented two ways: two hyphens or space/hyphen/space. In this program, use two hyphens for a dash.

SUBJECT'S CONSENT FORM

Phase III Study of the Effects of Selenium on ae Polyp Recurrence in Person with ae co po

Addendum B: Consent Form for Future Use of Blood, Toenail, and Tissue for Research

I AM BEING ASKED TO READ THE FOLLOWING MATERIAL TO ENSURE THAT I AM INFORMED OF THE NATURE OF THIS RESEARCH STUDY AND OF HOW I WILL PARTICIPATE IN IT, IF I CONSENT TO DO SO. SIGNING THIS FORM WILL INDICATE THAT I HAVE BEEN SO INFORMED AND THAT I GIVE MY CONSENT. FEDERAL REGULATIONS REQUIRE WRITTEN INFORMED CONSENT PRIOR TO PARTICIPATIONS IN THIS RESEARCH STUDY SO THAT I CAN KNOW THE NATURE AND RISKS OF ANY PARTICPATION AND CAN DECIDE TO PARTICIPATE OR NOT PARTICIPATE IN A FREE AND INFORMED MANNER.

1. Purpose: As a participant in the "Phase III Study of the Effects of Selenium on ae po Recurrence in Persons with ae co po," I am being invited to voluntarily participate in an additional component of the study. The purpose of this additional component is to store samples (tissue, blood, buccal cells, and toenail clippings) at the Colorado Cancer Center for future co cancer prevention research.

2. If I agree to participate, samples that have been collected during the study will be stored for future research. These samples include tissue from my colonoscopies performed immediately before and during the study, blood drawn during my regularly scheduled visits, buccal cells, and toenail clippings. No sadditional sample collection will be required.

3. My samples may provide important information that will help researchers understand which factors increase the risk of co po and/or cancer or possibliy cause co po and/or cancer. Additionally, the samples may provide information that could be helpful in preventing or treating co po and/or cancer.

4. The future research that may be done with my tissue samples, blood, buccal cells, and toenail clippings, is not designed specifically to help me. It may help future generations of people who are at risk for developing co po and/or cancer and other related cancers in the future.

5. Selection Criteria: I am being invited to participate in this component of the study because I am currently a participant in the Selenium Study. I have had co po removed from my colon before my participation in the Study and may

Continued on next page

ONE-MINUTE TIMINGS

Goal: 30 WAM, 2 errors

Take a 1-minute timing on each paragraph.

1   There has been a fantastic growth in the United States in the use of in-line roller skates, sometimes called Rollerblades, which is a trade name. People are using their in-line skates in conjunction with their employment. Couriers in New York City deliver their packages using their in-line skates to move quickly through the crowded streets. USA Hockey created an in-line hockey division in 1994.

2   Two-way radio systems are used by selected groups such as the police, ambulance services, and taxi cab companies. Users are limited to a single, manually selected channel. If the channel is in use, then the person must wait until it is free. There is no privacy for two-way radio systems; all others on your channel can listen to your conversation.

18.10 ## THREE-MINUTE TIMING

Goal: 25 WAM, 2 errors

So far all timings have been 1 minute long. Now you will take a 3-minute timing to help prepare you for keying longer documents such as reports. In most cases, speeds drop and errors increase when the length of the timing is extended. Your goal for this timed writing is to reach at least 25 WAM with no more than 2 errors per minute. Try to come within 5 WAM of your 1-minute rate while maintaining your accuracy at no more than 2 errors per minute. Remember to start over if you finish the paragraph before time is up.

1   Nails date back to 3000 B.C. They have been found in diggings and sunken ships that sailed in the years around 500 A.D. The Romans hand-forged nails and began the new trend toward complete use in building with wood. Most nails were first made in small shops; demand for nails grew so fast that the small, but well-made supply of handmade nails was not quite enough for the demand. Today, most companies that make nails can trace their own beginnings back to those early times.

ENDING THE SESSION

Now you may print this session's files, continue to the next session, or exit the program.

Print

To print Exercises 18.1–18.10 proceed as follows:

1   Click the Close ⊠ button in the top right corner of the screen.
2   At your Paradigm Keyboarding with Snap Welcome page, point to Reports on the Snap menu bar, and click View Submissions Report.

For women: Intravenous fl is usually not administered to pregnant women, although there is no scientific evidence to suggest that it might harm unborn babies.

I agree to undergo fl ag _____ (Place an X if you agree)

No, I do not wish to undergo fl ag _____ (Place an X if you decline)

| _____ | _____ | _____ |
| Patient Signature | Printed Name | Date |

| _____ | _____ | _____ |
| Witness Signature | Printed Name | Date |

51.6

Document B

Changing a Consent Form Using Search and Replace

1 At the *Session 51 Document B* screen open document 051proa.
2 Using PWP's Search and Replace feature, change the two-letter codes to their full words:
   fl = fluorescein
   ag = angiography
3 Proofread to make sure that the replacements didn't cause formatting problems.
4 Name, save, and print the document as **051wprb**.

51.7

Document C

Edited Consent Form

1 Review the edited copy of the Consent Form for Document C; check for errors that may have been overlooked in the editing process.
2 At the *Session 51 Document C* screen key the document as follows:
   a Throughout this document the codes for three medical terms have been used. Key the two-letter codes as shown. These codes will be changed using PWP's Search and Replace feature in the next document.
      ae = adenomatous
      po = polyps
      co = colorectal
   b Bold, underline, and capitalize your document as shown in the text.
   c Number the paragraphs on pages 1–3 as shown. On each of the three pages begin with the number 1. References to specific paragraphs can be made by stating a page number and a paragraph number. (For help see Session 42, page 202.)
   d Insert hard page breaks as shown on pages 1–3 of Document C in the text.
   e Refer to the index at the back of the text if you need to review proofreader's marks.
   f Use PWP's Header/Footer feature to number pages 2–4. (For help see page 227 in Session 45)
3 Proofread and correct the document, then check and print it.
4 The document is automatically saved as **051proc**.
5 Click Next Exercise.

3   At the View Submissions Report Wizard, click <u>Show session files</u> to see the drill lines text (Exercises 18.1–18.8), or <u>Show timings files</u> to see the timings text (Exercises 18.9–18.10).

4   Click Show Report.

5   Click the name of the file you want to print.

6   At the Word Processor dialog box, click Launch.

7   Click <u>F</u>ile, and then click <u>P</u>rint.

8   At the Print dialog box, click OK.

9   Click the Close button to close the Paradigm Word Processor.

10   Click Home on the Snap menu bar to return to the Welcome page.

Continue

To continue on the next session, click the Next Exercise 🠖 button **twice**. This will take you to Exercise 19.2. (You will bypass Exercise 19.1 <u>Warmup</u> since you are already warmed up.)

Exit

To exit, do the following:

1   Click the Close ☒ button in the top right corner of the screen.

2   At your Paradigm Keyboarding with Snap Welcome page, click <u>Logout</u>.

Ergonomic Tip

Try using a document stand to hold your source materials—position it so that the distance from your eyes to the copy is the same distance as your eyes to the screen.

51.5

Document A

Consent Form

1 Before keying Document A, read the copy in the text to check for errors that need to be corrected.
2 At the *Session 51 Document A* screen key Document A. Throughout this document, the codes for two medical terms have been used. Key the two-letter codes as shown. These codes will be changed using the Search and Replace feature in the next document.

    fl = fluorescein
    ag = angiography

3 Proofread and correct the document, then check and print it.
4 The document is automatically saved as **051proa**.
5 Click Next Exercise.

Document A

RETINAL CONSULTANTS OF NY., LTD

Practice Limited to Diseases and Surgery of the Retina and Vitreous
Donald W. Dugel, M.D.
Pravin O. Thach, M.D.

CONSENT FORM FOR fl ag

The purpose of fl ag is to further study blood flow patterns of the retina by photography to provide a baseline examination for future reference should any changes occur later, and to determine what treatment, if any, is required for any existing problems.

Ag is a diagnostic procedure in which a rapid sequence of photographs is taken to document the blood circulation of the retina. The dye is injected into a vein in the arm, forearm, or hand.

As is the case with all drugs and many medical tests, there can be some side effects. Thirty to sixty seconds after the dye is injected, approximately 1 – 4 percent of patients will develop a very transient and fleeting nausea that will pass in a minute or two. Vomiting is rare. More rare reactions to the dye include hives, asthmatic symptoms, laryngeal edema, respiratory or cardiac arrest, or shock, and can be life threatening . If these occur, they usually do within the first few minutes after beginning the test and can usually be controlled with oral or intravenous medications.

After the test, you will see a red after-image from the photo flash. Your skin may have a temporary yellowish-brown color from the dye. Your urine will have a brilliant yellow discoloration for several voidings. For several days following this test, the dye will interfere with many chemical blood test. If you have blood work drawn within the next two weeks, inform you physician that you've had this test done.

This information is provided so that you may make an informed decision to undergo fl ag.

Continued on next page

Session Goals

Apostrophe, Quotation Mark **1-Minute: 30 WAM/2 errors**	**Using apostrophes** **3-Minute: 25 WAM/2 errors**

19.1-19.4 ## ON-SCREEN EXERCISES: GETTING STARTED

If you exited the program at the end of the previous session, refer to page 71 of Session 18 to review how to open the next session or to continue from where you left off.

19.5 ## TEXTBOOK EXERCISES: REINFORCEMENT—PART ONE

After reviewing the proper reaches to the apostrophe and quotation mark keys, you will use these keys as you complete drills on keying word contractions, conversations, and titles of written works. Read the introductory material for each topic before you key the corresponding drill. When you have finished the drills, click Print (if desired), then Next Exercise.

Reviewing the Apostrophe and Quotation Mark Keys

Apostrophe Drill

Students in Online Classes

Note that the apostrophe and the quotation marks are on the same key.

Key lines 1–3 twice: first for speed, then for control.

1 Al's Dad's Ted's Allen's Jane's Jan's Ken's Len's

2 Alfie's neat sedan hasn't had a dent; he's tense.

3 Dale's latest theft hadn't shaken Jeanne's faith.

1   If you have never had the opportunity to glide through the skies at a very high rate of speed, you might be somewhat nervous or overly concerned about the first flight. You can be sure that flying is always safer than driving your own vehicle from your garage to school, work, or on a shopping trip.

Traveling via the fantastic jet airplane is the fastest and most economical way to travel for a person if the distance traveled is at least 200 miles. If two or more individuals will be covering fewer than 500 miles, traveling by car will be considerably more economical. If the distance is more than 1,000 miles, traveling by jet airplane is the fastest way to go and is usually considered to be more economical. The time saved is valuable, especially if your time is limited.

Traveling across an entire ocean to another country can be quite an enjoyable experience, especially if traveling in one of the newest wide-bodied jet planes. All seating is quite comfortable, and all the aisles are wide. These jumbo jets have a staircase that leads to an upper cabin for the first-class passengers to enjoy. Some airplanes now have a closed-circuit television screen that enables everyone to observe the take-off and landing and the cockpit gauges and controls. On longer flights, you might enjoy a full-length movie in addition to delicious meals and snacks.

TEXTBOOK EXERCISES: PREPARING MEDICAL CONSENT FORMS

Doctors and medical researchers in the field of medicine are constantly involved in looking for new and improved methods for treating medical problems. Drugs, medical methods, and procedures must be tested and results verified before they can be approved by the Federal Food and Drug Administration (FDA) for use by the general public. Human beings are sought to participate in medical research.

To address legal issues, individuals who are asked to participate in medical research studies must be given a consent form that provides details of the research and the risks/side effects involved. Before accepting or declining to participate, the potential participant is encouraged to read carefully what is involved before making a decision. It is critical that the consent form is easy to read and comprehend, clearly outlines the risks/side effects, and is error free.

Consent forms can be printed or stored in the computer where they can be accessed and printed for distribution. Generally, multiple copies are made of the forms so that the researchers and participants have copies of what has been signed and dated. In this session you will prepare two original consent forms and then make changes to the forms using the PWP features of Search and Replace and Cut and Paste. In one of the consent forms you will use the PWP Paragraph Numbering and Page Numbering features.

In the Reinforcing Writing Skills section you will find a discussion on the use of charts and graphs to improve the readability of documents and compose a memo to your instructor on what information in a selected document might be used as a chart or graph.

Quotation Mark Drill

Key lines 1–3 twice: first for speed, then for control.

1 "hello" "Help" "gasp" "Fiddle" "Ha" "Hi" "splash"
2 "At last," said Sal, "is that lad's knee healed?"
3 "At least," said Al, "Jake ate the jelled salad."

19.6 ON-SCREEN ACTIVITIES: THINKING DRILLS

General Guidelines for the Apostrophe

1 An apostrophe is used in a contraction—a shortened spelling of a word, substituting an apostrophe for the missing letter.

| cannot | can't |
| could not | couldn't |

2 An apostrophe can be used to show possession by adding an 's.

a hat belonging to John	John's hat
the voices of the people	people's voices
the guess of anybody	anybody's guess

For plural nouns that end in s, add the apostrophe only.

| the carts of the golfers | golfers' carts |
| the clothes of the girls | girls' clothes |

3 An apostrophe can also be used as a symbol for feet.

| 100 feet | 100' |
| 255 feet | 255' |

Note: Some individuals have trouble determining if a word is a personal pronoun or a contraction.

Example: their   they're   its   it's

Remember: The apostrophe indicates a missing letter. Therefore, *they're* indicates *they are*, and *it's* stands for *it is*.

Additional examples:

They're taking their own sleeping bags.

not

They're taking they're (they are) own sleeping bags.

It's a treat to give the dog its bone.

not

It's a treat to give the dog it's (it is) bone.

Thinking Drill

Now you have an opportunity to apply the apostrophe guidelines in a Thinking Drill. Follow the instructions on the screen. After you have completed the drill, return to the text and review the information that follows on using quotation marks correctly.

MEDICAL CONSENT FORMS

Session Goals

1-Minute: 40 WAM/1 error
3-Minute: 35 WAM/1 error

Search and replace, cut and paste, numbering paragraphs, and page numbering

Enhancing reports with charts and graphs.

51.1-51.2 ON-SCREEN EXERCISES: GETTING STARTED

If you exited the program at the end of the previous session, refer to page 11 in Session 3 to review how to open the next session. If you are continuing immediately from Session 50, start with Exercise 51.2. Click the Next Exercise or Previous Exercise button if you are not at the correct exercise.

51.3 ONE-MINUTE TIMINGS

Goal: 40 WAM/1 error

SI: 1.47

- Take two 1-minute timings. Start over if you finish before time is up.

- Use your most recent timing score to set a speed or accuracy goal. Note that the error goal has dropped to only 1 (per minute). If you are below 40 WAM push for speed. If you have 40 or more WAM but are making more than 1 error, push for accuracy, otherwise push for speed.

1   Betty is going to ski the best there is. Her imagination runs rampant. The mountains, trees, and powder all come together in one great rush of joy. Betty breaks into a wide, bright grin. Her face is covered with powder-white snow, and her limbs are frozen in motion. She has skied the ultimate run and still stands. Betty is free to ski, tumble, fly, and embellish to her heart's delight. She is a fleeting traveler among these huge, snowy monuments.

51.4 THREE-MINUTE TIMINGS

Goal: 35 WAM/1 error

SI: 1.48

- Take two 3-minute timings. If you finish the three paragraphs before time is up, start over with the first paragraph.

- Note that the error goal has dropped from 2 to 1 (per minute). Push for speed or accuracy depending on your needs.

When you have finished the drills on quotation marks, along with the additional drills, click Print (if desired), then Next Activity.

General Guidelines for Quotation Marks

The three most common uses for quotation marks are to indicate conversations, to indicate emphasis, and to highlight titles in published material.

Using Quotation Marks in Written Conversation

1 Quotation marks are used to indicate spoken words in written materials. When each new speaker says something, the text begins on a new line and is indented. Study these examples:
   "The weather is really nasty," said Nancy.
   Relaxed, Jan yawned and said, "Oh, I really hadn't noticed."
   "That's because you have been sleeping all morning," murmured Nancy with a slight sneer in her voice.
2 The comma and period are placed inside the quotation marks. (See the previous examples.)
3 The question mark is placed either inside or outside the ending quotation mark, depending on the sentence logic.
   a Place outside if the entire sentence is a question.
      When did he say, "I shall not return"?
      Did he say, "I saw ten paintings at the exhibit"?
   b Place inside if the quotation **only** is a question.
      The owner shouted, "Why don't you just leave?"
      She asked, "Do you know if the train is late?"
4 The semicolon and colon **always** go outside the end quotation mark.
   Last week she announced, "Recreation time will be lengthened"; however, we have not experienced it yet.

Quotation Mark Drill

Now test your knowledge of quotation mark guidelines by keying the following sentences. (The correct answers are shown on pages 81–82.)

Key the three sentences, inserting quotation marks where appropriate.

The computer is old, stated Mr. Barlow, and must be replaced.
Why did the pilot say, We'll be 30 minutes late?
Catherine sleepily said, Why don't you just be quiet?

Key the following three sentences as conversation, adding quotation marks as appropriate.

We will be landing 30 minutes late, announced the pilot. Deanna muttered, I suppose that means we miss dinner. The flight attendant smiled and said, Perhaps we'll be on time after all.

Key the following as conversation, adding quotation marks as appropriate.

50.9

Document E

Memo Containing Directions

Compose a memo to your instructor that contains the directions on how to get from school to your place of residence. Be sure that the instructions are clear; for example, instead of saying "Turn north on Main Street…," it is clearer to say "Turn left on Main Street…."

Proofread and correct any errors. Save and name your memo as follows:

Students in Online Classes

Key Document E as an e-mail message to your instructor and attach Document E.

1 Click the Save button 🖫 on the toolbar.
2 At the *Save As* dialog box, key **050wpre**.
3 Press *Enter* or click Save.
4 Close the document by choosing File→Close.

ENDING THE SESSION

Now you may print this session's files, continue to the next session, or exit the program.

Print

To print Exercises 50.1–50.9 proceed as follows:

1 Click the Close ☒ button in the top right corner of the screen.
2 At your Paradigm Keyboarding with Snap Welcome page, point to Reports on the Snap menu bar, and click View Submissions Report.
3 At the View Submissions Report Wizard, click <u>Show session files</u> to see the drill lines text (Exercises 50.1–50.2), <u>Show timings files</u> to see the timings text (Exercises 50.3 and 50.4), and <u>Show production files</u> or <u>Show unchecked production files</u> to see the production documents (Exercises 50.5–50.9).
4 Click Show Report.
5 Click the name of the file you want to print.
6 At the Word Processor dialog box, click Launch.
7 Click <u>F</u>ile, and then click <u>P</u>rint.
8 At the Print dialog box, click OK.
9 Click the Close button to close the Paradigm Word Processor.
10 Click Home on the Snap menu bar to return to the Welcome page.

Continue

To continue on the next session, click the Next Exercise button **twice**. This will take you to Exercise 50.2. (You will bypass Exercise 50.1 <u>Warmup</u> since you are already warmed up.)

Exit

To exit, do the following:

1 Click the Close button in the top right corner of the screen.
2 At your Paradigm Keyboarding with Snap Welcome page, click <u>Logout</u>.

Ergonomic Tip

Perform stretching and breathing exercises at your desk frequently during the day to relieve stress and physical discomfort.

The pilot announced, Due to fog, we will be forced to land in Omaha instead of Minneapolis. Deanna's fears were confirmed. Omaha? she blurted. Yes, it's a wonderful city. I vacation there often, replied the flight attendant. The pilot was heard again, We may not be able to leave Omaha for 36 hours. Be prepared to spend the night in the airport. An unexpected treat, said the smiling flight attendant.

Using Quotation Marks in Titles and for Emphasis

1   Quotation marks are used to enclose titles of works such as poems; short stories; chapters, essays, or articles in magazines and other larger works; radio and television programs; and short musical works.

> "The Midnight Ride of Paul Revere" is a good poem.
>
> The last episode of "Star Trek" was really interesting.
>
> The plot of "Last Rays of Daylight" was dull for a short story.
>
> Did the band perform "Stardust" last evening?
>
> I read the article "Thirty Ways to Avoid Work" in the magazine.

2   Quotation marks may be used within a sentence to give a word or words special emphasis, for example, a technical word used in a nontechnical sentence, slang expressions, humorous expressions, or defined words. (In typeset material, defined words are usually set in italics.) Be careful not to overuse the quotation mark in this manner.

> The "Aglaonema" is commonly called the Chinese evergreen.
>
> Marvin thought the concert was "far out" and enjoyable.
>
> Their idea of "fast" service is serving one customer at a time.
>
> According to Webster's dictionary, a wren is a "brown singing bird."

Quotation Mark Drill

Key each of the following sentences, inserting quotation marks to enclose titles or special words of emphasis. When finished, compare your results to those found on page 82.

> The story was a real corker.
>
> The gemot was used largely in early English government.
>
> With friends like you, who needs enemies?
>
> A narrow path or ledge is sometimes called a berm.

> The poem entitled Barney's Revenge is not very long.
>
> At midnight, Joan saw The Light of Laughter on television.
>
> The author's last short story, Bars on the Doors, was a mystery.
>
> Her favorite song is Thunder Serenade by Mario Zahn.

was slightly dilated and the pancreatic duct filled easily. Postoperatively, the patient has done well. The morning after surgery, he was ambulatory, eating a general diet, and comfortable with oral pain medication. He is being discharged at this time. He had a Jackson-Pratt drain placed at surgery, and this was removed on the morning of discharge. I will see him in my office in about too weeks. He has no restrictions on his diet or activity. He will continue his preadmission colchicine 0.6 mg, and he will be on Vicodin 5 mg 1-2 every four to six hours as needed for pain.

FINAL DIAGNOSIS: Chronic cholecystitis with cl.

OPERATION: Laparoscopic ch with operative cholangiogram, 06/23/xxxx.

_____

T. R. WOLMACK, M.D.

TRW/xx
DD: 06/24/Current year
DT: 06/25/Current year
DOCUMENT: 8891-DS

Changing a Discharge Summary Report Using Search and Replace

50.8

Document D

1 At the *Session 050 Document D* screen, open Document 050proc.
2 Using PWP's Search and Replace feature, change the two-letter codes to their full words. Remember to select the <u>W</u>hole word only check box.

      pn = pancreatitis
      ch = cholecystectomy
      cl = cholelithiasis

3 Proofread to make sure that the replacements didn't cause formatting errors.
4 Name, save, and print the document as **050wprd**.

REINFORCING WRITING SKILLS

Providing Essential Information

Frequently when you write memos or other short documentation, you're in a hurry. You need to relay a brief piece of information, for example, or you may be telling other staff members about an upcoming meeting. In haste, you may write as if the other person knows what you are thinking. For example, assume that you are writing to a business associate to set up a meeting for 1 p.m., Wednesday, June 14. In your memo to this person, suppose that you state the following:

Let's meet from 1–3 p.m., Wednesday. If you have questions about the proposal, we can discuss them at that time.

    Analyze the material. Did you tell the receiver which Wednesday? (There are at least four Wednesdays every month.) Where is the meeting to be held: your office or the other person's office? What proposal are you referring to? Make sure you review your document from your reader's perspective to ensure that you have included the essential information.

Additional Drill

Key the following drill. Press **Enter** after each line.

1 .'.' .'..'..'..'..'.' .' .' '.'..'..'..'.' .' .'
   ; ';' ;' ;;' ;;' ;;' ; ; ; ; ';' ;;' ;;' ;;' ;' .'

2 can't couldn't John's hat, people's voice, anybody's guess

3 Keat's sonnets, girls' clothes, 100', 255', they're, it's

4 .'.'.'.' .' .'' .'.'.'' .'..'' .'' .'' .'..''..''..'' .'' .'' .'
   ; ';' ; ' '' ; ' ; ; ; ;' ; ; ; ;;' ;;' ;;' ;' ;' ;'

5 "The weather is really nasty," said Nancy.

6 When did you say, "I shall not return"?

7 She asked, "Do you know if the train is late?"

8 "The Midnight Ride of Paul Revere" is a good poem.

9 Marvin thought the concert was "far out" and enjoyable.

19.8 ONE-MINUTE TIMINGS

Goal: 30 WAM/2 errors

Take a 1-minute timing on each paragraph.

1   This new book on soccer has an excellent chapter on coaching soccer that offers 14 "awesome" tips to be used in working with young people new to the sport. There are some excellent suggestions on how to get positive support from the parents of the players. It's a great resource for coaches and their assistants.

2   A personal computer's components determine the limitations. For example, a computer without a video adapter and a video "codec" wouldn't be able to store the filming done via a camcorder. What can be done with the right components in today's microcomputers is amazing. It wouldn't take long to think of 101 things that could be done on a computer with the "right" components.

19.9 THREE-MINUTE TIMINGS

Goal: 25 WAM/2 errors

- Take a 3-minute timing on the following paragraph.
- If you finish before time is up, start the paragraph again.
- Take a second 3-minute timing; try to increase your speed while maintaining your accuracy.

RIVERSIDE MEDICAL CENTER
PORTLAND, OREGON

NAME: MEDICAL RECORD #:
ADMITTED: ROOM:
PHYSICIAN: DISCHARGED:

DISCHARGE SUMMARY

SUMMARY:
FINAL DIAGNOSIS:
OPERATION:

_____

50.7

Document C

Discharge Summary

1   At the *Session 50 Document C* screen, insert Document 050prob. Enter the
    information for the heading as follows:
    a   NAME: **Eldon Leonard**
    b   MEDICAL RECORD #: **60344**
    c   ADMITTED: **06/23/**Current year
    d   ROOM: **S-540**
    e   PHYSICIAN: **T. R. Wolmack, M.D.**
    f   DISCHARGED: **06/24/**Current year
2   Key the body of the discharge summary report. Correct any errors in Document C
    that may have been overlooked. Use the current year for **xxxx** in the dates.
    Throughout this document, the codes for three medical terms have been used. Key
    the two-letter codes as shown. These will be changed using the Search and Replace
    feature in the next document.

    pn =   pancreatitis
    ch =   cholecystectomy
    cl =   cholelithiasis

3   Proofread and correct the document, check document, and print.
4   The document is automatically saved as **050proc.**
5   Click Next Exercise.

Document C

DISCHARGE SUMMARY

SUMMARY: The patient was in the hospital with severe gallstone pn in May of xxxx.
At that time, the patient had an ultrasound, which showed cl. Once the pn subsided and
his CAT scan findings had reverted to normal, he was admitted and a ch was performed
on June 23, xxxx. The procedure went well but was quite difficult because the
gallbladder was serverely scarred, contracted, and packed with stones. The ductal system

Continued on next page

1   Fair time is near. Last year, our county had a great fair. Lots of people came to see the fine views and have a good time. Just imagine that 539,437 people attended, which was a record. We are hoping that by the next year we can have over 600,000 at the fair. The new rides were colorful and exciting. Both the young and old had a great time. We hope that the same old amusement company will come back and bring some of those new rides and fun shows that are bigger and better.

Answers to Quotation Mark Drills

"The computer is old," stated Mr. Barlow, "and must be replaced."

Why did the pilot say, "We'll be 30 minutes late"?

Catherine sleepily said, "Why don't you just be quiet?"

"We will be landing 30 minutes late," announced the pilot.

Deanna muttered, "I suppose that means we miss dinner."

The flight attendant smiled and said, "Perhaps we'll be on time after all."

The pilot announced, "Due to fog, we will be forced to land in Omaha instead of Minneapolis."

Deanna's fears were confirmed. "Omaha?" she blurted.

"Yes, it's a wonderful city. I vacation there often," replied the flight attendant.

The pilot was heard again, "We may not be able to leave Omaha for 36 hours. Be prepared to spend the night in the airport."

"An unexpected treat," said the smiling flight attendant.

The story was a real "corker."

The "gemot" was used largely in early English government.

With "friends" like you, who needs enemies?

A narrow path or ledge is sometimes called a "berm."

The poem entitled "Barney's Revenge" is not very long.

At midnight, Joan saw "The Light of Laughter" on television.

The author's last short story, "Bars on the Doors," was a mystery.

Her favorite song is "Thunder Serenade" by Mario Zahn.

ENDING THE SESSION

Now you may print this session's files, continue to the next session, or exit the program. See pages 75–76 of Session 18 if you need to review procedures.

Ergonomic Tip
Clean your monitor regularly with an anti-static screen cleaner recommended by the manufacturer.

50.5

Document A

Medical Terminology

1. At the *Session 50 Document A* screen, key Document A as a two-column table.
2. Be sure to include an appropriate border and gridlines in your table, and use different levels of shading for the first two rows.
3. Proofread and correct any errors.
4. Name, save, and print the document as **050wpra**.
5. Click Next Exercise.

MEDICAL TERMINOLOGY	
Term	**Definition**
Ambulatory	Able to walk about; not confined to a bed
Cholecystectomy	Surgical removal of the gallbladder
Cholecystitis	Inflammation of the gallbladder
Cholelithiasis	Presence of solid materials in the gallbladder or bile ducts
Colchicine	An alkaloid used in chronic treatment of gout
Ductal	Relating to a duct
Laparoscopy	Examination of the contents of the abdominopelvic cavity with a laparoscope
Pancreatitis	Inflammation of the pancreas

50.6

Document B

Creating a Discharge Summary Report Form

1. At the *Session 50 Document B* screen, key Document B as a template for a discharge summary report form.
2. In case the report goes beyond one page, insert the header **Discharge Sum. Rept.** and a page number field; align both at the right margin.
3. Proofread and correct the document, check document, and print.
4. The document is saved automatically as **050prob**.
5. Click Next Exercise.

Session 20

EXCLAMATION POINT, POUND SIGN, DOLLAR SIGN, AMPERSAND

Session Goals

 !, #, $, &

 Using exclamation points

1-Minute: 30 WAM/2 errors
3-Minute: 25 WAM/2 errors

20.1–20.6 ON-SCREEN EXERCISES: GETTING STARTED

If you exited the program at the end of the previous session, refer to page 71 of Session 18 to review how to open the next session or to continue from where you left off.

20.7 TEXTBOOK EXERCISES: REINFORCEMENT

After reviewing the proper reaches to the symbol keys (exclamation point, pound sign, dollar sign, and ampersand), you will use these keys as you complete punctuation drills. Read the appropriate material in the text before you key each drill. When you are finished, click Print (if desired), then Next Exercise.

Reviewing the Symbol Keys

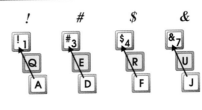

Symbols are located on the number keys. You have mastered the necessary reaches; now all you have to do is reinforce the location of each symbol. ***Remember:*** Be sure to press the ***Shift*** key.

Exclamation Point Drill A

Key lines 1–3 once. Space once after the exclamation point (except at the end of the line).

1 Help! Stop! No! Yes! Go! Wait! Begin! Halt! None!
2 Walter, stop right now! You had all better stop!
3 No, you cannot go right now! Listen to them now!

1   Plants that have been started can also be purchased at all local nursery or garden shops in the spring. Usually, these flowers are in full bloom at the period when they are offered for sale; the gardener can then select the colors and kinds of plants that will look best in the specific garden sites and areas. After the flower garden bed has been prepared, the gardener can simply place the fine blooming plants in the earth and soon there will be a bright garden.

Planning flower displays is a time-consuming but rewarding task. For example, a mass of brilliant colors and textures could brighten a dark corner or highlight darker foliage and shrubs. Some annuals are better suited for border planting or edging. Others that grow quite tall can be used for unique backgrounds or for screening. There are many annuals that make gorgeous bouquets of cut flowers. The gardener can enjoy the fruits of his or her labor with vases of beautiful blossoms placed all around the house.

Growing annuals in containers has become very popular. Creative gardeners will move containers from one place to another to highlight the most beautiful plants in bloom. A movable or mobile green garden allows for the maximum use of color.

TEXTBOOK ACTIVITIES: MEDICAL TERMINOLOGY AND DISCHARGE SUMMARY REPORTS

You will continue to review medical terminology by completing a table of medical terms and their definitions. Next you will prepare a template for a discharge summary report, and then you will use this template to prepare a report.

When a patient is discharged from a hospital or medical center, a discharge summary is prepared. The discharge summary contains much of the same information as the history and physical examination form and includes any surgical procedures performed, radiology reports, consultation information, and the condition of the patient upon discharge. The discharge summary includes instructions for follow-up care.

Before proceeding with Document A, notice that throughout Unit 10 you have been working with a variety of specialized reports for the medical field. In the medical reports you may have noticed the lack of paragraphing. A doctor doesn't have to decide where paragraphs belong. The headings, whether centered or at the left margin, are bolded and keyed in all caps. There is no extra spacing between the sections in the body of medical reports. As you move from field to field—for example, medicine, law, banking, manufacturing—you will find specialized reports that are formatted in unique ways. It is always a good idea to check an organization's procedures manual to note what types of reports are generated and how they are formatted.

Pound/Number Sign Drill

Key lines 1–3 once for control.

1 #33 33# 39 9# #168 168# #106 106# #3 3#3 21# #122
2 Items #10, #7, #3, #6, #4, #12, and #19 are mine.
3 Get #61 weighing 10# and #2299 weighing 189,756#.

Students in Online Classes

Note that the # sign has two meanings: pound and number. The # sign after a number represents pounds. The # sign before a number represents the word *number*.

Dollar Sign Drill

Key lines 1–3 once for control.

1 $1 $2 $3 $4 $5 $6 $7 $8 $9 $10 $11 $120 $16.00 f$
2 Add $1.16, $28.96, $17.44, $18.00, $21.13, $4.26.
3 The gifts cost $1.10, $6.90, $19.89, and $101.13.

Ampersand Drill

Key lines 1–3 once for control.

1 17 & 60 & 9 & 16 & 14 & 71 & 77 & 45 & 61 & 9891
2 Buy gifts from the J & K store and the R & Sons.
3 Contact Hart & Sons for the products you need.

Additional Drill

Key lines 1–12 for control. Press **Enter** after each line.

1 fff f4f ff ff f4f4 $$$ f$ f$ f4 f$ f$ f4 f4
2 $40.00 4$ $4.00 $$44 $4.00 $$44 44 $4 $4 f$f$ 444
3 $143,789.00 $1,640.68 $689.33 $17.31 $26.80 $1.44

4 d#d d3d# d#d# d#d# d3d3 ### d# d# d3 d# d# d3 d3
5 d#d d3#d #3 3# ##33 3# #3 ##33 33 #3 #3 3#3# 333
6 Buy 14#, 23#, 71#, 3#, 8#, 41#, 13#, 21#, and 6#.

7 j7j j7j& j&j& j&j& j7j7 &&& j& j& j7 j& j& j7j7
8 &j& j7j& j&j& && j7j& j7& &&77 77 &7 &7 7&7& 777
9 Patricia and Ron went to Samuelsons & Bigsby today.

10 a!a! a!a a!a a!a! a! a! a!a! a!a a!a a!a a! a! a!
11 What! How frightening! Mark your calendar!
12 My brother yelled, "Run for your life!" Wow!

Students in Online Classes

While the instructions for the drills for the four symbol keys say to key each line once, repeat any line where you feel more practice is needed.

Session 50

DISCHARGE SUMMARY REPORTS

Session Goals

1-Minute: 40 WAM/2 errors
3-Minute: 35 WAM/2 errors

Review tables, templates, and Search and Replace

Providing Essential Information

**50.1-
50.2** **ON-SCREEN EXERCISES: GETTING STARTED**

If you exited the program at the end of the previous session, refer to page 11 in Session 3 to review how to open the next session. If you are continuing immediately from Session 49, start with Exercise 50.2. Click the Next Exercise or Previous Exercise buttom if you are not at the correct exercise.

50.3 **ONE-MINUTE TIMINGS**

Goal: 40 WAM/2 errors

SI: 1.49

Take two 1-minute timings.

> 1   Firms take time and spend the money to train their workers. Every effort is made to involve employees in decision-making and to allow them to be creative. Employers who train workers are more profitable than employers who do not. Many studies have shown that one of the best roads to high profits and worker output is to treat those workers as assets to be developed rather than expenses to be cut. Gains to a firm's operation are high when needed changes are made by having training programs that are easy for workers to use on the job. The worker must be given time to absorb the new changes and to start using those changes. Workers must also be given a chance to make decisions that will affect their work.

50.4 **THREE-MINUTE TIMINGS**

Goal: 35 WAM/2 errors

SI: 1.49

Take two 3-minute timings. If you finish the three paragraphs before time is up, start over with the first paragraph.

General Guidelines for the Exclamation Point

1 The exclamation point is used to express a high degree of emotion or strong feeling.

2 The exclamation point may be used in any of these situations:

a *One word (space once after the exclamation point)*
> What! You mean the flight has been delayed for six hours?

b *A phrase (space once after the exclamation point)*
> How frightening! The fire broke out only 10 minutes after we had left.

c *A clause*
> The date of the meeting—mark it on your calendar!—is November 10.

d *A sentence (space once after the exclamation point)*
> So there you are, you rascal!

e *A quotation that is exclamatory*
> My brother yelled, "Run for your life!"

f *A complete sentence that is exclamatory*
> I simply do not believe the fiscal report that states, "The absentee rate was increasing by 500 percent"!

Exclamation Point Drill B

Key each sentence, inserting appropriate punctuation. Answers are shown on page 86.

Congratulations You won the first prize

Jan shouted What a mess

I emphatically restate my position: I will not resort to underhanded tactics

Help Help I'm locked in

Oh, how ridiculous He's never even seen the inside of a bank

20.8 ONE-MINUTE TIMINGS

Goal: 30 WAM/2 errors

Take a 1-minute timing on each paragraph.

1   State, county, and regional fairs provide wholesome entertainment for more than 150 million Americans each year. The Texas State Fair has an annual $160-million-dollar impact on the Dallas-Fort Worth area with more than 3.1 million attendees. From animals to high-tech displays, there's something for everyone, and the price is right!

2   When ordering team jerseys, be sure to include #223-852 in the category box on the order form. JB & K provides an additional 5-percent discount for orders in excess of 15 jerseys. There is a significant savings on two-color jerseys compared to those with three or more colors. Prices are listed on the attached sheet.

Now you may print this session's files, continue to the next session, or exit the program. See pages 230–231 in Session 45 to review the procedures.

Ergonomic Tip

Keep the angle between your trunk and thigh greater than 90 degrees when seated. If you learn forward when sitting, it puts pressure on your back muscles and vertebrae.

Goal: 25 WAM/2 errors

Take two 3-minute timings on the following paragraph.

1   Why should seat belts be fastened when a car is moving? Seat belts will reduce injuries and deaths. Many tests and studies have been done to prove this point. Half of all the traffic deaths happen within 25 miles from home. Traffic deaths can occur when an auto is moving just 40 miles an hour or less. If a car is moving at 30 miles per hour, the impact is like hitting the ground after hurtling from the top of a building that is three stories high.

Answers to Exclamation Point Drill B

Congratulations! You won the first prize.

Jan shouted, "What a mess!"

I emphatically restate my position: I will not resort to underhanded tactics!

Help! Help! I'm locked in.

Oh, how ridiculous! He's never even seen the inside of a bank.

ENDING THE SESSION

Now you may print this session's files, continue to the next session, or exit the program. See page 75 of Session 18 if you need to review procedures.

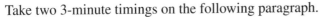

Ergonomic Tip

If you are experiencing eye pain, flashes of light, floaters, blind spots, or blurred vision, make an appointment immediately with a qualified professional.

the screw and sleeve, the set screw was placed with a torque wrench from proximal to distal. After it was secured, the two distal cortical interlocking screws were placed across jig and sleeve. The wounds were all irrigated with normal saline and polymyxin bacitracin solution. The band and the abductor fascia were closed with a #1 Vicryl simple running suture. A drain deep to the abductor fascia was inserted and then closed with 2-0 Vicryl running stitch. The patient tolerated the procedure well and returned to the recovery room in stable condition.

D. A. STRAUSS, M.D.

DAS/xx
DD: 03/23/Current year
DT: 03/24/Current year
DOCUMENT: 5529-OR

Students in
Online Classes

Reminder: Be sure to apply the Widow Orphan Guidelinie to leave and carry at least wo lines of a paragraph.

49.8

Document D

Changing an Operative Report Using Search and Replace

1. At the *Session 49 Document D* open document 049proc.
2. Using PWP's Search and Replace feature, change the two-letter codes to their full words:

   ic = intertrochanteric
   im = intermedullary
   tr = trochanter

3. Proofread to make sure that the replacements didn't cause formatting problems.
4. Name, save, and print the document as **049wprd**.

REINFORCING WRITING SKILLS

Communicating through printed documents or via e-mail offers distinct advantages over communicating by telephone or in person:

- A written (printed) message usually carries more authority.
- The reader can study and reread printed documents containing complicated instructions, but the same information conveyed orally is presented only once.
- A written message provides a permanent record.
- Writing the information gives the writer more control over the tone and desired outcome.

49.9

Document E

Composing an E-Mail Report

Use the Word Processor to compose an e-mail report that consists of at least one-and-a-half pages, written to your instructor on the subject of A SUMMARY OF THE REINFORCING WRITING SKILLS GUIDELINES IN SESSIONS 35–48. Prepare a double-spaced rough draft. Then save, print, and edit your e-mail report for complete, well written sentences and correct grammar, punctuation, and capitalization. Use subheadings to help direct the reader's attention. Send the report to your instructor as an attachment to an e-mail message.

Save the document as **049wpre** and close it.

PERCENT SIGN, ASTERISK, PARENTHESES, BRACKETS

Session Goals

 %, *, ( ), [ ]

Symbols

 1-Minute: 30 WAM/2 errors
3-Minute: 25 WAM/2 errors

21.1-21.7

ON-SCREEN EXERCISES: GETTING STARTED

If you exited the program at the end of the previous session, refer to page 71 of Session 18 to review how to open the next session or to continue from where you left off.

21.8

TEXTBOOK EXERCISES: REINFORCEMENT

This section offers a brief review of the proper reaches to the percent sign, asterisk, left and right parentheses, and left and right brackets keys. When you finish the drills, click Print (if desired), then Next Exercise.

Reviewing the Percent Sign, Asterisk, Brackets, and Parentheses Keys

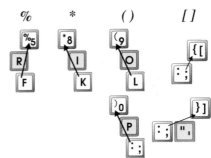

Percent Sign Drill

Be sure to press the **right Shift** key. Place both hands on the home row and practice the move from *f* to *percent sign*. Be sure to anchor your left little finger to the "A" key.

Key lines 1–4 twice: first for speed, then for control.

1. f5f f5f f5f f5f f5f f%f F%F f5f F%F5 f%f5 f%f f%f
2. 55% 555% 5% 5%5% 555% 55% 5% 5% 55% 555% 5%, 555%
3. A 6% discount and a 10% reduction will equal 16%.
4. They made 55% of their shots and 8% of the fouls.

Operative Report

1 At the *Session 49 Document C* screen, insert Document 049prob. Enter the information for the heading as follows:

a NAME: **Oscar Hernandez**
b MEDICAL RECORD #: **1109**
c SURG: **D. A. Strauss, M.D.**
d ROOM: **E-206**
e ASST: **L. S. Tuttle, ORT**
f DATE OF BIRTH: **06/23/1936**
g ANES: **A. V. Zajac, M.D.**
h PHYSICIAN: **D. E. White, M.D.**
i DATE/OPERATION: **03/23/**Current year

Note: When entering the Medical Record #, Room #, Date of Birth, and Physician information, use your right arrow key to move past the colon, press the space bar once, and enter the data. For the other entries in the heading and in the body of the report press the End key, then press the space bar once.

2 Key the body of the operative report. Correct any errors in Document C that may have been overlooked. Throughout this document, the codes for three medical terms have been used. Key the two-letter codes as shown. These will be changed using the Search and Replace feature in the next document.

> ic = intertrochanteric
> im = intermedullary
> tr = trochanter

3 Depending on where the page break falls, insert a hard page break if appropriate.
4 Proofread and correct the document, check document, and print.
5 The document is saved automatically as **049proc**.
6 Click Next Exercise.

Students in Online Classes

Reminder: Check the copy in the text before keying. You may find errors.

Document C

PREOPERATIVE DIAGNOSIS: Comminuted ic right hip fracture.
POSTOPERATIVE DIAGNOSIS: Same.
OPERATIVE PROCEDURE: Open reduction internal fixation right ic hip fracture; Richard's im hip compression screw system, 14 mm im rod, 95 mm lag screw, one set screw, sleeve and two 36 mm distal cortical interlocking screws. Spinal anesthesia. The patient was brought to the operating room and underwent spinal anesthesia followed by sterile prep and drape of the right lower extremity in a routine fashion. The patient was on the fracture table with the right lower extremity secured in a traction boot and the left lower extermity comfortably padded with Gelfoam and in a padded stirrup. An X-ray was utilized to demonstdrate desired reduction of fracture fragments. An incision was made proximal to the greater tr identifying the greater tr. A pin and drill allowed entrance into the im canal by lateral visualization. Serial reaming was done down the canal to judge the size of the 4-inch medullary rod. The rod went to 15 and accepted at 14 mm. It was reamed to 18 mm proximally and the rod was placed down the canal. The rod sounded without difficulty and the 14 mm rod was placed. Step reaming was accomplished and a lag screw was then placed that measured 95 mm. A sleeve was tapped across the outer cortex and through the channel of the bone. Upon placement of

Continued on next page

Asterisk Drill

In addition to signaling a footnote or indicating spacing, the asterisk serves as a multiplication sign in some programming languages. Anchor a finger on the "J" or ";" key to make the reach to the asterisk key.

Key lines 1–4 twice: first for speed, then for control. (Remember to press the *left Shift* key.)

1   k8k k8k k8k ki8k ki8k ki8*k k*k K*K k*k k*k *ki*k
2   8*8 8*8 8*8 k8*k ki8*k k*k 8*8*8 *** 8*8 ki8* k*k
3   The check was for $***4.65 and it should be $.46.
4   The * symbol is used in programming: A - B * 38.

Left Parenthesis Drill

Key lines 1 and 2 twice: first for speed, then for control. (Remember to press the left shift key.) Anchor your finger on the "J" key.

Students in Online Classes

Be sure to use the letter "l" and not the number "1" in this drill.

1   l9l l9l l9l l9l lo9l lo9l lo9(l l(l l(l lo(l lo9(
2   l(l l(l l9l l9l l9(l lo9(l lo(l lo9(l l9Ll l(l l9

Right Parenthesis Drill

Key lines 1–4 twice: first for speed, then for control. (Remember to press the left shift key.) Anchor your finger on the "J" key.

Students in Online Classes

Watch your little finger make the reach the first three times you key the bracket, then look at the text for the remainder of the drill.

1   ;0; ;0; ;0; ;0; ;p0; ;p0; ;p0; ;p0; ;p); ;p); ;0;
2   ;); ;); ;); ;); ;); ;0); ;); ;0); ;p0); ;p0); ;);
3   The price ($5.95) was more ($2 more) than I paid.
4   Most of the teams (at least 6) won all six games.

Left Bracket Drill

Key lines 1 and 2 twice: first for speed, then for control. (Do not use the shift key.) Anchor your finger on the "J" key.

1   ;[; ;[; ;[; ;[; ;[; ;[; ;[;[;[;[;[; ;[;[; ;[;[;
2   ;[;[;[;[; ;[;[; ;[;[; ;[;[;[; ;[;[; ;[; ;[;[;

Left and Right Brackets Drill

Key lines 1 and 2 twice for control.

1   ;[; ;]; ;[; ;]; ;[; ;]; ;]; ;[; ;]; ;[; ;[; ;];];
2   ;[ ]; ;[; ;]; ;[; [;] [;] [;] [;] [;] [;] [;] [;]

RIVERSIDE MEDICAL CENTER
PORTLAND, OREGON

NAME:
MEDICAL RECORD #:   SURG:
ROOM: ASST:
DATE OF BIRTH: ANES:
PHYSICIAN: DATE/OPERATION:

OPERATIVE REPORT

PREOPERATIVE DIAGNOSIS:
POSTOPERATIVE DIAGNOSIS:
OPERATIVE PROCEDURE:

Using Widow/Orphan Protection for Page Breaks

In Session 42 the Hard Page Break feature was introduced (page 200) along with two-page letters. Guidelines were presented for determining where page breaks were to occur. For example, there is to be a minimum of two lines of a paragraph at the bottom of a page. One line of a paragraph at the bottom is known as an orphan line. A minimum of two lines of a paragraph is to be at the top of a page. One line at the top is called a widow line.

Most commercial word processing packages have a feature called *Widow/Orphan Protection* that will eliminate one line of a paragraph being left at the bottom of a page or carried to the top of the next page. Since this feature is not available in PWP, it is up to you to see that there are no orphan or widow lines in your multiple-page documents. When you have occasion to use other word processing packages, check to see if the *Widow/Orphan Protection* feature is available. In the meantime, you will find the *Hard Page Break* feature helpful in making sure that your documents are properly formatted.

Additional Drill

Key the following drill. Press **Enter** after each line.

1. k* K*K k*k k8*k k8k*k k*k*k k8*k k8*k k*k K*K k*k
2. The * symbol is used in formulas: A1*B2-C2*49.
3. f%f f5%f f%f f5%5 f5%f f5%f f5%f f%5f 5%5 5%5 555

4. Did you know that 5% of 5,000 equals 250% of 100?
5. ;[;[; ;[;[; ;[;[;[;[;[;[; ;[; ;[; ;[; ;[;; ;[; ;[;
6. ;];]; ;]; ;]; ;]; ;];]; ;];];];];]; ;]; ;]; ;]; ;]];

7. [;] [;] [;] [;] [;] [;] [;] [;] ;]; ;[; ;]; ;[; ;[;]
8. ;[; ;]; ;]; ;[; ;[; ;]; ;]; ;[; ;]; ;[; ;[; ;]; ;[; ;];
9. 19 1(1 19L1 19(1 1(1 19(1 19(1 191 191 1(1 1(1

10. ;); ;0); ;0); ;0); ;); ;0); ;); ;); ;); ;); ;);(0)
11. The amount ($6.96) was more ($2 more) than I paid.
12. Most of the table (see Table 3.2) was accurate.

21.9 ONE-MINUTE TIMINGS

Goal: 30 WAM/2 errors

Take a 1-minute timing on each paragraph.

1.   The stock market gets a lot of people's attention. When Standard & Poor's index increases, many people will hold on to their stocks in anticipation of further gains. A 4% drop in durable goods orders would most likely increase short-term interest rates; this has an impact on the Federal Reserve Board's next move.

2.   The Radio Corporation of America (RCA) demonstrated the all-electronic 120-scan line television in the 1930s. In the same decade, Germany began regular TV broadcasting service. In the 1940s, coaxial (copper) cable was introduced as a more efficient method for telephone and television transmission. The progress in TV technology has been dynamic!

21.10 THREE-MINUTE TIMINGS

Goal: 25 WAM/2 errors

- Take two 3-minute timings on the following paragraph.
- Start the paragraph again if you finish before time is up.

MEDICAL TERMINOLOGY	
Term	**Definition**
Abductor	Muscle that moves a bone away from the body's midline
Comminuted or Compound	A fracture in which one or more areas of bone are displaced
Cortex	The gray matter covering the surface of the brain
Cortical	Involving or resulting from the action or condition of the cerebral cortex
Distal	A body part located far from an attachment point
Fascia	Fibrous tissue covering muscles, the skull, and some organs
Lateral	Furthest from the midline of the body
Medullary Cavity	The hollow center of long bones
Polymyxin	Any of several toxic antibiotics obtained from soil bacterium
Proximal	A body part located near an attachment point
Saline	Consisting of or containing salt

49.6

Document B

Creating an Operative Report Form

1 At the *Session 49 Document B* screen, key Document B as a template for an operative report form.
2 Insert the header **Operative Rept.** and a page number field; align both at the right margin.
3 Proofread and correct the document, check document, and print.
4 The document is saved automatically as **049prob.**
5 Click Next Exercise.

1   Firms from which persons order items have to charge an amount for shipping and handling. Many firms do pay for the shipping amount if the items you ordered weigh less than a certain amount. If you have to pay the charges, you may wish to have that order sent by UPS. UPS uses varying charges according to the zone in which you live. UPS now has 8 mailing zones. Zone 1 is on the West Coast and Zone 8 is on the East Coast with all the rest of the zones located between these two points.

ENDING THE SESSION

Now you may print this session's files, continue to the next session, or exit the program. See page 75 of Session 18 if you need to review procedures.

See page 75 of Session 18

Ergonomic Tip

Rest your forearms on the edge of a table. Grasp fingers of one hand and gently bend back wrist for five seconds to relax your hand and fingers.

---

1   During every moment of the day or night, all kinds of storms are in the process of raging over land and sea. More than 1,800 thunderstorms or blizzards pelt the earth with rain or snow. Somewhere over a high sea, a hurricane with an awesome wind may be forming. In some areas, the people may be looking at a cloudless sky, but not more than a few hundred miles away other people are sheltering themselves from a wild and furious snowstorm or a pelting rain.

     A storm is a disturbance of the upper atmosphere and contains an added element of strong winds. During many storms, destructive winds have been known to cause great damage. During a blizzard on the wide open prairie, snowdrifts pile high and block roads. Ice storms cause widespread damage to telephone and power lines.

     Distinctive forms of clouds and precipitation, as well as winds, are common to storms. Precipitation is the weather bureau's name for all forms of water falling from the sky. Clouds are the first signal of an incoming storm. Signals of the hurricane, for example, move in with little or no noise. An alert weather person is well aware of the danger signals. First, the wispy, veil-like cirrus clouds appear and dance on the horizon.

TEXTBOOK ACTIVITIES: MEDICAL TERMINOLOGY AND PREPARING OPERATIVE REPORTS

You will continue reviewing medical terminology by completing a table of medical terms and their definitions. Next you will prepare a template for a postoperative report, and then you will use this template to prepare a report.

    When surgery is performed on a patient, a report of the surgery is dictated by the surgeon. This report is transcribed and placed in the patient's record. Generally, the report contains preoperative and postoperative diagnoses and describes the condition of the patient after surgery.

49.5

Document A

Medical Terminology

1 At the *Session 49 Document A* screen, key Document A as a two-column table.
2 Be sure to include an appropriate border and gridlines in your table, and use different levels of shading for the first two rows.
3 Proofread and correct any errors.
4 Name, save, and print the document as **049wpra**.
5 Click Next Exercise.

Students in Online Classes

Reminder: Read to comprehend the terms and definitions before preparing the table.

Session Goals

@, =, +

1-Minute: 30 WAM/2 errors
3-Minute: 25 WAM/2 errors

Symbols

22.1-
22.6

ON-SCREEN EXERCISES: GETTING STARTED

If you exited the program at the end of the previous session, refer to page 71 of Session 18 to review how to open next session or to continue from where you left off.

22.7

TEXTBOOK EXERCISES: REINFORCEMENT

This section offers a brief review of the proper reaches to the "at" sign, equals sign, and plus sign keys. When you have finished the drills, click Print (if desired), then Next Exercise.

Reviewing the At Sign, Equals Sign, and Plus Sign Keys

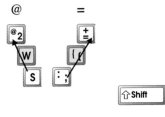

At Sign Drill

Key lines 1–4 twice for control. Be sure to press the *right Shift* key. Anchor the "f" finger when keying the "at" sign.

1 .s2s s2s s2s s2s s2s s2s s2s s@s s@s s2@s s2@s

2 14 @ $2.50, 16 @ $55.80, 1 @ $17.59, 13 @ $124.66

3 It is better to buy 99 @ 18 rather than 180 @ 10.

4 jjones@emcp.net; Xavier@emcp.net;
   vang@emcp.net

Students in Online Classes

In the next three sets of drills, watch your finger make the reach from the home row to the symbol key the first three times it is struck. Then concentrate on keeping your eyes on the copy to gain speed.

Session

49

OPERATIVE REPORTS

Session Goals

1-Minute: 40 WAM/2 errors
3-Minute: 35 WAM/2 errors

Widow/Orphan protection
Headers/Footers

Advantages of printed documents

49.1-49.2   ON-SCREEN EXERCISES: GETTING STARTED

If you exited the program at the end of the previous session, refer to page 11 in Session 3 to review how to open the next session. If you are continuing immediately from Session 48, start with Exercise 49.2. Click the Next Exercise or Previous Exercise button if you are not at the correct exercise.

49.3   ONE-MINUTE TIMINGS

Goal: 40 WAM/2 errors

SI: 1.45

• Take two 1-minute timings.

• Use your most recent timing score to set a speed or accuracy goal.

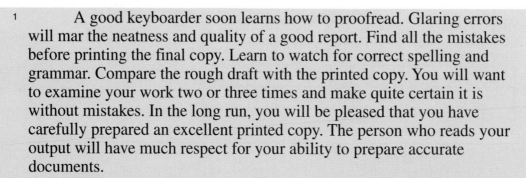

1   A good keyboarder soon learns how to proofread. Glaring errors will mar the neatness and quality of a good report. Find all the mistakes before printing the final copy. Learn to watch for correct spelling and grammar. Compare the rough draft with the printed copy. You will want to examine your work two or three times and make quite certain it is without mistakes. In the long run, you will be pleased that you have carefully prepared an excellent printed copy. The person who reads your output will have much respect for your ability to prepare accurate documents.

Editing is another task that requires careful attention. Once a document has been prepared, you may need to check it for correct word choice and use. Also, vary the sentence structure so readers enjoy the content.

49.4   THREE-MINUTE TIMINGS

Goal: 35 WAM/2 errors

SI: 1.48

Take two 3-minute timings. If you finish before time is up, start over with the first paragraph.

Equals Sign Drill

Key lines 1–4 twice for control. Anchor the "J" finger when keying the equals sign.

1   .;=; ;=; ;=; ;=; ;=; ;=; ;=; ;=; =;= =;= =;= =;= ;=
2   a = b c = d e = f g = g j = j k = k l = l ;=; ;=;;
3   A = D C = D J = J K = K L = L A = B C = D E = R =;
4   The = sign is generally used in math problems now.

Plus Sign Drill

Key lines 1–4 twice for control. Remember to press the *left Shift* key for the plus sign. Again, anchor the "J" finger when making this reach.

1   ;=; ;+; ;+; ;=+; ;+:+:+=; ;=; ;+; ;=; ;+; ;=; :+;
2   The equations were: A = D + F + G and E = E + RT.
3   The equations were: A = B + C + E and A = A + BC.
4   The computer program stated A = (B + C + C) * AD.

Additional Drill

Key lines 1–9 once for control. Press *Enter* after each line.

1   s2@s s@2s s2s s@s S@S S@S S@S s@s s@s s2s s@s
2   23 @ $2.31, 172 @ $8.91; 17 @ 57, 98 @ 34, 8,934 @ 90, 2 @ 4
3   dsmith@emcp.net; phantom@emcp.net; tmodl@emcp.net

4   =; =;= =;= =;= ;=; ;=; =;= =;= ;=; ;=; = =
5   a=b c=d e=f G=J H=I K=L m=n o=p q=r
6   The = sign is used in formulas when working in spreadsheets.

7   ;+; ;=; ;+; ;=; ;+; ;=; ;+:+:=; ;=+; :=+: :+=:
8   The formula A = C + BA is the same as A = (C+BA).
9   The spreadsheet formula stated D1 = (B2 + C3 + A1) * F4.

22.8 ONE-MINUTE TIMINGS

Goal: 30 WAM/2 errors

Take a 1-minute timing on each paragraph.

Document F

Memo with Misplaced Modifiers

1 At the *Session 48 Document F* screen key Document F, the memo to Megan Aarmodt.
2 Save the memo as **048wprf**; print a copy, and close the document.
3 Edit the memo; three of the sentences contain misplaced modifiers that make the meaning unclear. Find those sentences and rewrite them.
4 Open 048wprf and make the corrections you have identified.
5 Save the revised memo, print a copy for your instructor, and close.

Document F

DATE: (Current date)

TO: Megan Aarmodt

FROM: (Your name)

SUBJECT   SELLING TECHNIQUES FOR OUR MEDICAL SOFTWARE

(ds)

Megan, we had a meeting last week about some special techniques to use when selling our new medical software for patient records. Here's a brief description of them. We'll send complete information in the next two weeks.

- When giving your presentation, the medical staff members need to have access to a computer.
- Leave plenty of time for questions, which may be difficult in late-afternoon appointments.
- Mention the names of some of the other medical facilities using our software.

Watch your mail for samples of a dazzling new brochure that we can send to your best clients.

xx/048wprf

ENDING THE SESSION

Now you may print this session's files, continue to the next session, or exit the program. See pages 230–231 in Session 45 to review the procedures.

Ergonomic Tip
While legs are straightened to the front, circle feet to relax ankle muscles.

1   Symbols are used frequently in computer programming languages. Of course, the plus (+), minus (-), and equals (=) keys are used. The asterisk (*) is used as a multiplication sign, and the diagonal (introduced in the next session) is used for division. It is important that we key symbols just as quickly as we key numbers and letters.

2   Global area networks (GANs) are critical in today's business world. Many U.S. companies are selling their products in overseas markets. It is imperative that communication channels are established with branches, suppliers, and customers wherever they may be. Communication must be instant if a company is to remain competitive.

22.9   THREE-MINUTE TIMINGS

Goal: 25 WAM/2 errors

Take two 3-minute timings on the following paragraph. If you finish before the time is up, repeat the paragraph.

1   There is a new way to lay out a great garden that uses grids of neat 1-foot by 1-foot squares. Then, you plant the seeds and plants with certain spacings. The system is a simple one that allows persons to make the most of a garden space and at the same time conserve water and labor. Talented experts feel that 1-foot by 1-foot garden schemes let you grow the same amount of food as a regular garden does in less than one-fifth of the space.

ENDING THE SESSION

Now you may print this session's files, continue to the next session, or exit the program. See page 75 of Session 18 if you need to review procedures.

Ergonomic Tip
Use a desk lamp (task lighting) instead of overhead lights to eliminate screen glare.

One thing you haven't done so far is delete files no longer needed. It is a good habit to get into. By deleting files no longer needed you are making sure there is space on your electronic storage device(s) to store new documents. To delete a document proceed as follows:

1 Choose File→Open.
2 At the *Open* dialog box, select the document you want to delete.
3 Position the arrow pointer on the selected document, then click the *right* mouse button.
4 At the pop-up menu that displays click Delete.
5 At the *Confirm File Delete* dialog box, click Yes.

Renaming Documents

At the *Open* or *Save As* dialog boxes, you can use the Rename option from the pop-up menu to give a document a different name by doing the following steps:

1 Select and position the arrow pointer on the document to be renamed.
2 Click the *right* mouse button, then click Rename with the *left* mouse button. This causes a black border to surround the document name and the name to be selected.
3 Key the desired name, then press **Enter**.

48.9

Document
E

Deleting Files and Renaming a Document

1 Choose File→Save As.
2 At the *Save As* dialog box, select files 034wpra and 034wprb and delete them.
3 Rename document 048proa as **Selenium**.
4 Click Cancel to exit the dialog box.

REINFORCING WRITING SKILLS

One of the most common causes of unclear communication is the **misplaced modifier.** Words, phrases, and clauses can serve as modifiers. If these modifiers are not placed as closely as possible to the sentence elements they help describe, the meaning of the sentence becomes unclear. The following sentences, for example, are unclear because of the location of the modifiers:

Managing the office last week, the problems piled up for him.

The position of the phrase, *managing the office last week,* makes it modify *the problems,* but we know that the writer meant the phrase to describe the person. To correct the problem, rewrite the sentence: *Managing the office last week, he saw the problems pile up.* Or: *The problems piled up for him when he managed the office last week.*

The assistant took his boss to lunch, who was leaving next week.

Who was leaving next week, the assistant or his boss? The sentence construction does not make the writer's meaning clear. To correct the problem, rewrite the sentence so the modifying clause *who was leaving next week* is placed as closely as possible to the word it describes: *The assistant, who was leaving next week, took his boss to lunch.*

Session Goals

 ^, <, >, /, \

🕐 **1-Minute: 30 WAM/2 errors**
3-Minute: 25 WAM/2 errors

 Symbols

23.1-
23.7
ON-SCREEN EXERCISES: GETTING STARTED

If you exited the program at the end of the previous session, refer to page 71 of Session 18 to review how to open the next session or to continue from where you left off.

23.8
TEXTBOOK EXERCISES: REINFORCEMENT

This section provides a review of the proper reaches to the exponent sign, less than sign, greater than sign, slash/diagonal, and the backslash keys. When you have finished the drills, click Print (if desired), then Next Exercise.

Reviewing the Exponent Sign, Less Than, Greater Than, Diagonal, and Backslash

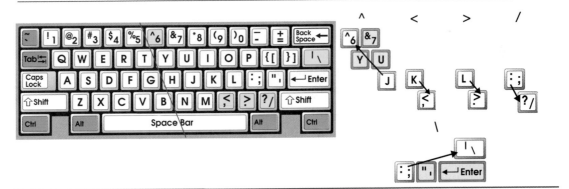

Exponent Sign Drill

Key lines 1–3 twice for control. Anchor the ";" finger when making this reach.

1 j6j j6j j6j j^j j^j j^j j^j j^j J^J J^J J^J J^J J^J J^
2 The ^ sign is used to raise an integer to a power.
3 For example, 2^2 is the square of the numeral two.

Changing a Radiology Report Using Search and Replace

Document D

1   At the *Session 48 Document D* screen, open Document 048proc.
2   Using PWP's Search and Replace feature, change the two-letter codes to their full words:

    bn = barium enteroclysis
    pj = proximal jejunum
    fl = fluoroscope

3   Proofread to make sure that the replacements didn't cause formatting errors.
4   Name, save, and print the document as **048wprd**.

MAINTAINING DOCUMENTS ELECTRONICALLY

Every medical facility maintains a filing system whether it consists of hardcopies or electronically stored patient records. The most common means of maintaining patient records electronically is to store these records on computer hard drives, CDs or DVDs, Read/Write (R/W) CDs or DVDs, and for larger systems "Write Once Read Many" (WORM) and "Write Many Read Often" (WMRO) optical disk technology where literally billions of records can be stored.

Patient records maintained on computer hard drives can be backed up on CDs, DVDs, and WORM optical disks. With these devices, patient records are stored and cannot be erased. With R/W CDs, DVDs, and WMRO technology, records can be edited, updated, and/or deleted. The electronic storage system selected for patient records is directly related to the number of patient records to be maintained by the medical facility. Once records have been stored in a digital format, including text, X-rays, ultrasound, or whatever type of imagery is used, they can be accessed in moments and displayed on the computer screen. Doctors and staff are able to access these records from distant locations miles apart.

Like a filing system, the computer-generated storage devices on which patient records have been saved need maintenance. Maintaining electronic storage devices may include such activities as deleting unnecessary documents, copying important documents to another file, and renaming documents.

In PWP, many document management tasks can be completed at the *Open* dialog box or at the *Save As* dialog box. Among these tasks are deleting and renaming documents. To display the *Open* dialog box, click the Open button on the toobar or chose File→Open. To display the *Save As* dialog box, choose File→Save As.

Deleting Documents

In Sessions 1–33 all the activities that you completed were controlled by the Paradigm Keyboarding software (PKB). You didn't have to worry about saving, deleting, and naming documents; this was done for you so that you could concentrate on mastering the keyboard. Once you began Session 34 a new feature was added to the program, in which you created documents in the Paradigm Word Processor (PWP).

PWP is similar to commercial word processing software packages such as MSWord and WordPerfect. The word processing software doesn't save files for you, doesn't name documents for you, and doesn't delete documents for you. These activities are your responsibility. Since Session 34 you have been naming, saving, and closing documents in all the sessions. This is good because that is what you will have to do when using commercial software packages for home use or on the job.

Less Than Sign Drill

The < symbol can be keyed with a space before and after it or with no space. Whichever you select, be consistent. Remember to use the left shift key, and anchor the "J" or the ";" finger for this reach. Key lines 1–3 twice for control.

1 2<7 3<8 4<9 5<6 8<9 1<2 5<7 6<8 k<l k<l 5<6 1<8<9
2 12 < 43 16 < 58 17 < 89 15 < 28 123 < 456 17 < 77
3 2 < 4, j < k, 1 < m, K < L; S < Z; K < L; JK < LM

Greater Than and Less Than Signs Drill

Follow the same spacing guideline as with the *less than* symbol. Key lines 1–3 twice for control. Anchor the "J" finger for this reach, and use the left shift key.

1 l<l l<l ;<; ;<; 6>4 6>2 5>1 9>7 l>l ;>>;;
2 L>M L>R ;>; 56 > 43 126 > 78 198 > 48 66 > 55 6>>
3 6 > 2 < 6; 6 > 1.2; 78 > 8; 1234 > 678; 56 < 234;

Forward Slash (Diagonal) Drill

The slash is used as a division sign in computer programming languages and in Web addresses such as http://www.emcp.com. It is also used to divide characters such as month, day, and year in the date (for example, 04/14/97).

Key lines 1–3 twice for control. Anchor the "J" finger when making this reach.

1 ;/; ;/; ;/; l;/ ;/; ;/; l;/ ;/; l;/ ;/ ;/ ;/;/ ;/
2 a = b/c d = f/g h=j/l t=k/j r = j / k fgh = rty/j
3 The equation: miles/hours will equal speed rate.

Backslash Key Drill

Key lines 1–3 twice for control. Anchor the "J" finger when making this reach.

1 The \ sign is used to designate a given file path.
2 For example, CD\ will return to the root directory.
3 The command, MKDIR\TGRADES, makes a DOS directory.

Specialized Punctuation Mark and Symbol Keys

Key each group of five lines once. If you need more practice, choose one or two groups to key again.

1 Two-thirds of the three-fourths are very gifted.
2 John said: Data Structures is a great textbook.

Document C

Radiology Report

1 At the *Session 48 Document C* screen, insert Document 048prob. Enter the information for the heading as follows:

a NAME: **Tabitha Rosemond**
b MEDICAL RECORD #: **4113**
c ADMITTED: **05/22/**Current year
d ROOM: **N-420**
e PHYSICIAN: **Y. A. Yakamura, M.D.**
f DATE/PROCEDURE: **05/22/**Current year

Note: When entering the Name, Admitted, and Physician information, use your right arrow key to move past the colon, press the space bar once, and enter the data. For the other entries in the heading and in the body of the report press the End key, then press the space bar once.

2 Key the body of the radiology report. Correct any errors in Document C that may have been overlooked. Throughout this document, the codes for three medical terms have been used. Key the two-letter codes as shown. These will be changed using the Search and Replace feature in the next document.

bn = barium enteroclysis
pj = proximal jejunum
fl = fluoroscope

3 Proofread, check, and correct the document; click Check; the document is automatically saved as **048proc**.
4 Click Next Exercise.

Reminder: Check the copy in the text before keying. You may find errors.

Document C

PROCEDURE: A bn through an Anderson tube was completed. Scout film was used, which shows small bowel loops. The long intestinal tube is noted to be coiled upon itself with its tip in the area of the pj. A diluted bn contrast material was administered via syringe and followed under fl control. The pj loops appeared normal. The fl reveals that loops begin to dilate within the area of gaseous dilation showing the slowest parssage of barium. Closer to the mid-ileum area there appears to be a narrowing in the pelvis after which the small bowel resumes normal caliber. The exact location of this is difficult to ascertain with certainty, but the finding is consistent with an adhesive band.
IMPRESSION: Partial small bowel obstruction in the mid-ileum.

Y. A. YAKAMURA, M.D.

YAY/xx
DD: 05/23/Current year
DT: 05/23/Current year
DOCUMENT: 8701-RR

3 Jerome's cat ran to Mary's house and said meow!!

4 "Hello," said Jim. "How are you this fine day?"

5 "Help!" yells the old man as the bees followed.

6 If the dress is $35.95, why is the coat $125.75?

7 Take #33 and move it to #66. Move #66 to #1234.

8 Farber & Daughters is the name of my law firm.

9 The check was made out for at least $*******.99.

10 You scored 89% on the exam and 78% on the drill.

11 Now is the time (11:45) for you (Ginny) to move.

12 I make $6 per hour, but I would like to make $9.

13 Sixteen @ $1.23 and 57 @ $23.45 is far too much.

14 If hours = 40 and rate = $5.00 then gross = $200.

15 The equation was A = B + C + F + D + G + H + I + J.

16 Jerry thought that A < B and F < G and JK < JKL.

17 However, Tom knew that A > B and F > G and I > IK.

18 If you raise 2^2 the answer will be squared now.

19 Enter your last name on the line that follows: _____.

20 LET B = A + B + C / D * H * (HH - K) + (HH + JJ).

21 Go to http://www.uwec.edu for information on course availability.

22 IF GH < AN AND TH > HJ OR TY < TU MOVE TRY TO A.

23 There will be a reaction—perhaps not good—if you do that.

24 PRINT TAB[17] "PLAYER" TAB[34] "FG PERCENT"; FG

25 The #12 category weights 18#; the #7 category weighs 6#.

23.9 ONE-MINUTE TIMINGS

Goal: 30 WAM/2 errors

Take a 1-minute timing on each paragraph.

1   Barlow, a shrewd fellow, winked as he waited in the shadows. A whistle warned him of the slow walk of his fellow worker. As he wallowed in the warmth of that workshop, Will worked in the wild, blowing wind. Barlow was worthless.

MEDICAL TERMINOLOGY

Term	Definition
Barium	A soft metallic element used with X-rays
Dilation	Expansion of an opening, organ, or vessel
Endotracheal tube	Tube used to make an airway through the trachea
Enteroclysis	Injection of a nutrient or medicine into the bowel
Fluoroscope	A device consisting of a fluorescent screen and roentgen tube; makes visible the shadows of objects placed between the tube and the screen
Ileum	Lower three-fifths of the small intestine
Jejunum	The second part of the small intestine from the duodenum to the ileum
Mediastinal drain	Drain in the septum or cavity between two main parts of an organ
Pneumothorax	A collection of air or gas in the chest cavity resulting from a cut through the chest wall
Sternotomy	The procedure of cutting through the breastbone

48.6

Document B

Creating a Radiology Report Form

1 At the *Session 48 Document B* screen, key Document B as a template for a radiology report form.
2 Proofread, correct, and check the document.
3 The document will be saved automatically as **048prob**.
4 Click Next Exercise.

Document B

RIVERSIDE MEDICAL CENTER
PORTLAND, OREGON

NAME: MEDICAL RECORD #:
ADMITTED: ROOM:
PHYSICIAN: DATE/PROCEDURE:

RADIOLOGY REPORT

PROCEDURE:
IMPRESSION:

2   Malaysia is in the process of shifting from an agricultural to an industrial economy. Their government has a plan entitled Vision 2020 that will make them fully industrialized by that year. Many government and business people feel that the ethnic balance of Malay, Chinese, and Indian races must remain intact. Banks are offering low-interest loans for Malay-owned businesses.

3   A lazy bicycle ride in the country is surely a healthy and worthy activity. A sunny sky and a dry day is surely an omen to any type of cyclist. Be wary of cloudy and windy days. A daily remedy for a healthy and spry body is a ride on a cycle. Energy is enjoyed by young and not so young.

23.10 | THREE–MINUTE TIMINGS

Goal: 25 WAM/2 errors

Take two 3-minute timings on the following paragraph.

1   Newer houses seem to cost more and have more space in them. Homes are built with large master bedrooms and have such things as walk-in closets, double sinks, and sitting space. Most homes also have two major rooms: a formal living room and a large family room. Houses that used to sell for reasonable amounts are now priced in the hundreds of thousands of dollars. In parts of the country people pay over $250,000 for a new, average-sized house.

ENDING THE SESSION

Now you may print this session's files, continue to the next session, or exit the program. See page 75 of Session 18 if you need to review procedures.

Ergonomic Tip

Use your entire hand to depress hard-to-reach keys rather than forcing hands into awkward positions. Make sure that you bring your fingers back to the home row keys.

1　　　In the autumn, when the grass begins to turn brown and the trees begin to lose their leaves, many people turn their attention to the upcoming sports season. Appearing high on the list for sports fans is professional football. Every weekend there are a variety of exciting games to attend, watch, or listen to. As the season progresses, much excitement is evident; the excitement culminates in the last big game of the year. In Canada, it's the Grey Cup; in the United States, it's the Super Bowl Game. The winning team in each country is declared to be "the" football league champion.

Other winter sports games draw the attention of many folks. Ice hockey has grown considerably as a professional sport during the past few years. The whizzing skaters, the delicate skills of the players, and the element of competition will add to a winter spectator's joy.

Basketball draws its share of attention during the long winters. The game of basketball is played at a steady pace and usually is very exciting. As in other professional sports, the teams travel all over the nation, giving the spectators one thrilling game after another.

TEXTBOOK ACTIVITIES: MEDICAL TERMINOLOGY AND RADIOLOGY REPORTS

You will continue reviewing medical terminology by completing a table of medical terms and their definitions. Next you will prepare a template for a radiology report, and then you will use this template to prepare a report.

Radiology is the branch of science dealing with radioactive substances and the diagnosis and treatment of disease by roentgen rays (X-rays) and/or ultrasound. During the course of treating a patient, a doctor may prescribe an X-ray or ultrasound. Upon completion of the procedure, a report is dictated and then keyed for the patient's records.

48.5

Document A

Medical Terminology

1　At the *Session 48 Document A* screen, key Document A as a two-column table.
2　Be sure to include an appropriate border and gridlines in your table, and use different levels of shading for the first two rows.
3　Proofread and correct any errors.
4　Name, save, and print the document as **048wpra**.
5　Click Next Exercise.

Students in Online Classes

Reminder: Read to comprehend the terms and definitions before preparing the table.

Unit

4

10-KEY
NUMERIC KEYPAD

Radiology Reports

Session Goals

1-Minute: 40 WAM/2 errors
3-Minute: 35 WAM/2 errors

Maintaining documents electronically (renaming, deleting)

Correcting misplaced modifiers

48.1-48.2   ON SCREEN EXERCISES: GETTING STARTED

If you are continuing immediately from Session 47, start with Exercise 48.2. Click on the Next Exercise or Previous Exercise button if you are not at the correct exercise.

If you exited the program at the end of the previous session, refer to page 11 in Session 3 for instructions on entering the program.

48.3   ONE-MINUTE TIMINGS

Goal: 40 WAM/2 errors

SI: 1.45

- Take two 1-minute timings.
- Use your most recent timing score to set a speed or accuracy goal.

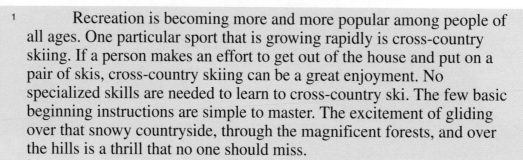

1   Recreation is becoming more and more popular among people of all ages. One particular sport that is growing rapidly is cross-country skiing. If a person makes an effort to get out of the house and put on a pair of skis, cross-country skiing can be a great enjoyment. No specialized skills are needed to learn to cross-country ski. The few basic beginning instructions are simple to master. The excitement of gliding over that snowy countryside, through the magnificent forests, and over the hills is a thrill that no one should miss.

48.4   THREE-MINUTE TIMINGS

Goal: 35 WAM/2 errors

SI: 1.46

- Take two 3-minute timings.
- On your second attempt, try to increase your speed while maintaining your accuracy goal.

24

HOME ROW (4, 5, 6), 0

Session Goals

Home Row (4, 5, 6), 0

10-Key Numeric Keypad: 25 WAM/0 errors
Alphabetic Keys: 30 WAM/2 errors

24.1-
24.3

ON-SCREEN EXERCISES: GETTING STARTED

If you are continuing immediately from Session 23, begin with Exercise 24.1. Click the Next Exercise or Previous Exercise button if you are not at the correct exercise.

If you exited the program at the end of the previous session, refer to page 11 of Session 3 for instructions on entering the program.

Before beginning the on-screen activities for Exercise 24.1, read the text on pages 99 and 100 titled "Typical 10-Key Numeric Keypad Configuration" and "Alternate 10-Key Numeric Keypad Configurations."

TYPICAL 10-KEY NUMERIC KEYPAD CONFIGURATION

Microcomputers have a 10-key numeric keypad located to the right of the alphabetic keyboard. The numeric keypad allows you to enter numeric data with one hand. This keypad may be used instead of the numeric row on the alphabetic keyboard. One example of using the 10-key numeric keypad is in working with spreadsheets and entering numbers in cells and rows. With a minimum amount of practice, you can enter numeric data at speeds well over 100 digits per minute. By industry standards, a rate of 250 digits per minute is considered average (equivalent to 50 WAM).

Copying Text

To copy a block of text from one place to another, you would follow these steps:

1   Select the text.
2   Click the Copy button on the toolbar.
3   Move the insertion point to the location where the text is to be copied.
4   Click the Paste button on the toolbar.

Deleting Text

To delete a block of text, you would follow these steps:

1   Select the text.
2   Press *Delete*.

47.8

Document D

Revising the SOAP Report Using Cut and Paste

1   At the *Session 47 Document D* screen, open document 047proc.
2   Using PWP's Cut and Paste feature move the section labeled as **X-RAYS** so that it comes before **PAST MEDICAL/SURGERY.**
3   Proofread the document to make sure that the changes didn't cause formatting errors.
4   Name, save, and print the document as **047wprd**.

47.9

Document E

Compose a Letter

Compose a rough draft of a letter to the top administrator of your school. Identify two things that you especially like about the school and two things that you would like to see changed (remember to be positive). Jot down key words of what you will cover before starting to compose.

Use the timing feature to have your WAM rate calculated. (When you are ready to start keying, click to start the timer.) Key the document. When finished, click to stop the clock—the system will calculate and display your WAM rate. Name (**047wpre**) and save your document.

Print a copy of your document and edit it for changes. Enter the changes into your document and save your document under the same name (047wpre); print the document and give the instructor both the rough draft (with the WAM rate) and your corrected copy, then close the document.

ENDING THE SESSION

Now you may print this session's files, continue to the next session, or exit the program. See pages 230–231 in Session 45 to review the procedures.

Ergonomic Tip
Getting up and walking down the hall relaxes your hands, wrists, arms, back, neck, eyes, and mind —by moving, you increase productivity.

The following illustration shows the general arrangement of most 10-key numeric keypads. The top row of numbers contains the 7, 8, and 9. The middle row contains the 4, 5, and 6. This row is identified as the *home row*. The bottom row of keys contains the 1, 2, and 3. The *0* (zero) key is at the very bottom. When working with spreadsheets, the **Tab** key ("a" finger) is used to move across the screen from cell to cell. The **Enter** key is a larger key located to the right of the *3* key. It is used to move vertically from one line to the next.

On a microcomputer the Num Lock key must be "on" to use the 10-key numeric keypad. When Num Lock is on, a green light displays by Num Lock in the upper-right corner of the keyboard. If Num Lock is not on, press **Num Lock** to turn it on. Press again to turn it off.

ALTERNATE 10-KEY NUMERIC KEYPAD CONFIGURATIONS

In addition to the standard numeric keypad configuration, there are several alternate key arrangements used among computer manufacturers. Typically, the symbol keys (**plus [+]**, **minus [-]**, **Enter**, and **decimal**) are rearranged. Other keys often rearranged include diagonal/forward slash (/) and asterisk (*). Generally, using the symbol keys next to the 10-key pad is more efficient.

Study the configuration of your 10-key pad and become familiar with the arrangement of the keys. Then proceed with the on-screen activities.

24.4 TEXTBOOK EXERCISES: REINFORCEMENT

Earlier in the session you completed new-key drills presented on the screen. Now you will repeat some of those drills and key some new ones to reinforce your sense of where the keys are on the 10-key numeric keypad. When you have finished the drills, click Print (if desired), then click Next Exercise.

Reviewing the Home Row and 0 Keys

Coumadin, and then, once his protime is back to a satisfactory level, stop the Lovenox. As I say, the biggest problem will be bleeding. It will be very important that we control the bleeding optimally during the surgery and take the best care of the soft tissues that we can. All of this has been understood and explained.

PLAN
Left knee replacement

_____

Ian M. Giangobbe

IG/XX
D: 06/07/XXXX
T: 03/30/XXXX

Cutting and Pasting Text

Some documents may need to be revised extensively, and those revisions may include deleting, moving, or copying blocks of text. This kind of editing is generally referred to as _cutting and pasting._

Cutting and/or _moving_ text means that text is deleted from its present location and reinserted in a new location. However, when text is _copied_, it remains in its original location _and_ a copy is inserted into the new location. There are two copies of the text in the document.

The basic steps for cutting and pasting text are:

1 Select the text. You can select the text one of two ways:
   a Go to the first character of the text to be selected, hold down the left mouse button and drag the mouse to the end of the material to be selected.
   b Go to the first character to the text to be selected, hold down the Shift key and press the down arrow to the end of the text to be selected. This method works best when you are selecting a paragraph or more of text.
2 Choose to move or copy the selected text.
3 Paste the selected text into the new location.

When cutting and pasting, you work with blocks of text. A block of text is a portion of text that you have selected. A block of text can be as small as one character or as large as an entire page or document.

Moving Text

To move a block of text from one place to another, you would follow these steps:
1 Select the text.
2 Click the Cut button ✂ on the toolbar.
3 Move the insertion point to the location where the text is to be moved.
4 Click the Paste 📋 button on the toolbar.

Drill Instructions

- Use the "a" finger of your left hand on the **Tab** key to space between groups of numbers. Anchor your "f" finger when making the reach to the Tab key.
- Press **Enter** at the end of each line.
- Keep your eyes on the copy.
- Read the numbers as combinations (review page 53 if necessary).

Note: If you want your numbers to appear in a single column rather than as a line, press **Enter** after keying each group of numbers. However, creating a single column requires extra paper when printing.

Home Row Drill

Place your right hand on home row (4, 5, 6). Use your right little finger for **Enter**, **plus,** and **minus**. Use your "a" finger to depress the **Tab** key.

Key lines 1–5 twice: first key the five lines for speed, then for control. Remember to think of the numbers in groups. Assume that you are in a spreadsheet application; tab after keying each group of numbers. Press **Enter** at the end of each line.

1 456 456 456 456 456 456 456 456 456 456 456 456 45
2 456 456 456 654 654 564 564 654 564 565 564 456 46
3 456 456 456 654 654 555 444 666 456 654 456 456 64

4 654 654 654 456 456 666 444 555 546 546 546 456 46
5 555 666 444 555 654 555 456 456 654 645 645 645 45

Students in Online Classes

If you look at your fingers or the screen as you are entering the numbers, it will slow you down. Also, when keying the lines for control, stop at the end of each line and proofread. If you have three or more errors, repeat the line.

0 Drill

Place the thumb of your right hand on the 0 key, your "a" finger on the **Tab** key. Tab after each group of numbers. Press **Enter** after each line.

Key lines 1–5 twice: first key the five lines for speed, then for control.

1 0 00 000 000 000 000 50 50 50 50 50 50 60 60 40 400
2 400 400 400 400 500 500 600 600 500 400 400 500 60
3 405 504 506 605 440 400 550 660 660 550 440 456 60

4 440 500 450 450 560 4560 4560 4560 6540 6540 56000
5 550 600 540 540 650 6540 6440 4560 6540 6054 56605

Students in Online Classes

After keying each line for control, proofread. If you have any errors, repeat the line until you can key it without error.

Additional Drill

Key the following drill for control. Press **Enter** after each line.

4 Correct any errors in Document C that may have been overlooked.

5 Proofread and correct the document you prepared.

6 Click the Check icon; Document C will be saved automatically as **047proc**.

7 Click Next Exercise.

Document C

CHIEF COMPLAINT

Left knee hurts when trying to walk.

SOAP REPORT

SUBJECTIVE

Kental Davis is the husband of DeeAnn Davis. Kental indicates that he has difficulty walking. His left knee hurts to the point that he has to limp. He has tried taking Tylenol, but there is no relief. Over the past 3 months, the pain has increased.

OBJECTIVE

MEDICATIONS: He is on Coumadin 7.5 mg four days, 5 mg three days. Other medicines are Allegra, Protonix, Diovan, Vitamin Eyes with lutein, Omega, and Selenium (study for colon cancer).

ALLERGIES TO MEDICATIONS: None, but **CODEINE** makes him nauseous and occasionally has made him disoriented.

PAST SURGERY: He had a Greenfield filter two years ago for a pulmonary embolism. He had his last DVT two years ago. He had cartilage removal from his right knee in 1978, but it is his left knee that bothers him

X-RAYS: X-rays show multicompartment arthritis of the left knee in varus. The right knee is similar, but not as severe.

OBSERVATIONS: He has good range of motion of both hips. The right knee functions well. He has a 1+ effusion and varus collapse and tenderness along the medial joint line of the left knee with some joint noise with range of motion. He has a lot of venous disease distal to the knee, but he has good palpable pluses. He wears compression stockings. There is no neuromuscular or motor deficit at the level of the foot or ankle.

ASSESSMENT

Mr. Davis has osteoarthritis of the left knee. Today we talked about knee replacement surgery, small knee incisions, standard knee incisions, pain medicine, and modification in great detail. The intent on Mr. Davis's part is that as I have done his wife's surgery, he would like me to do the surgery on his knee. I explained to him that I could not guarantee that I would do a small knee approach on him. What I would be more concerned about would be to control the bleeding and to make accurate bone cuts and that we would probably use a modified standard incision unless his tissue were a lot more flexible that I thought they were. The advantages of that of course, would be also they wouldn't take quite as long. He feels that is the way he would want to go. In preparation for his surgery, we would certainly want Doctor Lind to participate in his perioperative care. It sounds like we would stop the Coumadin and perhaps initiate Lovenox after the Coumadin was stopped, continue Lovenox postoperatively, resume the

Continued on next page

1 654 654 456 456 456 456 456 655 556 556 664 664 56

2 456 546 546 546 645 456 546 566 566 664 665 444 44

3 544 544 566 544 644 644 554 555 444 655 444 555 44

4 64 456 456 654 456 666 444 555 654 654 456 456 456

5 45 666 555 444 654 654 465 55 44 45 65 64 56 54 446

6 500 600 400 545 545 6545 4505 5460 5440 5540 50404

7 644 654 4560 4560 4560 4560 6540 6540 6540 450 406

8 556 654 6540 5460 5046 0564 0546 5040 5000 605 404

9 600 500 4000 4005 5004 6005 5004 6005 0665 044 606

24.5 TIMINGS: 10-KEY NUMERIC KEYPAD

Goal: 25 WAM with 0 errors

- Take a 1-minute timing on the lines in Group 1. Then take two 1-minute timings on the lines in Group 2.
- If you finish before time is up, start over.
- Press the **Tab** key with your "a" finger.
- Press **Enter** at the end of each line.

1
654	654	654	456	456	666	444	555	546	546	546	456	46
555	666	444	555	654	555	456	456	654	645	645	645	45
654	654	456	456	456	456	456	655	556	556	664	664	56
456	546	546	546	645	456	546	566	566	644	665	444	44
544	544	566	544	644	644	554	555	444	655	444	555	44

2
550	600	540	540	650	6540	6440	4560	6540	6054	56605
500	600	400	545	545	6545	4505	5460	5440	5540	50404
644	654	4560	4560	4560	4560	6540	6540	6540	450	406
556	654	6540	5460	5046	0564	0546	5040	5000	605	404
600	500	4000	4005	5004	6005	5004	6005	0665	044	606

24.6 ONE-MINUTE TIMINGS

Goal: 30 WAM with no more than 2 errors

- Take a 1-minute timing on paragraph 3, then take a 1-minute timing on paragraph 4.
- Press **Tab** to indent the first line.
- If you finish a paragraph before time is up, start over.

SUN WEST ORTHOPEDIC SURGEONS
SUN CITY WEST, ARIZONA

(ds)

PATIENT NAME: MEDICAL RECORD #:
DOB: DATE OF VISIT:

SURGEON:

CHIEF COMPLAINT

(ds)

SOAP REPORT

(ds)

SUBJECTIVE
OBJECTIVE
MEDICATIONS:
ALLERGIES TO MEDICATIONS:
PAST SURGERY:
X-RAYS:
OBSERVATIONS:
ASSESSMENT
PLAN

(ds)

_____
(Enter Name of Doctor)

DR/TM *(Enter Dr's initials and your initials as the Medical Transcriptionist)*
D:XX/XX/XXXX *(Current date)*
T:XX/XX/XX *(Current time)*

SOAP Report

47.7

Document C

1   At the *Session 47 Document C* screen, insert document 047prob using the following steps:
   a   Choose Insert→File.
   b   At the *Insert File* dialog box, double-click **047prob**.
2   Enter the information for the headings as follows:
   a   PATIENT NAME: Kental R Davis
   b   MEDICAL RECORD: 325260845
   c   DOB: 09/25/1942
   d   DATE OF VISIT: 06/07/current year
   e   SURGEON: Ian M Giangobbe
       Note: When entering the patient's name, DOB, and surgeon's name, use the right arrow key to move past the colon; press the space bar once, and enter the data. For the other entries in the heading and in the body of the report, press the End key, and then press the space bar once.
3   Key the body of the SOAP report.

Students in Online Classes

Reminder: Check the copy in the text before keying. You may find errors.

3   Current periodicals and programs are promoting the need for international business education courses. Another trend is to include international concepts in existing courses and programs. The global view of business and international protocols must be taught to students preparing for the world of work.

4   Basically, employers like a loyal employee. Honesty and courtesy always pay off in any job or assignment. Apathy and sloppy work are always very costly to a company. On the other hand, any employee who does consistently good work will be properly awarded and can expect to receive a salary increase of perhaps 8 percent.

ENDING THE SESSION

Now you may print this session's files, continue to the next session, or exit the program.

Print

To print Exercises 24.1–24.6 proceed as follows:

1   Click the Close ⊠ button in the top right corner of the screen.
2   At your Paradigm Keyboarding with Snap Welcome page, point to Reports on the Snap menu bar, and click View Submissions Report.
3   At the View Submissions Report Wizard, click Show session files to see the drill lines text (Exercises 24.1–24.4), or Show timings files to see the timings text (Exercises 24.5–24.6).
4   Click Show Report.
5   Click the name of the file you want to print.
6   At the Word Processor dialog box, click Launch.
7   Click File, and then click Print.
8   At the Print dialog box, click OK.
9   Click the Close button to close the Paradigm Word Processor.
10 Click Home on the Snap menu bar to return to the Welcome page.

Continue

To continue on the next session, click the Next Exercise button **twice**. This will take you to Exercise 25.2. (You will bypass Exercise 25.1 Warmup since you are already warmed up.)

Exit

To exit, do the following:

1   Click the Close ⊠ button in the top right corner of the screen.
2   At your Paradigm Keyboarding with Snap Welcome page, click Logout.

Ergonomic Tip
Keep neck and shoulders relaxed.

MEDICAL TERMINOLOGY

Term	Definition
Arthritis	An inflammation of one or more joints
DVT	Deep vein thrombosis; blood clot in a deep vein
Coumadin	A blood thinner
Codeine	A drug used in cough medicine; also used as a pain killer
Lutein	A supplement derived from marigold flowers used in medications for treating macular degeneration — strengthens the eye blood vessels
Pulmonary embolism	A blood clot that breaks away and lodges in the lung or heart
Cartilage	A translucent elastic tissue that resides between the bones of a joint
Effusion	The escape of a fluid from anatomical vessels by rupture or exudation
Varus	The position of a joint that is turned inward to an abnormal degree
Venous	Referring to blood that has passed through the capillaries, given up oxygen for the tissues, and become charged with carbon dioxide
Distal	Away from the point of attachment
Palpable	Capable of being touched or felt
Neuromuscular	That part of the nervous system that impacts muscle tissue
Osteoarthritis	Degenerative changes in the joints

47.6

Document B

Creating a Medical SOAP Report Form

1 For a review of setting tabs and using headers/footers in PWP, refer to page 227 in Session 45.
2 At the *Session 47 Document B* screen, key Document B as a template for a medical SOAP report form. Remember to set a tab at 3.0" and triple space after **PLAN** to insert the signature line.
3 Insert the header **SOAP Report, a**nd a page number field; align both at the right margin.
4 Be sure to check for errors in the printed copy of the document in the text. Proofread and correct any errors in the document you have keyed.
5 Click the Check icon; your document is saved at **047prob**.
6 Click Next Exercise.

7, 8, 9

Session Goals

7, 8, 9

10-Key Numeric Keypad: 25 WAM/0 errors
Alphabetic Keys: 30 WAM/2 errors

25.1-
25.5 ## ON-SCREEN EXERCISES: GETTING STARTED

If you exited the program at the end of the previous session, refer to page 99 of Session 24 to review how to open the next session or to continue from where you left off.

25.6 ## TEXTBOOK EXERCISES: REINFORCEMENT

Some of the drills presented on the screen earlier in the session are repeated in the text, along with some new ones, to reinforce your sense of where the keys are located on the numeric keypad. When you have finished the drills, click Print (if desired), then Next Exercise.

Reviewing the 7, 8, and 9 Keys

Drill Instructions

- Use your "a" finger to tap the **Tab** key.
- Press **Enter** at the end of each line.

7 Drill

Key lines 1–6 twice: first key the six lines for speed, then for control. Remember to read the numbers as groups.

1 444 47 47 47 47 47 47 47 74 74 74 74 74 74 74 74 4
2 57 57 57 57 57 57 57 75 75 75 75 75 75 75 75 5 666

¹ Since the first moment in time when two people traveled beyond a shouting distance of each other, humans have searched for a method of talking over a long distance. Earlier cultures tried drums and smoke signals for messages. Today, the traffic noises in most places would cover the sounds of a drum; fire engines would arrive on the scene to drown the fire.

People communicate easily today with our telephones. Most of us don't realize how advanced the technology of phone service has become. Old photos show endless miles of phone wires hung on poles; today we would find the wire buried. The switchboard operator has been replaced with automatic dialing handled by a big computer with the sound waves being relayed across the world by satellite. The repair person has now been replaced by a trained service person.

The changes that have taken place are numerous; however, the objective of the service is still the same: to allow people to talk with other people. The next time you have a chance, look for other changes; you will be amazed with what you will find.

TEXTBOOK ACTIVITIES: MEDICAL TERMINOLOGY AND SUBJECTIVE, OBJECTIVE, ASSESSMENT, PLAN (SOAP) REPORTS

In this session you will again continue reviewing medical terminology by reading and comprehending medical terms and their definitions and then prepare a table consisting of the terms and their meanings as Document A. In addition, for Document B you will prepare a template for a Subjective, Objective, Assessment, Plan (SOAP) report. Surgeons working with patients prepare SOAP reports that provide background information about a patient's medical history, tell what the surgeon has found via testing (X-rays, ultrasound, MRI, Doppler, etc.), prepare an assessment based on the findings, and identify a course of action. For Document C, you will prepare a SOAP report. For Document D, you will use the PWP Cut, Copy, and Paste feature.

47.5

Document A

Medical Terminology

1 Before creating the Medical Terminology Table, read and comprehend each of the terms and the definitions provided so that when these terms are used in Document C, you will know their meanings.

2 At the *Session 47 Document A* screen, key Document A as a two-column table.

3 Add an appropriate border and gridlines to your table, and use different levels of shading for the first two rows. Refer to pages 224–225 of Session 45 to review the instructions for creating tables.

4 Proofread and correct any errors.

5 Name, save, and print the document as **047wpra**, then close the document.

6 Click Next Exercise.

Students in Online Classes

Reminder: Read to comprehend the terms and definitions before preparing the table.

3   67 67 67 67 67 67 76 76 76 76 67 76 76 76 67 6 777

4   76 74 74 567 567 567 567 567 4567 4567 7 456 457

5   65 45 67 4567 6 777 765 7567 5560 57670 5666 056

6   70 45670 45670 567 5560 5456 6747 44760 547 645

8 Drill

Key lines 1–5 twice: first key the five lines for speed, then for control. Read the numbers as groups.

1   555 58 58 58 58 58 58 58 58 85 85 85 85 85 85 58 5

2   58 68 68 68 48 48 48 48 58 78 78 78 78 58 58 6 800 8

3   800 800 807 807 806 805 508 508 408 804 88 876 568

4   468 780 786 807 876 558 558 558 778 78 45678 87654

5   007 80765 876 8888 7787 7877 6778 5678 458 85 8685

9 Drill

Key lines 1–5 twice: first key the five lines for speed, then for control. Think of the numbers in groups.

1   69 69 69 69 99 99 99 66 66 66 69 69 69 69 69 66 66 990

2   90 90 90 98 98 98 97 79 79 89 89 69 69 96 96 96 789 78

3   9 456 456 475 678 789 908 908 970 970 987 09 890 890

4   690 906 960 978 589 479 690 978 890 89 6989 6989 697

5   9 6979 69879 69879 69857 96857 456789 9678 9687 898

Additional Drill

Key the following drill for control. Press **Enter** after each line.

1   456 45 67 67 65 64 675 456 456 456 456 4567 4567 67

2   765 657 654 475 476 457 45776 4576 45577 45567 467

3   576 475 777 777 667 666 65777 7445 57774 77745 774

4   876 568 678 468 780 786 807 876 558 558 558 778 788

5   45678 87654 80765 876 8888 7787 7877 6778 5678 458

6   80000 87778 88585 848 5858 8585 5857 5857 8575 885

7   789 789 456 456 475 678 789 908 908 970 970 987 09 9

8   900 909 909 969 969 696 898 797 690 578 589 987 95 9

Students in Online Classes

At the end of each line, proofread. If you have any errors, repeat the line until you can key it without error before going to the next line.

SUBJECTIVE, OBJECTIVE, ASSESSMENT, PLAN REPORTS

Session Goals

1-Minute: 40 WAM/2 errors
3-Minute: 35 WAM/2 errors

Cutting, copying, and pasting text

47.1-47.2 ON-SCREEN EXERCISES: GETTING STARTED

If you exited the program at the end of the previous session, refer to page 11 in Session 3 to review how to open the next session. If you are continuing immediately from Session 46, start with Exercise 47.2. Click the Next Exercise or Previous Exercise button if you are not at the correct exercise.

47.3 ONE-MINUTE TIMINGS

Goal: 40 WAM/2 errors

SI: 1.45

- Take two l-minute timings.
- Use your most recent timing score to set a speed or accuracy goal.

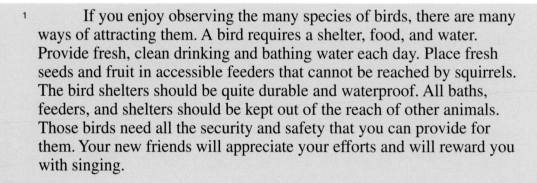

1   If you enjoy observing the many species of birds, there are many ways of attracting them. A bird requires a shelter, food, and water. Provide fresh, clean drinking and bathing water each day. Place fresh seeds and fruit in accessible feeders that cannot be reached by squirrels. The bird shelters should be quite durable and waterproof. All baths, feeders, and shelters should be kept out of the reach of other animals. Those birds need all the security and safety that you can provide for them. Your new friends will appreciate your efforts and will reward you with singing.

47.4 THREE-MINUTE TIMINGS

Goal: 35 WAM/2 errors

SI: 1.48

- Take two 3-minute timings. If you finish the three paragraphs before time is up, start over in paragraph one.
- On your second attempt, try to increase your speed while keeping errors at two or fewer per minute.

25.7   TIMINGS: 10-KEY NUMERIC KEYPAD

Goal: 25 WAM with 0 errors

- Take a 1-minute timing on the lines in Group 1. Then take two 1-minute timings on the lines in Group 2.
- If you finish before time is up, start over.
- Press **Tab** with your "a" finger.
- Press **Enter** at the end of each line.

1
99	89	89	79	79	66	69	69	59	59	49	49
789	789	456	456	475	678	789	908	970	970	987	09
900	909	909	969	696	898	797	690	578	589	987	95
9678	9687	8985	6978	96745	45678	56789	98765	987654			
9889	8899	9999	7999	69969	69969	94569	49566	594695			

2
9889	8899	9999	7999	69969	69969	94569	49566	594695	
9678	9687	8985	6978	96745	45678	56789	98765	987654	
900	909	909	969	969	696	898	797	690	578	589	987
789	789	456	456	475	678	789	908	970	970	987	09
99	89	89	79	79	66	69	69	59	59	49	49

25.8   ONE-MINUTE TIMINGS

Goal: 30 WAM with no more than 2 errors

Take a 1-minute timing on paragraph 3. If you finish before time is up start paragraph 3 over. Repeat the same process for paragraph 4.

3   Traveling in this vast land is a great experience. The endless rivers, vast prairies that stretch as far as the eye can see, and mountains that reach for the sky are all impressive. Rural villages reveal something of the past in terms of how they are laid out. These vivid scenes revive the mind and lift the spirits.

4   During your working life, you will meet and work with people of many different cultures. Although each of us is a member of a racial or ethnic group, our work groups make up one large community. The beliefs we share give us a common base and a list of topics to discuss.

ENDING THE SESSION

Now you may print this session's files, continue to the next session, or exit the program. See page 103 of Session 24 if you need to review procedures.

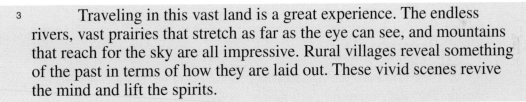

Ergonomic Tip

For relaxation, lightly clench hand and release, fanning out fingers, five times.

Current date

TO: Michael Chen, President

(your name)

SALARY ADJUSTMENT PROCESS

Many of the employees feel that the process for increasing our salaries is unfair. Some people seem to get salary reviews more often than others do. People get raises just because their manager likes them better. You've got to make some changes or the staff will get angry. They may even slow down their work and then you won't have products to sell.

A new system should be used that establishes a salary review schedule for all workers. You should also choose who will make the salary decisions and what factors they will use. A new process will make employees feel more satisfied.

Thank you for your consideration. I would be glad to discuss possible changes whenever you have the time.

xx/046wpre

ENDING THE SESSION

Now you may print this session's files, continue to the next session, or exit the program. See pages 230–231 in Session 45 to review the procedures.

Ergonomic Tip
Turn your head to look over your right shoulder, back to the front, and then over your left shoulder. This helps your neck muscles to relax.

Session

26

1, 2, 3

Session Goals

1, 2, 3

10-Key Numeric Keypad: 25 WAM/0 errors
Alphabetic Keys: 30 WAM/2 errors

26.1-
26.5
ON-SCREEN EXERCISES: GETTING STARTED

If you exited the program at the end of the previous session, refer to page 99 of Session 24 to review how to open the next session or to continue from where you left off.

26.6
TEXTBOOK EXERCISES: REINFORCEMENT

Earlier in the session you completed new-key drills presented on the screen. Now you will repeat some of those drills, along with some new ones, to reinforce your keyboarding skills. When you have finished the drills, click Print (if desired), then Next Exercise.

Reviewing the 1, 2, and 3 Keys

---

1 Drill

Key lines 1–5 twice: first key the five lines for speed, then for control. Read the numbers in groups and press **Enter** at the end of each line.

1 41 14 41 41 41 14 14 14 451 415 514 614 614 716 41
2 61 61 61 51 71 81 91 17 171 171 187 187 191 151 19
3 168 187 187 186 175 177 109 186 101 186 186 19658

4 145 156 195 157 145 198 966 919 818 717 616 515 41
5 1474 4010 4561 4561 4710 46678 15851 979711 5987

46.8 Changing Medical Consultant's Report Using Search and Replace

Document D

1 At the *Session 46 Document D* screen, open document 046proc.

2 Using PWP's Search and Replace feature (see Session 43, pages 207–208, for a review), change the two-letter codes to their full words. Remember to select the <u>W</u>hole words only check box. Also select the Case <u>i</u>nsensitive check box in order to find the occurrence of Hy in the numbered paragraph. After replacing Hy, check that the full word is capitalized as the two-letter code was.

    ic = intertrochanteric
    hy = hypercholesterolemia
    nr = neurovascular

3 Proofread the document to make sure that the replacements didn't cause formatting errors.

4 Name, save, and print the document as **046wprd**.

REINFORCING WRITING SKILLS

A number of words in the English language have a negative effect on readers. Words such as *hate*, *argue*, *wrong*, *poor*, and *problem* are examples of words that tend to produce an undesirable reaction. Think about how you would react to the following statement in a proposal for automating operations in your organization:

> Our project team uncovered numerous problems in the day-to-day operations of your medical facility.

The terms *uncovered* and *problems* immediately convey a negative perception that may cast all the information that follows in a poor light. Are workers trying to cover up something? And, are there that many problems with our system? By rewording the sentence and eliminating the negative words, the reader is more apt to accept what is being presented and to think about it in neutral or objective terms. Here's a more positive way to say the same thing:

> Our project team has identified areas where changes can be made in the day-to-day operations of your medical facility that will make the work flow more smoothly…

So, when communicating with others, choose your words carefully. Decide what tone you would like to convey in presenting the information. Then select language that helps achieve that mood or feeling. Put yourself in the position of the reader. Will you cause the reader to take issue with what you are saying before the details are presented? If so, reword your material.

46.9 Business Memo Edited for Tone

Document E

Review the following memo. Then rewrite the memo using more positive language. You are trying to convince the president of your company that the salary adjustment process needs to be improved.

Check your sentences for clarity and correct grammar, spelling, and punctuation. Save the memo as **046wpre**. Print the memo, if required by your instructor, and then close it.

2 Drill

Key lines 1–5 twice: first key the five lines for speed, then for control. Read the numbers in groups.

1 52 52 52 52 52 52 25 25 25 25 25 24 24 42 62 72 82 52
2 25 62 72 82 92 02 42 52 27 85 58 85 95 96 90 88 56 24
3 242 252 252 262 852 258 158 148 284 282 272 958 594

4 222 224 225 226 227 228 228 822 922 202 202 212 2169
5 2456 2789 2010 2456 2678 2525 24567 27890 12456 127

3 Drill

Key lines 1–5 twice: first key the five lines for speed, then for control. Read the numbers in groups.

1 63 63 63 63 63 36 36 36 36 36 93 39 39 39 69 69 63 34 35
2 36 73 73 93 83 23 13 30 54 65 63 36 83 49 34 234 354 345
3 456 383 838 938 736 373 369 936 963 33 568 936 947 373

4 464 585 484 737 363 922 291 302 30 4435 4344 3345 3443
5 2343 2334 4873 4848 3929 26282 4844 6673 8733 5663 55

Additional Drill

Key the following drill for control. Press **Enter** after each line.

1 41 41 51 61 71 81 91 11 141 141 141 141 145 146 14
2 100 104 145 414 151 149 109 011 084 171 155 109 1
3 4111 1444 4568 1787 1679 88981 98871 019091 001001

> At the end of each line, proofread. If you have any errors, repeat the line until you can key it without error before going to the next line.

4 24 56 25 58 47 71 89 80 20 20 20 50 50 20 70 45 86
5 456 789 125 125 128 124 126 129 125 128 982 982 12
6 2222 2525 2582 2582 9792 2728 26267 88771 07862 72

7 345 636 663 663 663 336 393 393 993 993 339 936 93
8 568 936 947 373 464 585 484 737 363 922 291 302 30
9 4844 6673 8733 5663 5543 3323 6788 6733 2343 23343

26.7 TIMINGS: 10-KEY NUMERIC KEYPAD

Goal: 25 WAM with 0 errors

• Take a 1-minute timing on the lines in Group 1. Then take two 1-minute timings on the lines in Group 2.

4 Use the Bullets and Numbering feature for the numbered paragraphs.
5 Correct any errors in Document C that may have been overlooked.
6 Proofread and correct the document you prepared.
7 Click the Check icon; Document C will be saved automatically as **046proc**.
8 Click Next Exercise.

Document C

CONSULTATION: Mr. Osaki is a 73-year-old male who slipped and fell at his home. He landed on his right hip and sustained a displaced comminuted ic hip fracture with fragmentation of the lesser trochanter areas as well. He is presently comfortable on bed rest in the Emergency Room. Pertinent medical problems include noninsulin-dependent diabetes mellitus, hy, and past history of unknown lower extremity surgery. The remainder of his social history and family history is noted in Dr. North's admission record. A review of systems is unremarkable. On physical examination, the patient is alert, oriented, and comfortable on bed rest with stable vital signs. The upper extremities have full range of motion whithout tenderness and nr status is intact, as well as the left lower extremity. No tenderness on lateral pelvic compression. Thoracic and lumbar spine is nontender to palpation, and he has full range of motion to his cervical spine. The remainder of the HEENT, lungs, cardiac, and abdominal exam is noted in Dr. North's pre-anesthetic medical evaluation. The right lower extremity rests in a foreshortened and externally rotated position with know swelling and no ecchymoses. His nr status is intact. Review of X-rays demonstrates a comminuted right ic hip fracture with comminution of the greater trochanter, as well as the lesser trochanter.

IMPRESSIONS:

1. Right comminuted ic hip fracture.
2. Noninsulin-dependent diabetes mellitus.
3. Hy.

RECOMMENDATIONS: The patient is being admitted and taken to surgery this evening for open reduction and internal fixation of high right ic hip fracture. The need for surgery was discussed with the family and patient. The risks, potential complications, and treatment alternatives were discussed. The plan is to proceed with surgery tonight. They understood the above and consent was obtained with the patient's understanding.

_____

A. L. BERMAN, M.D.

ALB/xx
DD: 05/15/Current year
DT: 05/15/Current year
DOCUMENT: 760-CR

Students in Online Classes

Reminder: Check the copy in the text before keying. You may find errors.

- If you finish before time is up, start over.
- Press **Tab** with your "a" finger.
- Press **Enter** at the end of each line.

1	34	35	36	73	93	83	23	13	30	54	65	63
	345	636	663	663	663	336	393	393	993	93	339	936
	568	936	947	373	464	585	484	737	363	922	291	302
	3748	3833	9374	0585	0392	0458	0382	0483	3230	30339		
	4844	6673	8733	5663	5543	3323	6788	6733	2343	23343		

2	4844	6673	8733	5663	5543	3323	6788	6733	2343	23343		
	3748	3833	9374	0585	0392	0458	0382	0483	3230	30339		
	568	936	947	373	464	585	484	737	363	922	291	302
	345	636	663	663	663	336	393	393	993	993	339	936
	34	35	36	73	93	83	23	13	30	54	65	63

26.8 ONE-MINUTE TIMINGS

Goal: 30 WAM with no more than 2 errors

Take a 1-minute timing on each paragraph.

3   Students in school today must be prepared to live and compete in a global economy. They must develop a respect for life and work in a society of diverse cultures. Being exposed to the cultures of other countries can open doors to the future in terms of job opportunities.

4   The vessel sank in 510 feet of water in Lake Superior during a raging storm. An adept team of divers salvaged 149,683 parts. Seven local residents were among those who assisted in this job. The additional divers were welcome. The salvage company made a profit on their investment.

ENDING THE SESSION

Now you may print this session's files, continue to the next session, or exit the program. See page 103 of Session 24 if you need to review procedures.

Ergonomic Tip
Personalize your work area by having pictures of family and friends.

46.6

Document B

Creating a Medical Consultant's Report Form

1 For a review of setting tabs and using the Header/Footer feature in PWP, refer to Session 45, page 227.

2 At the *Session 46 Document B* screen, key Document B (shown on page 235) as a template for a medical consultant's report form. Remember to set a tab at 3.0" and triple space after **RECOMMENDATIONS** to insert the signature line.

3 Insert the header **Consultant's Report** and a page number field; align both at the right margin.

4 Be sure to check for errors in the printed copy of the document in the text. Proofread and correct any errors in the document you have keyed.

5 Click the Check icon; your document is saved as **046prob**.

6 Click Next Exercise.

Using Search and Replace to Reduce Document Preparation Time

Commercial word processors generally contain an automatic correction feature that can be used to automatically correct text and also can be used to quickly insert terms in a document. For example, rather than continually keying hypercholesterolemia in a medical consultant's report, the keyboarder can use a code suc h as *hy* to replace keying the whole word. When the keyboarder enters *hy*, the software will automatically change it to hypercholesterolemia.

While PWP doesn't have this feature, it can be simulated by using the Search and Replace feature once the document is finished.

46.7

Document C

Medical Consultant's Report

1 At the *Session 46 Document C* screen, insert document 046prob using the following steps:

   a   Choose Insert→File.

   b   At the *Insert File* dialog box, double-click 046prob.

2 Enter the information for the headings as follows:

   a   NAME: **Carl A Osaki**

   b   MEDICAL REOCRD #: **5534**

   c   ROOM: **W-54**

   d   DATE OF BIRTH: **01/11/1934**

   e   ADMITTED: **05/14/**Current year

   f   DATE OF CONSULT: **05/14/**Current year

   g   PHYSICIAN: **S. J. North, M.D.**

   h   CONSULTANT: **A. L. Berman, M.D.**

      Note: When entering the Name, Room, Admitted, and Physician information, use your right arrow key to move past the colon, press the space bar once, and enter the data. For the other entries in the heading and in the body of the report, press the End key, and then press the space bar once.

3 Key the body of the consultant's report. Throughout this document, the codes for three medical terms have been used. Key the two-letter codes as shown. These codes will be changed using the Search and Replace feature in the next document.

      ic = intertrochanteric

      hy = hypercholesterolemia

      nr = neurovascular

Session Goals

Review   Review keys from Sessions 1–26

10-Key Numeric Keypad: 25 WAM/0 errors
Alphabetic Keys: 30 WAM/2 errors

**27.1–
27.2**   *ON-SCREEN EXERCISES: GETTING STARTED*

If you exited the program at the end of the previous session, refer to page 99 of Session 24 to review how to open the next session or to continue from where you left off.

27.3   *TEXTBOOK EXERCISES: REINFORCEMENT*

Earlier in the session you completed review drills presented on the screen. Now you will repeat some of those drills, along with some new ones, to reinforce your sense of where the alphabetic, number, and 10-key numeric keypad keys are located. When you have finished the drills, click Print (if desired), then click Next Exercise.

Alphabetic Sentences

Key lines 1–3 twice: first key the three lines for speed, then for control.

1. It seems that I missed the road; it makes me mad.
2. Those wrecked cars are in the ditch at the curve.
3. Endure the thousand, routine, suspended problems.

Top-Row Numbers

Key lines 1–9 twice: first key the nine lines for speed, then for control.

1. Find 5,000 medium weight legal size file folders.
2. The Merkel 9000 offers 23 channels with .6 watts.
3. Please trace orders 1169, 2978, 67890, and 14989.

4. Return the 420 reams of 16 lb. paper now, please.
5. She is purchasing a Group 4 857 Facsimile system.
6. I would like to have 9 shades and 16 gray scales.

Hematochezia	Passage of feces containing blood
Hypercholesterolemia	High levels of cholesterol in the blood
Hysterectomy	Operation that removes the uterus
Intertrochanteric	Located between the greater and lesser trochanter of the femur
Lateral	Referring to the side
Melena	Black tarry feces resulting from the action of intestinal juices on free blood. Common in newborns
Neurovascular	Involving both the nervous and vascular systems
Obstruction	Blocking of a structure that prevents normal functioning
Trochanter	Either of the two bony projections at the upper end of the femur
Vital signs	Breathing rate, pulse, and temperature

Document B

RIVERSIDE MEDICAL CENTER
PORTLAND, OREGON

NAME: MEDICAL RECORD #:
ROOM: DATE OF BIRTH:

ADMITTED: DATE OF CONSULT:
PHYSICIAN: CONSULTANT:

CONSULTANT'S REPORT

CONSULTATION:
IMPRESSIONS:
RECOMMENDATIONS:

_____

7 Send me 13 of Item 4 and 7 of Item 9 immediately.

8 West Arn 20 lb. paper has 99 percent rag content.

9 I have: 360 holders, 75 pencils, and 99 punches.

Additional Drill

Key the following drill for control on the 10-key numeric keypad. Press *Enter* after each line.

1 654 54 76 56 46 767 46 654 6054 567 7655 6054 456

2 687 577 575 876 754 796 697 757 885 855 644 54 66

3 78 81 8687 782 8422 789 987 432 8282 6732 321 989

4 08 080 797 580 680 4986 7984 47782 78853 88795 85

5 19105 05084 88 384 18 682 9764 7976 8828 55130 56

6 66938 88282 775 993 5549 7970 2810 82 879 8322087

> **Students in Online Classes**
>
> At the end of each line, proofread. If you have any errors, repeat the line until you can key it with out error before going to the next line.

7 10.18 7.85 8.94 15.63 40.38 .89 95.93 24.56 67.36 3.69

8 7.8 67.8 67.21 478.231 123.456 1.456 14.567 89.90 .65

9 4.8 21.6 41.72 687.452 4.872 48.729 72.94 729.45 65.8

27.4 TIMINGS: 10-KEY NUMERIC KEYPAD

Goal: 25 WAM with 0 errors

- Take a 1-minute timing on the lines in Group 1. Then take two 1-minute timings on the lines in Group 2.
- If you finish before time is up, start over.
- Press *Tab* with your "a" finger.
- Strike *Enter* at the end of each line.

1											
12	34	56	78	90	123	456	789	987	654	321	4321
98	76	54	32	10	321	654	897	978	456	123	1234
76	89	32	12	01	789	564	987	654	545	231	2413
54	12	12	34	28	897	546	978	123	466	132	1432
32	54	78	56	58	978	645	789	101	654	213	2431

2									
130	12.9	14.87	123.4	1.456	14.56	56.21	156.02	47
8	67.8	67.21	478.23	2.789	27.879	87.90	879.08	56.49
427	32.56	978.12	3.462	34.620	62.08	620.81	84.8	61
72	687.45	4.872	48.729	72.94	729.45	25.2	52.5	98.12
18724	9.678	96.78	8.69	687.89	2	672.3	598	390.26

27.5 TIMINGS: ALPHABETIC KEYS

Goal: 30 WAM with no more than 2 errors

Take a 1-minute timing on each paragraph.

TEXTBOOK ACTIVITIES: MEDICAL TERMINOLOGY AND MEDICAL CONSULTANTS' REPORTS

In this session you will continue reviewing medical terminology by completing a table of medical terms and their definitions. You also will prepare a template for a medical consultant's report. In medical centers, clinics, and hospitals, the primary physician may request a consultation by a surgeon or specialist. The surgeon or specialist examines the patient and then dictates a report of the examination and plan for treatment, surgery, and/or prognosis. You will key a consultant's report (Document C) using the template created as Document B. For Document D, you will have an opportunity to use the PWP Search and Replace feature introduced in Session 43, page 207.

Students in Online Classes

Reminder: Read to comprehend the terms and definitions before preparing the table.

Medical Terminology

46.5

Document A

1   Before creating the Medical Terminology Table, read and comprehend each of the terms and the definitions provided so that when these terms are used in Document C, you will know their meanings.
2   At the *Session 46 Document A* screen, key Document A as a two-column table.
3   Add an appropriate border and gridlines in your table, and use different levels of shading for the first two rows. Refer to pages 224–225 of Session 45 to review the instructions for creating tables.
4   Proofread and correct any errors.
5   Name, save, and print the document as **046wpra**, then close the document.
6   Click Next Exercise.

MEDICAL TERMINOLOGY	
Term	**Definition**
Abdominal	Referring to the abdomen and its function and disorders
Adhesion	A holding together or bringing together of two surfaces or parts
Bowel	The large intestine
Cardiac	Referring to the heart
Comminuted fracture	A crushed bone
Compression	State of being squeezed together
Diabetes mellitus	A metabolic disorder characterized by hyperglycemia and glycosuria resulting from inadequate production or use of insulin
Ecchymosis	Large, reddish blotches on the skin
Fragmentation	Breaking up into pieces or fragments

Continued on next page

1   The population of the United States has become more varied culturally. It is extremely important that individuals be made aware of the need to communicate with other cultures in ways that are satisfying to both parties. As people interact on a daily basis, meanings are discovered that form a bond for common understanding.

2   The first thing a visitor notices at the travel agency is a bronze statue of the founder. The agency is merging with another travel group that will give them 4,000 office locations in 125 countries. The merger of their business and information systems will take five years.

ENDING THE SESSION

Now you may print this session's files, continue to the next session, or exit the program. See page 103 of Session 24 if you need to review procedures.

Ergonomic Tip

Slowly lift shoulders while inhaling, and then slowly drop shoulders while exhaling; this will help you relax.

1   A person who owns a home and wishes to sell it has to identify an asking price. Most people who want to sell their homes don't have the background for putting a fair market value on their home. Often, the sale price is based on the original cost plus added improvements to the home. In other cases, sale prices are based on what the owner thinks the property is worth. For most people, their home is their largest investment, and if they plan to sell, it is a good idea to contact a real estate agent or an appraiser for input on the fair market value of a home.

Many factors have to be taken into account when arriving at a property's fair market value. Some of the most important factors are location, size of home, energy efficiency, eye appeal, decorating, age, floor plan, and landscaping, as well as many other minor points. One of the best indicators of the market value of a home is comparable sales, as that is what the buying public is willing to pay. Recent sales of properties that have been sold that are the most similar in size, style, location, and condition are most helpful in establishing a realistic sale price on a home.

No two properties are alike; it is important to review the pros and cons of each property being compared. However, the positives and negatives are really up to the buyer to decide. There are other factors to be considered in setting a sale price on a home. For example, at the time the house is to be listed for sale, is it a seller's or buyer's market? When there is a shortage of homes in a particular category and there are people wanting to buy, this represents a seller's market. Many times, new firms entering or leaving an area will have a direct impact on the market value of homes.

People who are planning to sell their homes should also be aware that at least 90 percent of all buyers will require new financing. Those lending the money to home-buyers will require an appraisal of the property to ensure that the asking price is realistic. In the process of selling a home, the seller wants to get the highest possible dollar for the sale while the buyer wants to purchase at the lowest possible amount. No doubt supply and demand are critical factors in arriving at the sale price of a home.

Unit

5

COMPOSITION

CONSULTANTS' REPORTS

Session Goals

1-Minute: 40 WAM/2 errors
5-Minute: 30 WAM/2 errors

Creating tables and templates and using Search and Replace

46.1- 46.2 | ON-SCREEN EXERCISES: GETTING STARTED

If you exited the program at the end of the previous session, refer to page 11 in Session 3 to review how to open the next session. If you are continuing immediately from Session 45, start with Exercise 46.2. Click the Next Exercise or Previous Exercise button if you are not at the correct exercise.

46.3 | ONE-MINUTE TIMINGS

Goal: 40 WAM/2 errors

SI: 1.45

- Take two 1-minute timings. If you finish before time is up, start over.
- Take your most recent timing score to set a speed or accuracy goal.

> 1   When considering the purchase of any article of clothing, do not let any sales person convince you to take a garment that does not fit well. If you decide to buy something that does not fit, be sure that the store from which you buy the clothing has an excellent alteration department. Make sure that they understand that the clothing must be altered to fit before you make the final arrangements to purchase the item. To be completely assured and satisfied, take a friend along to give you another opinion on how you look.

46.4 | FIVE-MINUTE TIMINGS

Goal: 30 WAM/2 errors

SI: 1.46

- Take two 5-minute timings.
- On your second attempt, try to increase your speed while keeping errors at two or fewer.

Session Goals

**Compose at
Word-Response Level**

**1-Minute: 35 WAM/2 errors
3-Minute: 30 WAM/2 errors
5-Minute: 25 WAM/2 errors**

28.1-28.2 ON-SCREEN EXERCISES: GETTING STARTED

If you are continuing immediately from Session 27, begin with Exercise 28.1. Click the Next Exercise or Previous Exercise button if you are not at the correct exercise.

If you exited the program at the end of the previous session, refer to page 11 of Session 3 for instructions on entering the program.

28.3 TEXTBOOK EXERCISES: REINFORCEMENT

This section provides practice in thinking and composing at the keyboard. Mastering this skill will speed up your preparation of documents. When you have finished this section, click Print (if desired), then Next Exercise.

Composing at the Keyboard

Now that you have learned the keyboard and have developed your skills further, it is time to learn to think and compose at the keyboard so you can use a computer efficiently.

There are four stages in building composition skills:

1 Developing skill at the **word-response** level. (You already began working at this level when you keyed the Thinking Drills.)
2 Developing skill at the **phrase-response** level.
3 Developing skill at the **sentence-response** level.
4 Developing skill at the **paragraph**, or "**complete**," level.

5 Click the name of the file you want to print.
6 At the Word Processor dialog box, click Launch.
7 Click File, and then click Print.
8 At the Print dialog box, click OK.
9 Click the Close button to close the Paradigm Word Processor.
10 Click Home on the Snap menu bar to return to the Welcome page.

Continue

To continue on to the next session, click the Next Exercise button. This will take you to Exercise 46.1.

Exit

To exit, do the following:

1 Click the Close ⊠ button in the top right corner of the screen.
2 At your Paradigm Keyboarding with Snap Welcome page, click Logout.

Ergonomic Tip

Keep your neck straight or bent slightly forward to minimize straining your neck muscles.

Word Response: Yes or No

Key answers to the questions that follow. For the first question in each group, key the question number followed by a period, press **Tab**, then key the letter followed by a period, one space, and either **yes** or **no** or **not sure**. Press **Enter** and go to the next question. For the second and remaining questions in each group, just press **Tab**, then key the letter and a period, one space, and then the answer. Press **Enter** after each response. **Remember:** Do not hesitate. Key your answer as quickly as possible.

Students in Online Classes

For Groups 1 and 2, after keying the letter and period, space once, and key the question. Key a space after the question mark and then key your Yes, No, or Not Sure response. This will give you more practice keying the alphabetic characters.

1. a. Do you like the weather today?
   b. Do you like animals?
   c. Are you hungry?
   d. Do you read the newspaper?
   e. Would you like to go into politics?
   f. Do you participate in any sport?
   g. Do you like animals?
   h. Are you hungry?
   i. Do you read the newspaper?
   j. Do you watch television every day?

2. a. Are you tired?
   b. Do you have any brothers?
   c. Do you have any sisters?
   d. Do you have a job?
   e. Are you a "good" speller?
   f. Are you going on vacation soon?
   g. Do you like English?
   h. Do you like coffee?
   i. Would you like to travel overseas?
   j. Do you like to cook?

Word Response: Which One?

Answer the following questions with one of the two choices or with the word **neither**. Follow the same procedure you used in the first drill. Press **Enter** after each response. **Remember:** Do not hesitate. Key your answer as quickly as possible.

Students in Online Classes

For Groups 1–4, after keying the letter and period, space once, and key the question. Key a space after the question mark and then your response.

1. a. Would you rather ski or swim?
   b. Would you rather drive or ride?
   c. Would you rather eat or cook?
   d. Would you rather walk or talk?
   e. Would you rather hike or bike?

REINFORCING WRITING SKILLS—REVIEW

Tips on how to improve your writing skills have appeared throughout Units 8 and 9 (Memos, E-Mails, and Letters). Your effectiveness as a writer will be enhanced by applying these tips. Here is a brief review of these tips:

- Compose documents at the keyboard—it's faster than writing in longhand. These documents serve as your rough draft and can be edited and changed accordingly.

- Identify your reader(s) so that your writing focuses on the recipient's ability to understand.

- Keep sentences short (15 to 25 words), use simple words, keep paragraphs short (8 to 10 lines), write as though you were talking face to face with the reader of your document.

- Make sure your paragraphs have only one topic sentence and that the other sentences in the paragraph relate to the topic sentence.

- Eliminate excess verbiage—cut out words that are not needed.

- Use positive words.

- Get action from your readers—don't let them procrastinate.

Students in Online Classes

Use the Word Processing timing feature. When finished, center the letter vertically.

45.8 **Document D** **Letter to Instructor**

Compose a rough draft of a letter addressed to your instructor that includes the names of your three favorite cars. After the salutation, start your first paragraph with the following statement:

> My three favorite cars are:

Compose a paragraph for each of the three cars that includes the reasons why these cars are your favorites choices. Save the document as **045wprd**. Print a copy of the document. Edit your draft to enhance its readability by focusing on the writing reinforcement techniques that have been presented in Units 8 and 9. Then make the changes noted in your rough draft. Save the document under the same name (**045wprd**), print it, and close it. Give your instructor both copies of the letter.

ENDING THE SESSION

Now you can print any files you have created, continue with the next session, or exit Paradigm Keyboarding with Snap.

Print

To print Exercises 45.1–45.8 proceed as follows:

1 Click the Close ☒ button in the top right corner of the screen.
2 At your Paradigm Keyboarding with Snap Welcome page, point to Reports on the Snap menu bar, and click View Submissions Report.
3 At the View Submissions Report Wizard, click Show session files to see the drill lines text (Exercises 45.1–45.2), Show timings files to see the timings text (Exercises 45.3–45.4), and Show production files or Show unchecked production files to see the production documents (Exercises 45.5–45.8).
4 Click Show Report.

2. a. Are you a female or a male?
   b. Are you right- or left-handed?
   c. Is the instructor of this class male or female?
   d. Would you rather drink milk or tea?
   e. Would you rather dance or read?

3. a. Would you rather dance or sing?
   b. Would you rather eat hot dogs or hamburgers?
   c. Would you rather write or read?
   d. Would you rather study or play?
   e. Would you rather own a dog or a cat?

4. a. Do you like summer or winter best?
   b. Would you rather be short or tall?
   c. Would you rather be dirty or clean?
   d. Would you rather win or lose?
   e. Would you rather run or walk?

Word Response: Opposites

Read a word and then key the word's opposite, using the same procedure you followed in the previous drills. If you cannot think of an opposite, key the word shown. Press **Enter** after each response. **Remember:** Do not hesitate. Key your answer as quickly as possible.

1. a. day
   b. salt
   c. mother
   d. uncle
   e. grandmother
   f. rich
   g. war
   h. young
   i. love
   j. hot

Students in Online Classes

For Groups 1 and 2, after keying the letter and period, space once, key the word. Press tab and then key your one-word response. Do this for each of the words in the two groups.

2. a. clean
   b. male
   c. minus
   d. seldom
   e. floor

HISTORY OF PRESENT ILLNESS: Mr. Carr is a 40-year-old male admitted to Riverside Medical Center for treatment of deep vein thrombophlebitis in his left lower extremity. Mr. Carr has always been healthy, has never been hsopitalized, and has had no medical problems until recently. About six weeks ago, he developed a superficial thrombophlebitis of the left lower extremity. He was treated for this without incident and seemed to improve. About one week ago, he was trying to get back into shape and started working out on a treadmill. He noted some discomfort in hisleft calf, which he attributed to muscle pain and contininued his exercise. Over the past 24 hours, the left lower extremity has become more painful and swollen. He was seen by Dr. Winston at the Riverside Medical Center and a Doppler ultrasound was performed demonstrating clear evidence of deep venous thrombosis. He is now admitted for treatment of that condition. He has not hand any undue shortness of breath nor has be hand any palpitations, cough, or chest pain. He notes that he usually runs a rapid pulse in the range of 80 or 90.

PAST MEDICAL HISTORY: Mr. Carr has had the usual childhood diseases without rheumatic or scarlet fever, yellow jaundice, pneumonia, or kidney infections. He has had no previous surgeries. He does not smoke and drinks alcohol only rarely. He currently is taking Motrin for pain but no other medications. He has no drug allergies.

FAMILY HISTORY: Mr. Carr's mother and father are both living, as weel as one brother and one sister. There is no family history of cancer or coagulation disorders.

PHYSICAL EXAMINATION: This is a well-developed male, who appears somewhat older than his stated age.

VITAL SIGNS: Blood pressure 140/80, pulse 100.

HEENT: Normal. Jugular venous pressure was normal. Neck was supple.

LUNGS: Clear.

HEART: Not enlarged. First sound single, second sound normally split.

ABDOMEN: Obese, without hepatosplenomegaly. Bowel sounds were normal.

EXTREMITIES: Edema in the left lower extremity below the mid thigh. Peripheral pulses were normal. There was calf tenderness and a positive Homans'.

NEUROLOGIC: Normal.

DIAGNOSIS:
1.   Deep vein thrombophlebitis left lower extremity.
2.   Tachycardia.

_____
C. K. WINSTON, M.D.

CKW/xx
DD: 03/08/Current year
DT: 03/08/Current year
DOCUMENT: 4312-HP

f. stop

g. no

h. winter

i. sick

j. True

Syllabic Intensity

Beginning with this session, the **syllabic intensity** (the average number of syllables per word) is listed for all 1-, 3-, and 5-minute timings. Syllabic intensity (SI) is an approximate indication of how difficult material is to key. The lower the SI, the easier the material is to key; the higher the SI, the more difficult the material, since the words are longer.

When you take timings, your goal is to improve either your speed or your accuracy. You must concentrate on one or the other. Your goal will probably change daily—or even during a particular class period. Note that with this session, the speed goals for the 1- and 3-minute timings have been raised by 5 WAM.

28.4 ONE-MINUTE TIMINGS

Goal: 35 WAM/2 errors

SI: 1.27

Take two 1-minute timings on the following paragraph.

1   Long ago, pilgrims loved to indulge in blunt folklore. Tales, sometimes false, were told with glee daily. One old tale included a blazing clash of sailors in balky sailboats on a bottomless lake. The last sailor alive was a lad that was blind. As he lay clinging to a slim balsa log in filth and slimy silt, the leader's falcon led help to him. Balmy days followed as the lad's leg healed slowly and the salves applied to his eyes let the light in.

28.5 THREE-MINUTE TIMINGS

Goal: 30 WAM/2 errors

SI: 1.33

Take two 3-minute timings on the following paragraph. If you complete the paragraph in less than three minutes, start over.

1   To change a U.S. unit of measure to a metric unit of measure takes practice and knowledge. To change back and forth, a table of metric measures and U.S. units of measures is great to have. For instance, 1 mile is equal to a metric measurement of 1.6 kilometers. One yard is about the same as a metric measure of 0.9 meters. One can change a larger metric unit to a smaller one by moving the decimal point one place to the right.

5 Proofread and correct any errors.
6 The document is automatically saved as **045prob**.
7 Click Next Exercise.

Document B

> Reminder: Check the copy in the text before keying. You may find errors.

RIVERSIDE MEDICAL CENTER
PORTLAND, OREGON

NAME: **MEDICAL RECORD #:**

DATE OF ADMISSION: **PHYSICIAN:**

HISTORY AND PHYSICAL EXAMINATION

HISTORY OF PRESENT ILLNESS:
PAST MEDICAL HISTORY:
FAMILY HISTORY:
PHYSICAL EXAMINATION:
VITAL SIGNS:
HEENT:
LUNGS:
HEART:
ABDOMEN:
EXTREMITIES:
NEUROLOGIC:
DIAGNOSIS:

(¼)

45.7

Document C

Medical History and Physical Examination Report

1 At the *Session 45 Document C* screen, insert Document 045prob using the following steps:
  a   Choose Insert→File.
  b   At the *Insert File* dialog box, double-click **045prob**.
2 Enter the information for the heading as follows:
  a   NAME: **Jacob D. Carr**
  b   MEDICAL RECORD #: **21345**
  c   DATE OF ADMISSION: **03/08/**Current year
  d   PHYSICIAN: **C. K. Winston, M.D.**
    Note: When entering the Name and Date of Admission information, use your right arrow key to move past the colon, press the space bar once, and enter the data. For the other entries in the heading and in the body of the report press the End key to move to the point of entry, then press the space bar once.
3 Key the body of the report. Correct any errors in Document C that may have been overlooked.
4 Use the Bullets and Numbering feature for the numbered paragraphs.
5 Proofread, check, print, and correct the document.
6 The document is automatically saved as **045proc**.
7 Click Next Exercise.

Goal: 25 WAM/2 errors

SI: 1.29

Take a 5-minute timing on the following paragraphs. If you finish the three paragraphs before the five minutes are up, start over with the first paragraph and continue.

1   The most important piece of furniture in an office is the chair. Workers will spend most of their day doing their work while seated. If people are uncomfortable, they will not be as productive as they could be with the right chair. It has been stated that a person's productivity will increase 15 to 20 percent when using a chair that fits his or her body.

There are several features to look for in selecting a chair to be used in an office setting. First, make sure it has a five-star base so that it won't tip over. Next, make sure that the seat adjusts upward and downward to fit the person using it. The back rest must be adjustable up and down so that it supports the worker's back. The front of the chair must have a "water fall," or downward-curved cushion, so that there is no pressure behind the knees while the worker is seated.

Any adjustments to be made to chair height, back support, or tilt must be easy to do. There are chairs on the market that adjust as the person sits down; no manual adjustments need to be made. Another important part of a chair is the covering. Some coverings are warm (they don't breathe). Chairs can be purchased with arms that drop so that the chair can be moved closer to the desk.

ENDING THE SESSION

Now you may print this session's files, continue to the next session, or exit the program.

Print

To print Exercises 28.1–28.6 proceed as follows:

1   Click the Close ☒ button in the top right corner of the screen.
2   At your Paradigm Keyboarding with Snap Welcome page, point to Reports on the Snap menu bar, and click View Submissions Report.
3   At the View Submissions Report Wizard, click Show session files to see the drill lines text (Exercises 28.1–28.3), or Show timings files to see the timings text (Exercises 28.4–28.6).
4   Click Show Report.
5   Click the name of the file you want to print.
6   At the Word Processor dialog box, click Launch.
7   Click File, and then click Print.
8   At the Print dialog box, click OK.
9   Click the Close button to close the Paradigm Word Processor.
10   Click Home on the Snap menu bar to return to the Welcome page.

SETTING TABS

To set a left tab on the ruler, first click the right button of the mouse on the left edge of the bottom half of the ruler and confirm that the box next to Left tabulator is checked. Position the arrow pointer just below the tick mark (the marks on the ruler) where you want the tab(s) to appear, then click the left mouse button. When you set a tab on the ruler, any default tabs to the left are automatically deleted by PWP.

A tab can be removed from the ruler by selection Format→Tabs, selecting the tab from the Tabulator box, and clicking Clear. To remove all tabs, click Clear all.

USING PWP'S HEADER/FOOTER FEATURE

PWP's Header/Footer feature can create a header or a footer for every page of a document. One advantage of using a header or footer feature is that the text is keyed only once, but will appear at the top or bottom of every page in a document except the first page, which in PWP is left blank. Using a header or footer feature also allows you to make editing changes in the text of a document without having to reposition the header/footer. If text is added, deleted, or moved, PWP adjusts the location of the header/footer text accordingly. To create a header/footer in a document, follow these basic steps:

1 Choose View→Header and Footer.
2 The screen will be divided in two, with the top half the text window for a header and the bottom half a text window for a footer. Key the text you wish to have in the header window.
3 To include a page number in the header, choose Insert→Field. Select {page}, click Insert, then click Close.
4 Choose View→Header and Footer again to return to your document. To see the header in relation to the rest of the document, choose File→Print Preview.

Preparing History and Physical Examination Reports

Commercial word processing software programs generally include features such as templates that allow you to create forms for portions of a document that remain the same. All the keyboarder has to do is enter the variable information. In Document B that follows, note that all the information that is bolded and capitalized remains the same from one report to the next. These forms can also be set up so that when filling in the heading information, the system tabs automatically to the next entry.

Although the PWP software doesn't include all the features and functions available in commercial word processors, it is possible to create a form template that can be used over and over again. The next document will be created as a form template for history and physical examination reports.

45.6

Document B

Creating a History and Physical Examination Form

1 At the *Session 45 Document B* screen, key Document B as a template for a medical history and physical examination report form.
2 Set a tab at 3.0" for the MEDICAL RECORD: and PHYSICIAN: headings and the signature line.
3 Triple space after DIAGNOSIS: and key the signature line.
4 Insert the header **History and Physical Exam Report** and page number field; align both at the right margin.

Continue

To continue on the next session, click the Next Exercise ▣ button. This will take you to Exercise 29.1.

Exit

To exit, do the following steps:

1 Click the Close ⊠ button in the top right corner of the screen.
2 At your Paradigm Keyboarding with Snap Welcome page, click Logout.

Ergonomic Tip

Take small breaks as short as 10 seconds every 30 minutes to stretch; this will help you relax and relieve tension.

Document A

Medical Terminology

1 Before creating the Medical Terminology Table, read and comprehend each of the terms and the definitions provided so that when these terms are used in Document C, you will know their meanings.

2 At the *Session 45 Document A* screen, key Document A as a two-column table.

3 Add an appropriate border and gridlines in your table, and use different levels of shading for the first two rows. Follow the instructions above for preparing your table.

4 Proofread and correct any errors.

5 Name, save, and print the document as **045wpra**, then close the document.

6 Click Next Exercise.

MEDICAL TERMINOLOGY	
Term	**Definition**
Coagulation	The clotting process
Edema	A condition in which the body tissues contain excessive fluid
Hepatosplenomegaly	Enlargement of the liver and spleen
Jugular	Referring to the throat
Palpitation	Rapid, violent, or throbbing pulsing or fluttering of the heart
Pneumonia	Inflammation of the lungs caused by bacteria, viruses, or chemical irritants
Rheumatic fever	A systemic, inflammatory disease that varies in severity and duration
Scarlet fever	An acute contagious disease characterized by sore throat, strawberry tongue, fever, red rash, and rapid pulse
Tachycardia	Abnormally rapid heart rate, over 100 beats per minute
Thrombophlebitis	Inflammation of a vein along with the formation of a blood clot
Thrombosis	The formation, development, or existence of a blood clot within the circulatory system
Ultrasound	Inaudible sound in the frequency range of about 20,000 to 10,000,000,000 cycles per second; an imaging process to outline the shape of various tissues and organs in the body
Venous	Referring to the veins or blood passing through them
Yellow fever	An acute infectious disease characterized by jaundice, throat tenderness, vomiting, and hemorrhages

Session Goals

Compose at Phrase-Response Level

1-Minute: 35 WAM/2 errors
3-Minute: 30 WAM/2 errors
5-Minute: 25 WAM/2 errors

29.1-29.2 ON-SCREEN EXERCISES: GETTING STARTED

If you exited the program at the end of the previous session, refer to page 114 of Session 28 to review how to open the next session or to continue from where you left off.

29.3 TEXTBOOK EXERCISES: REINFORCEMENT

In this section you will continue learning to think and compose at the keyboard. You will practice keying whole phrases and sentences in response to questions offered in the following drills. When you have finished the drills, click Print (if desired), then click Next Exercise.

Composing Phrases

Now that you have completed the word-response level, you can move on to the phrase-response level and sentence-response level. At a clear editing window, read the questions and then answer them by keying the question number, period, one space; then press **Tab**, key the letter, a period, one space, then the answer. Press **Enter** and go to the next question. For the second and remaining questions in each group, just press **Tab**, then key the letter, a period, one space, and the answer. Press **Enter** after each response. Do not make complete sentences—just answer the question. If you do not know the correct answer, invent one. **Remember:** Do not hesitate. Key your answer as quickly as possible.

Short Phrases

1. a. What is the name of a town and state/province that you would like to visit?
   b. What is your instructor's first and last name?
   c. What is the president's/prime minister's last name?
   d. What is the name of this book?
   e. What is the name of this course?

Students in Online Classes

For Groups 1–4, after keying the letter and period, enter a space, then key each question followed by a question mark. Enter a space, then key the phrase for your response.

Adjusting the Width of a Column Using ⊣⊢

To adjust the width of a column, you can position your insertion pointer on the column line to be moved so that it becomes ⊣⊢, and drag the border to the desired width.

Selecting Cells

A table can be formatted in special ways. To identify the cells that are to be formatted, select those specific cells.

You can select individual cells or groups of cells with the mouse by clicking the first cell to be selected and dragging the mouse past the right edge of the cell. You can select a row of cells by placing the insertion point in the left-most cell of the row and choosing Table→Select Row. You can select an entire table by placing the insertion point within any cell and choosing Table→Select Table.

Merging Cells in a Table

Select the cells to be merged and choose Table→Merge cells. A new, large cell will be created from the selected cells.

Aligning Data within Cells

The information entered into cells defaults to a left alignment. To center, right justify, or left and right justify, click on the appropriate icon in the format tool bar. For example, to center data in a cell you would click on the icon ▤ on the format tool bar.

Adding Borders

The gridlines in a table do not print. If you want horizontal and vertical lines between cells to print, you must add borders to the table. Borders can be added to one cell, selected cells, or an entire table.

Borders can be added to selected cells by choosing Tables→Borders and Shading. At the *Tables Borders and Shading* dialog box, choose either Box to select a single cell or Grid to select multiple cells, then select the desired line width in the Style box. You can select which parts of a cell have a border by clicking on the sides of the sample cell within the Border box.

Adding Shading

Shading can be added to cells to add visual appeal to a table. As with borders, shading can be added to selected cells in the *Table Borders and Shading* dialog box (choose Table →Borders and Shading). Click the Shading tab, click Custom, select the kind of shading you want for the selected cells, then click OK.

2. a. What is your first and last name?
   b. What is your friend's first and last name?
   c. What is the title of your favorite song?
   d. What is the name of the last movie you saw?
   e. What is the name of the last television show you saw?

3. a. Where were you born?
   b. Where did you attend elementary school?
   c. Where did you go on your last vacation?
   d. Where are you going after class today?
   e. Where will you be tomorrow at this time?

4. a. What are your favorite sports?
   b. What are your favorite colors?
   c. What will you be doing five years from now?
   d. What is the name of your favorite class?
   e. What is the name of your best friend?

Longer Phrases

Think of a phrase that completes each sentence. Number each sentence, followed by a period, press Tab, and then key the sentence to include your response. There are 20 sentences in this group. Press **Enter** after each response.

Because the clock was wrong, I _____ .
Because the road was icy, I _____ .
Because the team won, I _____ .
Because I was late, I _____ .
Because I can/cannot drive, I _____ . (Choose either *can* or *cannot*.)

If I pass this test, I _____ .
If I finish early, I _____ .
If I get the job, I _____ .
If the price is right, I _____ .
If the beach is crowded, I _____ .

I do/do not like loud music because _____ .
I do/do not study at the library because _____ .
I do/do not obey the speed limit because _____ .
I do/do not like math because _____ .
I do/do not play sports because _____ .

History and Physical Examination Reports
Consultants' Reports
Subjective, Objective, Assessment, Plan Reports
Radiology Reports
Operative Reports
Discharge Summary Reports
Consent Forms
Lab Forms

Creating Tables

Tables are frequently used in today's written communication, because data are often difficult and impractical to present in sentence and paragraph form. Tables are used in memos, e-mail, letters, reports, and manuscripts as well as in stand-alone applications. The reader has an opportunity to see the total picture when the data are presented in a well-planned table.

Inserting Tables and Data Review

In PWP, there are two methods of creating tables:

1   Chose Table→Insert Table and then enter the number of columns and rows needed in the *Insert Table* dialog box.

2   Click the insert Table button [⊞] on the toolbar. This command causes a grid to appear. Hold down the left mouse button and drag the arrow pointer down until the grid shows the number of rows and columns you want, then release the mouse button.

Although you can add and delete rows and columns in a table, it is a good idea to analyze your data ahead of time to determine the number of columns and rows needed.

Where the rows and columns intersect, a cell is formed. Alphabetic and/or numeric data are keyed in cells. Cells in a table contain a cell designation. Columns in a table are letters from left to right beginning with A. Rows are numbered beginning with the first one as 1. Therefore, the cell in the upper left corner of the table is cell A1. The cell to the right of A1 is B1. The cells below A1 are A2, A3, and so on. Gridlines are the lines that form the cells of the table.

Entering Data in Cells

To enter data in a cell, click within the cell to place the insertion point, then key or edit the data. To move the insertion point to the next cell on the right press *Tab*. To move to the previous cell on the left press *Shift + Tab*. Another way to enter data is to position the I-beam pointer in the desired cell and click the left mouse button. Then Up or Down Arrow keys will move your insertion point vertically to another cell.

If the data you key do not fit on one line, they automatically wrap to the next line within the same cell. Or, if you press *Enter* within a cell, the insertion point is moved to the next line within the same cell. The cell lengthens vertically to accommodate the data, and all cells in that row also lengthen.

When all the information has been entered in the cells, move the insertion point below the table by positioning the I-beam pointer below the table and clicking the left mouse button or pressing the *Down Arrow* key.

A hammer is used to _____ .

A lawn mower is used to _____ .

Scissors are used to _____ .

A pencil is used to _____ .

An eraser is used to _____ .

Sentences

Read a question and then answer it by keying a complete sentence. Number each sentence. The first one is done as a sample. **Remember:** Do not hesitate. Key your answer as quickly as possible. Press **Enter** after each response.

What does a police officer do? A police officer enforces the laws.

What does a plumber do?

What does a firefighter do?

What does a lawyer do?

What does a teacher do?

What does an auto mechanic do?

What does a medical doctor do?

What does a dentist do?

What does an accountant do?

What does a chef do?

29.4 ONE-MINUTE TIMINGS

Goal: 35 WAM/2 errors

SI: 1.27

Take two 1-minute timings on the following paragraph.

1   The news on the network newscast might spawn a winning wealth of followers. If the newscaster can draw a wider range of viewers, the rewards are power and wealth. Watchers and followers of a witty newscaster are won when the daily news is written well. It is not a waste to rewrite the worst of interviews when witless words can wreck a well planned show or review. They who dawdle in the newsroom will not work or write very long. Their reward will be awful reviews.

29.5 THREE-MINUTE TIMINGS

Goal: 30 WAM/2 errors

SI: 1.33

Take two 3-minute timings on the following paragraph. If you complete the paragraph in less than three minutes, start over.

1   From the time we were young, most of us have learned to share. We learned that one result of sharing was gaining new knowledge from some other person. In the world of computers, sharing also takes place as a network. When two computers are linked, the computers are networked.

     When computers were first built, they were networked differently. The concept of networking was started with just one computer set up as the sender of information. All the other computers were set up as the receivers of data. The machines that received the data could not send one word to the sender and were known as "dumb" terminals.

     Networking today is diverse and unique. Although the concept of a dumb terminal is still in use, the sharing of data has changed. Now, both ends of the network can share; both ends can send and receive data. Users of a network can share files and cut down on the amount of paper used. Networks also let workers who are not in the same place share the same data without ever leaving their cubes. Other hardware in the office, such as printers and scanners, can be used by many persons joined to the network. When office hardware is shared, the result is more money saved.

     The concept of a network is not limited to sharing among offices in one building. Many large firms have offices all over the country. It would be impossible to walk down the hall to confer with a fellow worker. Through a worldwide network, large firms can confer with other offices that may be set up in other states or in other countries.

     Networking is an important part of the computer world. New concepts are developed and tried out each day. One day soon, we can look at a watch on our wrist and talk to another person who is thousands of miles away. We can only dream of the exciting future of computing. And, some of us will be part of producing the new things to come.

TEXTBOOK EXERCISES: PREPARING MEDICAL REPORTS AND FORMS

Every day medical reports and forms are prepared with word processing programs in doctors' offices, clinics, and hospitals. In this and the following eight sessions, you will use word processing features and functions to prepare a variety of medical reports and forms.

     The medical reports and forms you will prepare represent only a sampling of the kinds of documents used. Each office, clinic, or hospital will have specific requirements for formatting medical documents. The information presented in this unit is not intended to replace a regular course in medical terminology and/or transcription. The purpose of the following sessions is to provide you with the opportunity to apply word processing features and functions in the preparation of common medical documents.

     In this and the next eight sessions, you will prepare the following representative medical reports and forms and generate tables containing medical terms and their definitions and prepare templates to simplify the preparation of reports and forms:

1   Taking photos with a good camera can be fun. Most photo equipment has some method of setting a variety of focal lengths. A focal length setting of 35mm gives a wider picture angle, and it can be used for group portraits or photos of landscapes. A focal length setting of 70mm has a narrow angle for making a portrait or taking a good photo of a good scene or object that is far away. Using the zoom lens requires some practice before a picture can be a work of art.

29.6 FIVE-MINUTE TIMING

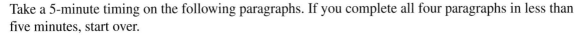

Goal: 25 WAM/2 errors

SI: 1.29

Take a 5-minute timing on the following paragraphs. If you complete all four paragraphs in less than five minutes, start over.

1   Education has become a lifelong process. No longer can we say that a person's formal schooling will last for a lifetime. Business spends almost as much for training programs as is spent for our public school system. The average age of students in schools offering programs above the high school level is on the rise.

      Adult learners enter school programs with needs and wants that differ from the requirements of traditional students. They are goal-oriented. They are looking for skills and knowledge that will help them keep a job, prepare for a new job, or advance to a higher-level job. Adults don't want to waste time in reaching new skills; they want to spend their time on those things that relate to their goals.

      Teachers and trainers of adult learners are faced with a tough task. In most cases, they must narrow the focus of their programs to meet the needs of the learners. Courses must be designed that draw upon the learners' skills and knowledge. To design a good program, you must assess what the learners know and what their goals are.

      The next step in the process is to design a performance outcome that shows that the person can demonstrate a mastery of what was presented in the course. Once the outcome has been set, the instructor can choose teaching methods, course length, texts needed, and program content. Problem-solving, learn by doing, and case studies are methods of teaching that help adult students.

ENDING THE SESSION

Now you may print this session's files, continue to the next session, or exit the program. See page 118 of Session 28 if you need to review procedures.

Ergonomic Tip

Sit up straight, drop your shoulders back, and let your arms and hands hang loosely. This takes the strain off your back and allows your lungs and other organs to function correctly.

Session

HISTORY AND PHYSICAL EXAM REPORTS

Session Goals

1-Minute: 40 WAM/2 errors
5-Minute: 30 WAM/2 errors

Creating tables, templates, setting tabs, and using Header/ Footer features

---

45.1- 45.2   *ON-SCREEN EXERCISES: GETTING STARTED*

If you exited the program at the end of the previous session, refer to page 11 in Session 3 to review how to open the next session. If you are continuing immediately from Session 44, start with Exercise 45.2. Click the Next Exercise or Previous Exercise button if you are not at the correct exercise.

45.3   ONE-MINUTE TIMING

Goal: 40 WAM/2 errors

SI: 1.48

- Take a 1-minute timing.
- Use your most recent score to set a speed or an accuracy goal.

> 1   You can extend the life of your computer by leaving it on during the day. When the switch is turned on, there is a large power surge inside the CPU. You can "save" the switch life by leaving the computer turned on. The temperature inside should stay as even as possible. When you turn the computer off and on many times during the day, the inside temperature will change. This change could cause the joints on the board to become brittle and crack. If you do leave your computer on for a long period of time and you do not have a screen saver, just turn off the monitor.

45.4   FIVE-MINUTE TIMING

Goal: 30 WAM/2 errors

SI: 1.48

Take a 5-minute timing. If you finish the five paragraphs before time is up, start over with the first paragraph.

Session Goals

Compose sentence/paragraph levels
Choosing the right word

1-Minute: 35 WAM/2 errors
3-Minute: 30 WAM/2 errors
5-Minute: 25 WAM/2 errors

30.1-30.2 ON-SCREEN EXERCISES: GETTING STARTED

If you exited the program at the end of the previous session, refer to page 114 of Session 28 to review how to open the next session or to continue from where you left off.

30.3 TEXTBOOK EXERCISES: REINFORCEMENT

This section offers more composition activities that include a review of correct word use. When you have finished these activities, click Print (if desired), then Next Exercise.

Choosing the Right Word

One of the most common problems a writer faces is choosing the correct word to convey a certain thought or idea to the reader. Writing must be precise; vague words or the misuse of words may change the author's meaning. Review the "General Guidelines for Correct Word Use" that follow. Keep them in mind as you key responses in the composing drills.

General Guidelines for Correct Word Use

1   **Use concrete nouns and descriptive adjectives, adverbs, and phrases; do not use vague or abstract words**. Vague words can mean many different things. Words such as **nice**, **good**, **bad**, **thing**, and **work** do not give the reader much information. Read each of the following and notice the differences.

Examples:

Vague:	The lecture was good, and I learned a lot.
Better:	The lecture solved two problems for me. I learned how to balance a checkbook and how to calculate interest.
Vague:	a nice color
Better:	an emerald green, a vivid scarlet, a dull black
Vague:	He said
Better:	He shouted defiantly, he muttered, he demanded

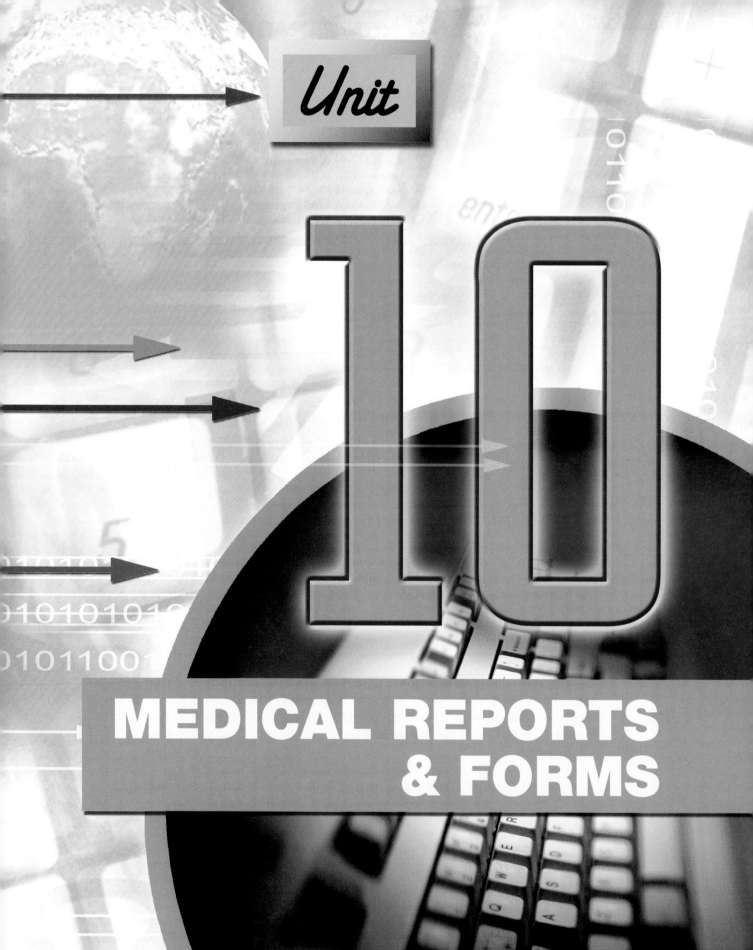

Unit

10

MEDICAL REPORTS & FORMS

2   **Use English idioms correctly.** An idiom is an expression peculiar to a culture and is perfectly acceptable if used correctly.

Examples:

Correct	Incorrect	Correct	Incorrect
acquitted of	acquitted from	in search of	in search for
aim to prove	aim at proving	kind of (+ noun)	kind of a (+ noun)
can't help feeling	can't help but feel	aloud	out loud
comply with	comply to	try to	try and
independent of	independent from	different from	different than

3   **Use the correct word;** the words shown below are often misused.

Examples:

accept *to take or receive*

advice *a recommendation*

biannual *twice a year*

council *a governing body*

fewer *(use with nouns that can be counted: fewer apples)*

good *modifies a noun or pronoun*

angry at *(things and animals)*

angry about *(occasions or situations)*

except *to leave out; aside from*

advise *to recommend*

biennial *once every two years*

counsel *to give advice*

less *(use with nouns that cannot be counted: less noise)*

well *modifies a verb or adverb*

angry with *(people)*

Sentence Response

Drawing from your experience and observations, think of descriptive words or phrases to make the following five sentences more interesting. Then key the sentence number, a period, and press **Tab** (Indent) before keying your revised sentence. In sentences 6–20 select the correct word/phrase. After you have keyed all twenty sentences, correct any errors you made. If your sentence goes beyond the right margin, let word wrap work for you. At the end of each sentence, press **Enter** and continue with the next sentence.

For a review of how to correct errors, go to Session 4, page 17, "Correcting Errors: Review." To reinforce proofreading techniques go to Session 7, page 27, "Common Keyboarding Errors."

1   The last book I read was good.
2   Today is a nice day.
3   My favorite sport is fun.
4   My favorite color is a nice color.
5   My best friend is nice.

Students in Online Classes

For sentences 1–5, key the number, period, space, and then key the sentence. Press the Enter key, Tab, and then key your entry. Press Enter. Proceed in the same manner for the remaining four sentences.

Select the correct idiom in the following sentences, and key each sentence using the correct words. Check the "General Guidelines for Correct Word Use" if you have a question about which alternative to use.

6   (Try to, Try and) key the data without any errors.
7   Juan went (in search for, in search of) a new printer ribbon.
8   My book is (different from, different than) Harriet's book.
9   I will try to (comply with, comply to) your wishes.
10   This (kind of a, kind of) paper is easier to store.

Select the correct word in the following sentences, and key each sentence using the correct word.

Document E

Compose a Personal Letter

Compose a rough draft of a letter to the top administrator of your school. Discuss your reasons for enrolling in the Medical Assisting (or oher medical program if different) program at your school and why you selected this school to complete your program.

Use the timing feature to have your WAM rate calculated. (When you are ready to start keying, click 🖳 to start the timer.) Key the document. When finished, click 🖳 to stop the clock—the system will calculate and display your WAM rate. Name (**044wpre**) and save your document.

Print a copy of your document and edit it for changes. Enter the changes into your document and save your document under the same name (044wpre); print the document and give the instructor both the rough draft (with the WAM rate) and your corrected copy. Then close the document.

ENDING THE SESSION

Now you may print this session's files, continue to the next session, or exit the program. See page 182 in Session 39 to review the procedures.

Ergonomic Tip

Turn your head to look over your right shoulder, back to the front, and then over your left shoulder. This helps your neck muscles to relax.

11 (Accept, Except) for Henry, the entire class went on the trip.
12 Our teacher strongly (adviced, advised) us to study for the exam.
13 There have been (fewer, less) absences this winter than last winter.
14 We have (fewer, less) flour than we need.
15 He is a (good, well) student.
16 Martha doesn't feel (good, well) today.
17 Sean plays the violin (good, well).
18 I am angry (at, about, with) my best friend.
19 I am angry (at, about, with) the rising costs of the textbooks.
20 I am angry (at, about, with) Whiskers, my cat.

Compose a complete sentence about each of the following items. Be sure to key the sentence number, period, and press the **Tab** key before keying your response. Let the sentence automatically wrap to the next line if your sentence extends beyond the right margin. At the end of each sentence, press **Enter** and proceed with the next sentence. Be sure to correct any errors.

1   ballpoint pen
2   ice cream
3   gas station
4   bank
5   elevator
6   fire
7   gain
8   dance
9   apple
10 water

Compose a complete sentence about each of the following items. Be sure to correct errors.

1   mirror
2   television
3   dollar bill
4   door
5   chair
6   radio
7   shoe
8   building
9   sunset
10 clock

Now you are ready to move on to the paragraph-response level, the fourth stage in building composition skills. Read the following guidelines for composing paragraphs. Study the guidelines and apply them in your composition activities.

General Guidelines for Paragraph Response

A paragraph is a group of related sentences—an organized and meaningful unit in a piece of writing. A paragraph contains a topic sentence and several supporting sentences. The sentences are organized in a logical manner and flow from one to the next. Transitional words connect one paragraph to another.

Your LDL (Low Density Lipoprotein) is to high. It should be 130 or below. LDL is **bad** because it carries cholesterol to the artery walls, where it is deposited. Reducing LDL will decrease your risk of developing heart disease.

Next, you asked what can be done to lower these levels. Here are some guidelines to follow:

1. Cut back on foods high in saturated fat and cholesterol. Saturated fat is found mostly in foods from animals and some plants. Choose fats with 2 grams or less of saturated fat per serving, such as liquid and tub margarines, canola oil and olive oil.
2. Eajt at least five servings of fruits and vegetables daily. One serving of vegetables is 1/2 cup cooked vegetables or 1 cup of raw vegetables. Fruits should be unsweetened, fresh, or canned without sugar.
3. Eat non more than 6 ounces per day of meat, seafood or poultry.
4 Use chicken or turnkey (without the skin) or fish in most of your main meals.
5. Eat at least 2 serving of fish per week.
6. Choose lean cutts of meat, trim all visible fat, and throw away the fat that cooks out of the meat.
7. Use fat free milk.
8. Use a minimal amount of fats and oils when preparing food, usually no more than 5 to 8 teaspoons per day. Try to broil or bake meat rather than frying to lower the fat intake.
9. Limit your intake of organ meats and other foods high in cholesterol.

Mr. Dominick Reilly
Page 2
Current date

Thank you, Mr. Reilly, for taking the time to share your questions. For you as a participant in our study on "Colon Cancer Prevention," we will do everything we can to help improve your health. I've enclosed a pamphlet on *"Your Cholesterol: Why it is Important to you."* Please read it; it will help you understand more about cholesterol. Your next blood work is scheduled for October 15, 20xx.

Sincerely yours,

Barbara Springer-Davis, R.N.
Office Manager
xx/044prod
Enclosure

A **topic sentence** expresses the main idea or subject of the paragraph. The topic sentence usually opens the paragraph, since most readers like to know what the paragraph is about before they read on. The topic sentence is bolded in the following example. **Supporting sentences** describe, explain, or further develop the topic sentence, as in this paragraph:

> **In a small office, the receptionist has a wide variety of duties.** Answering the telephone and receiving callers are primary responsibilities of any receptionist. Sometimes an employer asks a receptionist to take an important client to lunch or to contact a business customer. The correspondence in a small office varies from simple letters to complicated reports, and so the receptionist handles many types of communication.

Now, compose a paragraph about how you will use your keyboarding skills.

30.4 ONE-MINUTE TIMINGS

Goal: 35 WAM/2 errors

SI: 1.35

Take two 1-minute timings on the following paragraph.

1   At sunset, it is nice to enjoy dining out on a bank of a pond. Unless uninvited insects and swarms of ants invade the picnic, you will certainly unwind. As those soft night sounds enfold you, frenzied inward nerves and the decisions that haunt you drain from your mind. You may enjoy napping on a nearby bench. Next, swing into action after your rest and inhale much air into your lungs. Unpack the nice lunch and munch away. Don't deny yourself this experience.

30.5 THREE-MINUTE TIMINGS

Goal: 30 WAM/2 errors

SI: 1.39

Take two 3-minute timings on the following paragraph. If you complete the paragraph in less than three minutes, start over.

1   Simple salt and pepper shakers are very easy and quite simple to collect today. Lots of "fun" and very colorful pairs are available, either new or pre-owned. The bargains can be found at those family or group sales. Most folks try to see how many kinds they can find and buy. Some collect a mass of shakers that number over 500. The person or persons who are really collectors have shakers that number from 2,000 to 3,000 pairs. If anyone would like to begin the hobby of collecting, just look around and start a collection.

Current mammography guidelines recommend that women aged 40 and older should have a screening mammogram every year.

Thank you for allowing us to help in meeting your health care needs.

Sincerely,

DeeAnn Davis
Women's Diagnostic Services

xx/044proc

Two-Page Letter

44.8

Document D

1 At the *Session 44 Document D* screen, key Document D as a block-style letter.
   a Use the default margins and alignment.
   b To start the document, press *Enter* three times, key the date, and press *Enter* five more times before keying the inside address.
   c Be sure to make the changes noted by the proofreader's marks.
   d Use bullets instead of numbered items to highlight the topics and activities.
   e Enter a hard page break after the line that begins with "9. Limit your."
   f Provide the appropriate heading for page 2.
2 Proofread and correct any errors.
3 Click Check to automatically name (**044prod**), save, and check the letter.
4 If required by your instructor, print the letter with errors highlighted.
5 Correct errors the software has identified, then recheck the document.
6 Click Next Exercise.

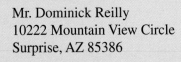
Students in Online Classes

After checking letter D and printing it, refer to the copy to correct any errors.

Document D

Current date

Mr. Dominick Reilly
10222 Mountain View Circle
Surprise, AZ 85386

Dear Mr. Reilly:

Here are the answers to your questions regarding the results of your blood test results. As noted on your report, your cholesterol count was 218 and your LDL Cholesterol was 156.   lc

First, you asked what the terms and initials meant. Cholesterol is a fat-like substance in the blood that, if elevated, has been associated with heart disease. Less than 200 is recommended by the National heart, lung, and Blood Institute. You are over the 200 level by 18 points. This is not to far from the 200 level, but you will want to reduce this count so that you are below 200.

Continued on next page

Goal: 25 WAM/2 errors

SI: 1.35

Take a 5-minute timing on the paragraphs that follow. If you complete the four paragraphs in less than five minutes, start over with the first paragraph and continue with paragraph 2, 3, and 4.

1   Most of the major events in communications grew out of a series of discoveries that took place over many years. Present-day systems can be traced to many great men and women who brought together the tools of their day to meet the needs of people on the job and in the home. The basis of this technology had its start in the 1830s.

One of the first events occurred in Germany when their government built a telegraph network that spanned 8,000 feet. By the next decade, the use of this device had spread to the United States. Congress funded a line that ran from Washington to Baltimore. During the same time frame, Samuel F.B. Morse finished a new telegraph device and code that came to be known as the Morse Code.

In the next few years, more developments took place. European telegraph wires and underwater cables became widely used. While the telegraph would continue to be used for many more years, other types of technology were taking shape. Bell developed the telephone in 1875, and he and Gray filed for a patent the next year. Bell later offered to sell his patents to Western Union, but they turned him down.

By the late 1880s, there were 140,000 homes in the U.S. with telephone service. The growth of this system has been impressive. Today there are 200 million lines that reach 93 percent of the homes in the U.S. The copper wire that has been used for so many years is being replaced by fiber optic cable that will bring voice, data, and video into our homes.

ENDING THE SESSION

Now you may print this session's files, continue to the next session, or exit the program. See page 118 of Session 28 if you need to review procedures.

Ergonomic Tip

Remember, you can make many adjustments in your own environment at little or no cost to you or your employer.

the details of your report and for assistance in setting up an appointment./Your exam was provided by the Sun Health Mammography Center, and is being stored with a copy of the report at the Sun Health Memorial Hospital, 14519 W Granite Valley Drive, Sun City West, AZ 85374. When you obtain your next mammogram, please inform the provider when and where you had this exam./Sincerely,/Julie Mansoor/Sun Health Mammography Center.

Block-Style Letter

44.7 **Document C**

1   At the *Session 44 Document C* screen, key Document C as a block-style letter. Change the margins to 1.25 inches and left and right margin alignment.
2   Proofread and correct any errors.
3   Click Check to automatically name (**044proc**), save, and check the letter.
4   If required by your instructor, print the letter with errors highlighted.
5   Correct errors the software has identified, then recheck the document.
6   Click Next Exercise.

Document C

Current date

Mrs. Doris A. Galloway
17931 Whispering Oaks Drive
Cayote Lakes, AZ 85373

Dear Mrs. Galloway:

We are pleased to inform you that the results of your mammography exam appear to be normal.

Your breast images and report will be kept on file here as part of your permanent medical record and are available for your continuing care. It is your responsibility to inform any new physician or new mammography center of your medical record with us.

Remember that a negative mammogram does not exclude the possibility of breast disease. You should never ignore a breast lump or any other change in your breasts, even if the mammogram is normal. Of you find a lump or other change talk to your health care proider about it as soon as possible. Please keep in mind that good breast care invovles a combination of three important steps: monthly breast self-examination, an annual examination by a helath care professional, and periodic mammograms.

Continued on next page

6

SKILLBUILDING
REINFORCEMENT

It is your responsibility to review each document before it is keyed. The document may be missing required features such as the date, reference initials, and/or filename. In addition, there may be enclosure notations, punctuation or capitalization errors.

44.5 Document A

Block-Style Personal Business Letter

1 At the *Session 44 Document A* screen, key Document A in the block-style letter format.
2 Proofread and correct any errors in the letter.
3 Click Check to automatically name (**044proa**), save, and then check the document.
4 Print the document.
5 To correct errors, click View Original. Make any necessary changes, then recheck the document.
6 Click Next Exercise.

Document A

Roy Olson, M. D./Miller Eye Clinic/143 W. Clairemont Road/Eau Claire, WI 54705/Dear Doctor Olson:/My wife, Doris, and I were long time patients of yours prior to moving to Sun City West, AZ, five years ago. You had diagnosed that I had dry macular degeneration. I recently have been invited to participate in a research study entitled "Complications of Age Related Macular Degeneration Prevention."/I have reviewed the details of the study and am not sure that this is something I should pursue. My wife and I feel that you are a top-notch eye specialist, and we value your opinion. Would you please review the details of this study (a copy is enclosed) and let me know whether, in your opinion, I should participate. Thank you./Sincerely,/Charles VanThornout/ 15128 Crown Ridge Drive/Sun City West, AZ 85374

44.6 Document B

Block-Style Letter

1 At the *Session 44 Document B* screen, key Document B in the block-style letter format.
2 Proofread and correct any errors in the letter.
3 Click Check to automatically name (**044prob**), save, and check the document.
4 Print the document.
5 To correct errors, click View Original. Make any necessary changes, then recheck the document.
6 Click Next Exercise.

Document B

Doris A. Galloway/17931 Whispering Oaks Drive/Coyote Lakes, AZ 85373/Dear Mrs. Galloway:/Thank you for your recent visit to Sun Health Mammography Center. Based on the views obtained, there is an area on your exam for which we recommend further evaluation. This is necessary to obtain a more definite diagnosis./We have sent the results to your physician, Rachel McGuire, M.D. Please contact Dr. McGuire to review

Continued on next page

Session 31

SKILLBUILDING REINFORCEMENT: LETTERS A–I

Session Goals

A Review A–I, Numbers, and Punctuation Keys

30 WAM/2 errors

ON-SCREEN EXERCISES: GETTING STARTED

There are nine exercises in Session 31. Each Exercise emphasizes a letter of the alphabet (letters **a** through **i**) and includes three activities. For example, Exercise 31.1 emphasizes the letter A. From the screen you will be directed to a page in the text to take a one-minute timing that includes many words with the letter A. To reinforce locational security, the second activity is screen-generated where you will key many words with the letter A. For the third activity, you will repeat the one-minute timing featuring the letter A to see how much you have improved on your speed and accuracy.

If you are continuing immediately from Session 30, start with Exercise 31.1. Click the Next Exercise or Previous Exercise button if you are not at the correct exercise.

If you exited the program at the end of the previous session, refer to page 11 of Session 3 for instructions on entering the program.

TIMINGS

31.1 **Emphasis on A**

That happy play has an amazing climax. It affects all 27 watchers. The absorbing last act is majestic with an array of blazing ideas. Many apt actors who speak well may apply and qualify for a part. The author is apt and adept; he is ascending toward a lavish share of awards. He is aware and now aims to avoid mistakes in reaching goals ahead. He had to fire an agent who made absurd demands and squandered all the cash on large purchases. He was a fraud and a hoax.

Students in Online Classes

Do the activities for all letters. It will help reinforce your keyboarding skills on letters, numbers, and frequently used punctuation marks.

[1]   As a direct result of the strides being made in telecommunications, the new systems that we have are hard to believe. The number of systems adds to the task we have of knowing how these systems function. It is next to impossible for one person to know about all the systems now being used in transmitting voice, data, and video, much less all of the products and services being developed.

One way to help understand telecom systems in use today is to study technical concepts used in sending and receiving all forms of information. While the number of systems is huge, the number of concepts is small by comparison. If one knows the basic concepts used in systems, then that person need not study in detail each device or system by itself. He or she can apply the concepts that relate to the system being reviewed to grasp how and why it works the way it does. This applies not only to current systems but to new ones being released each day.

The concepts of telecom can be divided into six parts. They are encoding, transmitting, receiving, storing, retrieving, and decoding. A person who wants to know how and why a system works can start by dividing the process into each of the six parts noted. This will make it easier to learn and compare since the parts will not be as complex as the whole.

One of the concepts used in telecom systems relates to transmitting. This is the part that moves the data from one point to another point. Often, a signal is sent right after the encoding step is done. This step takes many forms that we use daily, such as the wire that connects our phone to a local telephone office. Other means include radio waves that go between antennas that are found in many places such as towers, cars, homes, and buildings. Satellite networks and fiber optic networks provide another means to send data between and among two or more points.

Whatever system is used, it must move data from its origin to its destination as fast and efficiently as possible. Transmitting is done by putting the data in or through space or by sending it through a copper wire or optical fiber. By being able to break a system into parts, we can digest the concepts for each part.

TEXTBOOK EXERCISES: PRODUCTION PROGRESS CHECK

Now that you have completed the instruction on formatting letters, it is time to assess how quickly and accurately you can key them. Each completed letter is to be "mailable," which means that it could be mailed or sent without any other corrections.

Your goal is to key each document in mailable form at 25 WAM or higher. If you are below 25 WAM and/or are missing errors that should have been corrected, your instructor may ask you to repeat documents.

31.2 Emphasis on B

While the 15 boys scrambled about, Barb baked a big batch of bars. The bleak cabin needed a good scrubbing. She had been able to buy a bulb for the amber lamp. The bright and probing beam chased the gloom away. A cheery robin sitting on a limb called to other birds. The tasty leg of lamb and herb dressing would soon be ready. The slight haze of that day made the family feel an abounding sense of peace. Soon they would climb aboard the boat and return to urban life.

31.3 Emphasis on C

The chief and the crew did concur. That ocean cruiser could be launched at once. It was a fact: The cursed, cruel pirates had discovered their recent acquisition of sacks of gold coins. As the panic arose, the excited crew scanned a curving cedar grove along the coast. Those ancient cypress boards crackled as the excess load caused the boat to crawl and cease almost all movement. The acute crisis excluded a quick chance at a complete escape.

31.4 Emphasis on D

Even the steadfast must agree that some birthdays are dandy with abundant kindness and others seem to be dark and dull. Adults have undue qualms when adjusting to becoming 40 and older; a child stampedes through the days with wild abandonment. No doubt a small child full of daring and dynamic energy deals with life in a candid way. All the bedlam and wild dashing dispel any dim attitudes of dour adults. To avoid adverse thoughts on birthdays, spend them with children.

31.5 Emphasis on E

That eccentric thief scares me. He swears that he did not steal the wealthy lady's 11 rings. He is either embarking on an evil route of crime, or else he is a cheap cheat. At best, he knows how to effect an illegal entry. Each of his creeping moves suggests a false value. He prizes money and exerts extra effort to obtain it. In any event, it appears that he has the stolen jewelry. He is edgy and tired. His tale may change soon.

Session Goals

1-Minute: 40 WAM/2 errors
5-Minute: 30 WAM/2 errors

**Apply features
presented in Sessions
34-43**

Choosing positive words

**44.1-
44.2** | ***ON-SCREEN EXERCISES: GETTING STARTED***

If you exited the program at the end of the previous session, refer to page 11 of Session 3 to review how to open the next session. If you are continuing immediately from Session 43, start with Exercise 44.2. Click the Next Exercise or Previous Exercise button if you are not at the correct exercise.

44.3 ONE-MINUTE TIMINGS

Goal: 40 WAM/2 errors

SI: 1.45

- Take two 1-minute timings.
- Focus on speed or accuracy, depending on your most recent 1-minute timing score.

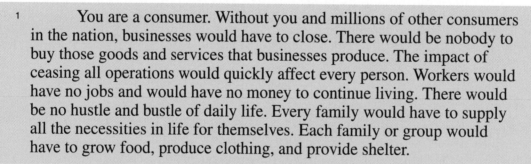

¹   You are a consumer. Without you and millions of other consumers in the nation, businesses would have to close. There would be nobody to buy those goods and services that businesses produce. The impact of ceasing all operations would quickly affect every person. Workers would have no jobs and would have no money to continue living. There would be no hustle and bustle of daily life. Every family would have to supply all the necessities in life for themselves. Each family or group would have to grow food, produce clothing, and provide shelter.

44.4 FIVE-MINUTE TIMINGS

Goal: 30 WAM/2 errors

SI: 1.45

- Take two 5-minute timings.
- On the second attempt, try to increase your speed while maintaining your accuracy.

31.6 Emphasis on F

Often, before we face all the facts, our own fears may begin to defeat us. Life seems filled with deep strife and failures. We become inflamed at ourselves and fuss in 50 futile ways. This is the time to stop fretting and inflate our egos with a firm, fresh start. Swiftly, our spirits are lifted. We have a fine feeling of being free from cares or defeat.

31.7 Emphasis on G

The boy is going to grab a bag of hamburgers after the game. That last game was grim. The team's energy ought to be higher, for the rough, gripping coughs are gone. The last germs have given way to good health through better hygiene. It is our guess that the girls will get eight goals. Those grounds are genuinely great. The eight dingy lights, which were illegal, glow brighter. When the gala bash is in full swing, the manager will give the guests a grand gift.

31.8 Emphasis on H

Those happy chaps hope to hike to the south shore. It is 72 miles from their homes. If harsh weather hinders them, each has a small, tight tent. When they are en route, the head chef can prepare wholesome meals. Breakfast might be ham and eggs or hotcakes. A hearty lunch of milk, fresh fruit, and sandwiches will be eaten in haste. The plans for night meals include hash, mashed chickpeas, and other delights. They are healthy and hearty. The whole group may catch fresh fish.

31.9 Emphasis on I

That stadium by the river isn't immune to crime. Last night a thief seized 18 expensive radios from a taxi driver, who was picking up a rider. The thief ditched the radios in the river. A diver fished them out quickly. The weird irony is that the thief is out of jail on bail. It's likely that he bribed an ignorant civil aide. In spite of this, he has been identified. His alibi is nullified. Irate voices are being raised to swiftly close the issue.

Now you may print this session's files, continue to the next session, or exit the program. See page 182 of Session 39 to review the procedures.

Ergonomic Tip

Blink often and take frequent opportunities to look away from your screen at an object farther away. Give your eye muscles a break.

Now you may print this session's files, continue to the next session, or exit the program.

Print

To print the drill lines and timed writings for this session, take the following steps:

1. Click the Close ☒ button in the top right corner of the screen.
2. At your Paradigm Keyboarding with Snap Welcome page, point to Reports on the Snap menu bar, and click View Submissions Report.
3. At the View Submissions Report Wizard, click <u>Show session files</u> to see the drill lines text or <u>Show timings files</u> to see the timings text.
4. Click Show Report.
5. Click either <u>031sess</u> (for drill lines) or <u>031tim</u> (for timings).
6. At the Word Processor dialog box, click Launch.
7. Click <u>F</u>ile, and then click <u>P</u>rint.
8. At the Print dialog box, click OK.
9. Click the Close button to close the Paradigm Word Processor.
10. Click Home on the Snap menu bar to return to the Welcome page.

Continue

To continue on the next session, click the Next Exercise ➡ button. This will take you to Exercise 32.1.

Exit

To exit, do the following:

1. Click the Close ☒ button in the top right corner of the screen.
2. At your Paradigm Keyboarding with Snap Welcome page, click <u>Logout</u>.

Ergonomic Tip

Use wrist pads to help keep wrists in a neutral position and support forearm on desk when using a mouse.

RICHARD T. WARD
13821 Via Manana
Wickenburg, AZ 83568
(623) 555-1395
Rtward5821@emcp.com

OBJECTIVE:
Secure a position as a Medical Assistant where I can use the knowledge and skills I have acquired to benefit the medical facility.

EDUCATION
In June 2006, I graduated with honors from the Estrella Mountain Community College with an Associate Degree in Medical Assisting. The course of study for this degree included the following:

Anatomy & Physiology	Medical Terminology
Medical Law & Ethics	Psychology
Medical Assisting Administrative Procedures	Medical Assisting Clinical Procedures
Diagnostic Testing	Medical Records
Communication	Windows
Word Processing (MS Word)	Machine Transcription
Accounting	Health Insurance

PERSONAL QUALITIES:

Conscientious	Responsible
Cooperative	People-oriented
Detail-oriented	Hard-working

EXPERIENCE:
Medical Assistant: Astro Medical Clinic, Sun City West, Arizona, spring semester, 20xx. As an intern, I helped set up an electronic filing system for medical records and worked with two physicians (Dr. Charles Bickett and Dr. Elon Booker) to establish a voice recognition system for inputting medical reports.

Laboratory Clerk: Boswell Hospital, Sun City, Arizona, summers of 20xx and 20xx. Helped admit patients, recorded data, filed patient records, gave instructions to patients, and prepared specimen labels.

Volunteer: Physical Therapy Unit, Del Webb Hospital, weekends during my first year at Estrella Mountain Community College, 20xx. I helped physical therapists exercise patients following surgical procedures.

References provided upon request.

Figure 43.1 Résumé

Session Goals

| J-R | Review J–R, Numbers, and Punctuation Keys |

 30 WAM/2 errors

SKILLBUILDING: GETTING STARTED

 **Students in Online Classes**

If you exited the program at the end of the previous session, refer to page 130 of Session 31 to review how to open the next session or to continue from where you left off.

Session 32 provides an opportunity to reinforce your keyboarding skills on the letters **j** through **r**. The directions for completing all keyboarding activities appear on the screen.

> Do the activities for all letters. It will help reinforce your keyboarding skills on letters, numbers, and frequently used punctuation marks.

TIMINGS

32.1 Emphasis on J

The object of the jury is to judge that subject and to be just. The adjacent jail adjoins the courtroom. A jaunt to the jail is not enjoyable. The judge's job is to remain judicious when the final judgment must be made. All 12 jurors must be adults; juveniles are not allowed on the jury. The jokers who jeer and jest will be ejected. Adjournment will take place after the judicial question has been resolved.

32.2 Emphasis on K

That old worker knows his work is risky. His kind of weakness is in his knees. He checks the skyline stockpiles from an airplane cockpit. It is awkward to go backwards or clockwise and keep a keen eye out for cracking walls. When he has checked the skyline, he has breakfast. His business is on the edge of bankruptcy. He needs a workable new plan for a husky bankroll. He hopes he will hit a $100,000 jackpot soon.

Document D

Letter of Application Search and Replace

1 At the *Session 43 Document D* screen, open document 043proc.
2 Do a Search and Replace for the following:
 a Replace *Core Clinic Institute* with *Core Clinical Institute.*
 b Replace *medical assisting* with *Medical Assisting.*
3 Save the revised letter with *Save As* and name it **043wprd**.
4 Print and then close the letter.
5 Click Next Exercise.

43.9

Document E

Composing a Letter of Application

1 At a clear editing window compose a draft for a letter of application for a full-time job. For Document E you will prepare a résumé to accompany the letter of application. Remember your goal is to get an interview. Use the block-style letter format.
2 Use either an actual job advertisement or a job that you would like to have in business, government, or education. If you don't have the name of a person to send your letter to, address it to your instructor as the Personnel Manager. Be sure to include the company/agency name, street address, city, state, and ZIP in the inside address. Assume that you are completing the educational program in which you are currently enrolled.
3 Use the word processing features presented so far to enhance the readability/appearance of your letter.
4 Save the letter with the filename **043wpre**.
5 Print a copy of your letter and edit the document using the proofreader's marks presented in the Appendices. Review the three parts of the letter:
 a Introduction
 b Your qualifications
 c Next step
 Is there anything that could be changed to improve your letter? Be specific about your experiences, activities, and education; keep them brief and to the point.
6 Make the changes noted on your edited copy.
7 Save and close the document.

Students in Online Classes

Since the letter and résumé to follow are not checked electronically, be sure to proofread carefully for format, spelling, and grammatical errors.

43.10

Document F

Résumé

Prepare a rough draft of a résumé to accompany the letter of application completed as Document E. Figure 43.1 shows a résumé. Review it for ideas on how you will prepare your résumé and what it will contain.

The format for the résumé is your choice and is to be one and a half to two pages in length. The résumé provides an excellent opportunity to use word processing features such as the indent function, underlining, italicizing, bolding, and bullets. The format must be developed with the reader in mind—easy to read, logical order, and a professional appearance. The content of the résumé is to highlight the features that set you apart from others applying for the same job—you want that interview.

When finished save your résumé as **043wprf**. Use the same procedure as with the letter of application—print and edit your résumé and make changes in format and content using the proofreader's marks presented in the Appendices. Then make the changes as shown on your edited document. Resave the document under the same name; this will replace your original rough draft. Unless instructed otherwise, print a copy of Documents E and F for your instructor, then close both documents.

32.3 Emphasis on L

Long ago, pilgrims loved to indulge in blunt folklore. Tales, sometimes false, were told with glee daily. One old tale included a blazing clash of 94 sailors in balky sailboats on a bottomless lake. The last sailor alive was a lad that was blind. As he lay clinging to a slim balsa log in filth and slimy silt, the leader's falcon led help to him. Balmy days followed as the lad's leg healed slowly and the salves applied to his eyes let the light in.

32.4 Emphasis on M

The merger of an academy and the campus may take place in the autumn. It might bring mixed emotions from the 2,000 men and women. The stormy economic issue might make an anatomy class impossible at the academy. Some who must commute for months are not amused; many think that the merger is clumsy and dumb. There is not much warmth among the enemies. The teamwork is not smooth. The amount of stormy mass meetings must be diminished. An amendment must be made.

32.5 Emphasis on N

At sunset, around 8:30 p.m., it is nice to enjoy dining out on the bank of a pond. Unless uninvited insects and swarms of ants invade the picnic, you will certainly unwind. As those soft night sounds enfold you, frenzied inward nerves and the decisions that haunt you drain from your mind. You may enjoy napping on a nearby bench. Next, swing into action after your rest and inhale much air into your lungs. Unpack the nice lunch and munch away. Don't deny yourself this experience.

32.6 Emphasis on O

An oldtime cowboy often chose a lonely life out on the open range. Hoards of prowling foxes snooped among the 25 old cows and their young ones. Owls often hooted as an obscure and occasional sound annoyed them. The food was often cold and soggy. Cooking his food and boiling his coffee over an orange-hot fire offered some enjoyment, however. Through a long night his mournful songs poured out. He was a proven, loyal worker who overcame obstacles or coped with problems.

43.7 Letter of Application

Document C

1 At the *Session 43 Document C* screen, key Document C. In the first paragraph, bold the months of June, July, and August.
2 Proofread and correct any errors in the letter.
3 Click Check to automatically name and save as **043proc**, and check the letter.
4 Print the document.
5 To correct errors, click View Original. Make any necessary changes, then recheck the document.
6 Click Next Exercise.

Document C

March 12, 20xx

After checking document C, refer to the printed copy to correct any errors. Center the letter vertically.

Mrs. Cheryle Reinertsen
Office Manager
Core Clinic Institute
14532 Greenway Drive
Surprise, AZ 85467

Dear Mrs. Reinertsen:

Jack Pleger, a medical assistant on your staff, suggested that I contact you about a summer appointment (June, July, and August) at the Core Clinic Institute. Jack completed the two-year program in medical assisting at Glendale Community College last year. He speaks highly of the Core Clinic Institute.

I will complete the first year of a two-year medical assisting program at Glendale Community College in May. The courses I will have completed so far have focused on the administrative responsibilities of a Medical Assistant. I feel most comfortable in greeting patients face-to-face and conversing with them on the telephone. In addition, I am prepared to register and schedule appointments, take care of insurance matters and basic accounting activities, prepare correspondence, and maintain and transcribe medical records.

I have no classes in the afternoon on Wednesday, March 19. Are you available any time between 1 and 5 p.m. so that I can meet with you to discuss a summer appointment? My phone number is (623) 555-2274, and my e-mail address is kyamanochi@emcp.com.

Sincerely,

Ken Yamanochi
15434 Cactus Lane
El Mirage, AZ 85382

32.7 Emphasis on P

If the plan for upgrading the park in the spring would be accepted, the plot could be plowed now. Adept employees can plant the 225 maple and pine trees by the pond with the new equipment. Those sprigs of spindly aspens should be pulled up or snipped off. Most spaces for pleasant picnics should be paved, as well as the paths to the ponds. The chipmunks and other park pets won't be upset and peevish if the plans are to plant all spots with pleasant posies.

32.8 Emphasis on Q

At the request of an old acquaintance from the Equator city, quotations for equipment will be sent quickly. Those earthquakes ruined her unique antique aquariums. The 13 techniques of restoring them require liquid lacquer and the equipment in question. Answer her inquiry and quote a good price to her. Ask her to reply quickly as to the quantity. The question of her delinquent account must be settled when the equipment is ordered.

32.9 Emphasis on R

A rapid rise in industrial prices is normally absorbed by the consumers. Large firms that need raw materials work hard to realize a profit. It is a marvel that the poor and weary customer can afford to purchase services or products that have increased 15 percent. The grim race to raise prices must be curbed early. Scores of workers who earn small salaries find no mirth in fierce, sharp rises in the market. The rows and rows of bright and sparkling products are a farce to all concerned consumers.

ENDING THE SESSION

Now you may print this session's files, continue to the next session, or exit the program. See page 133 of Session 31 if you need to review the procedures.

Ergonomic Tip

Place your monitor at a right angle (perpendicular) to a window to reduce glare on your monitor and sun in your eyes.

Current date

Ms. Mary Alcorn
Human Resources Coordinator
Astro Medical Clinic
Meeker Boulevard and Granite Valley Drive
Sun City West, AZ 85374

After checking letter A, refer to the printed copy to correct any errors. This letter is not to be centered vertically.

Dear Ms. Alcorn:

Jayne VanWinkle, Chair, Medical Assisting Department at Estrella Mountain CC told me about the 18 hour per week Medical Assisting Internship at the Astro Medical Clinic. Please consider me an applicant for this internship.

Currently I am a full-time student at Estrella Mountain CC majoring in the four-semester Medical Assisting program. Next month I will have completed two semesters of the four-semester certificate program in Medical Assisting. My previous medical work experience includes working as a volunteer at the Epoch Hospice in SCW for the past 12 months. In addition I was a caregiver for one year to my grandfather who passed away last year at the Del Webb Hospital in SCW. The experience I have attained in these situations plus the course work completed at Estrella Mountain CC will prove most valuable.

Please review the attached resume that provides additional information about my qualifications. May I talk with you in person about the internship? I can be reached at (623) 555-9145 before 7:30 a.m. and after 3:30 p.m. on weekdays.

Sincerely,

Gayle Kerr
13485 Aleppo Drive
Peoria, AZ 85373

Attachment

43.6

Document B

Letter of Application Search and Replace

1   At the *Session 43 Document B* screen, open document **043proa**.
2   Do a Search and Replace for the following:
   a   Replace *Estrella Mountain CC* with *Estrella Mountain Community College*.
   b   Replace *SCW* with *Sun City West*.
3   Save the revised letter with *Save As* and name it **043wprb**.
4   Print and then close the letter.
5   Click *Next Exercise*.

33

SKILLBUILDING REINFORCEMENT: LETTERS S–Z

Session Goals

 H E   Review S–Z, Numeric, and Punctuation Keys

    30 WAM/2 errors

SKILLBUILDING: GETTING STARTED

 *Students in Online Classes*

If you exited the program at the end of the previous session, refer to page 130 of Session 31 to review how to open the next session or to continue from where you left off.

Session 33 provides an opportunity to reinforce your keyboarding skills on the letters **s** through **z**. The directions for completing all keyboarding activities appear on the screen.

> Do the activities for all letters. It will help reinforce your keyboarding skills on letters, numbers, and frequently used punctuation marks.

TIMINGS

33.1 Emphasis on S

The 14 sulky, sad losers are scorned by most of us. A dismal loss or misfortune doesn't have to end in disgrace. Surely most folks in such spots show disgust at a loss. But those persons briskly squelch those feelings and smile because life goes on. There is always a lesson to be learned from every mistake or loss. Stay in the driver's seat and see all the good things that come along. Solving basic problems easily is necessary to reduce tensions.

33.2 Emphasis on T

Tenseness while keying causes costly mistakes. Take a gentle tip or two and practice them as you key. Watch out for fatigue: A tired receptionist tends to clutch at the keys and doesn't tap them with a gentle touch. Twirling or twisting in your seat is a typical trick at the computer. Talking a lot as you key is first on the list of bad techniques. Do not try too hard, as this often turns those keys into something frustrating. Don't let the keyboarding mistakes continue.

3 Press *Tab*. This moves the insertion point to the Replace With text box.

4 Click the Replace button. The first instance of the word to be replaced will be highlighted in the text and a *Replace* dialog box will appear asking you if you want to replace it. Click Replace, or, if you are certain that you want to find and replace all occurrences of the text, click Replace all.

The Search and Replace feature includes several options that allow you to customize your search. For example, you may need to limit your search to instances of whole words, which is what you will do in Document A. In a later session, you will learn to use other options.

Conducting Whole Word Searches

If there is no check mark in the Whole words only option at the *Search and Replace* dialog box, PWP will find any occurrence of the search text. For example, if you key *her* in the Search text box, PWP will stop at *there*, *hers*, *rather*, and so on, because each word contains the letters *her*. If you want to find a specific word such as *her*, insert a check mark in the Whole words only check box.

TEXTBOOK EXERCISES: PREPARING LETTERS OF APPLICATION

A letter of application by itself generally doesn't get you a job. But if the letter is written well, it could get you an interview. The challenge is to prepare a letter and a résumé that will make you stand out among all the job applicants. In planning the letter of application, think of it in three parts:

1 **Introduction:** How did you find out about the job opening? Why is the job so interesting to you? What do you know about the company? What can you do for them?

2 **Your qualifications:** What sets you apart from the crowd? Here you can identify educational qualifications, past employment, personal skills, achievements, and/or experiences that make you especially qualified for the job opening. This may require two or three short paragraphs.

3 **Next steps:** What can you do to create a positive reaction to your letter?

Although Documents A and C are letters of application that are keyed for other people, evaluating them in terms of the three parts named above will help you plan how to write your own letter, which you will do for Document E.

43.5

Document A

Letter of Application

1 At the *Session 43 Document A* screen, key Document A with left and right margins of 0.75 inches.

2 Proofread and correct any errors in the letter.

3 Click Check to automatically name and save the document as **043proa**, and check the letter.

4 Print the document.

5 To correct errors, click View Original. Make any necessary changes, then recheck the document.

6 Click Next Exercise.

33.3 Emphasis on U

The impulse to judge individuals quickly causes faulty results. It is unwise and unfair to jump to conclusions in a hurry. Actually, a useful guide to a sound understanding of humans is to quietly assess the situation. A subtle and thorough query can subdue doubts and evaluate behavior. An ugly and cruel deduction about another's values could cause undue suffering. You are urged to utilize more time (even if it's only 15 to 20 minutes) if you are puzzled and used to useless, quick guesses.

33.4 Emphasis on V

A visit to a village in a quiet valley gives vitality, vim, and vigor to the 46 tired individuals. Nothing rivals the vacation voyage to revive the spirits. Heavy problems seem to vanish and vexing tribulations evaporate. Vivid visions of a diverse way of living evoke valuable impressive vistas of rest. Save those fevered nerves and prevent grievous or adverse tribulations. Endeavor to take advantage of events that elevate the spirits; you deserve the very best.

33.5 Emphasis on W

The news on the network newscast might spawn a winning wealth of followers. If the newscaster can draw a wider range of viewers, the rewards are power and wealth. Watchers and followers of a witty new reporter are won when the daily news is written well. It is not a waste to rewrite the worst of interviews when 18 witless words can wreck a well planned show or review. Workers who dawdle in the newsroom will not work or write very long. Their award will be awful reviews.

33.6 Emphasis on X

An example of a tedious exercise is the flexing of lax muscles daily. Excess anxieties are exhausting to all who are under extreme pressure. A program of extensive, complex exercises is a vexation. Most experts agree that exertion to exhaustion is wrong. A flexible, yet exuberant exercise involves exhaling noxious air and inhaling oxygen. Explore the exotic experience of a brisk 30-minute daily walk. That expended energy will excite you and extend your life.

¹ One of the finest fruits on the market today is the mango, which is a fruit found in the tropics. The mango has become more popular all over the nation. The papaya is also a very good tropical fruit that has lots of vitamins and is good to eat. A carambola is quite a strange looking fruit. It has a waxy appearance and contains a solid meat. The cherimoya, or custard apple, is shaped like the strawberry and is green in color and oval in shape. The fruit is not very attractive, but it has a delicious and delicate flavor. Kiwifruit, the Chinese gooseberry, is grown in New Zealand; thus the name "kiwi" has been given to this fruit in honor of the native kiwi bird. The taste is mild and quite enjoyable.

The celery root has an ugly appearance. The outside of the root is deceiving; inside the ugly wrapping lies a great surprising flavor treat for vegetable lovers. Fine Jerusalem artichokes, also known as sunchokes, have lots of uses. The crispy, crunchy food has a nutlike flavor and makes a great finger food. A jicama is sometimes known as a Mexican or Chinese potato. The brownish vegetable looks like a raw turnip. The crispy and crunchy taste treat is quite good when served with a dip of some sort.

Although all of us seem to be creatures of habit, there is a new world of eating delights right in the produce bins, waiting for us to discover new taste treats. All it takes is some searching and a very sincere desire to try something new. Maybe a recipe or two would add to the variety of these exotic vegetables and fruits. Many cookbooks contain delightful recipes with which to vary our menus.

TEXTBOOK EXERCISES: REVISING BUSINESS LETTERS

Read the following information on *Search and Replace*. Then proceed with Documents A–D. Be sure to read the instructions in the text for each document.

Finding and Replacing Text

With PWP's *Search and Replace* feature, you can look for specific characters or formatting and replace with other characters or formatting. You can:

- Use abbreviations for common phrases when entering text, then replace the abbreviations with the actual text later.
- Set up standard documents with generic names and replace them with other names to make personalized documents.

To use Search and Replace, complete the following steps:

1   With the insertion point positioned at the beginning of the document, select Edit→Search. Then select Replace.
2   At the *Search and Replace* dialog box, key the text you want to find in the Search text box.

33.7 Emphasis on Y

A hobby is healthy for nearly everyone. A typical and unhealthy symptom of an extremely busy employer is anxiety. You may enjoy skydiving or flying as an activity. Yet, you might fill joyful and happy days by playing the rhythm of a song on a piano keyboard with its 88 keys. Analyze your daydreams and style your life to trying entirely new ways of living. I usually have enjoyed a foray into the dynamic joy of geology as a hobby. Prying through mystical layers of dirt is always fun.

33.8 Emphasis on Z

That wizard of zoology amazes zillions of zoo visitors daily. The dazzling display of the 55 puzzling zebras daze people of all sizes. Lazy lizards zigzag into a dizzy speed on an oozing pond. Monkeys puzzle many folks by the crazy antics on the hazardous horizontal bars. The graceful gazelles in brown graze in the park plazas. After a day at the zoo, it is fun to stop at a bazaar and have a zesty pizza.

ENDING THE SESSION

Now you may print this session's files, continue to the next session, or exit the program. See page 133 of Session 31 if you need to review the procedures.

Ergonomic Tip

Have a complete eye exam by a qualified professional at least every two years.

Session **43**

LETTERS OF APPLICATION AND RESUMES

Session Goals

1-Minute: 40 WAM/2 errors
5-Minute: 30 WAM/2 errors

Writing requests that get action

Using search and replace

43.1-
43.2   *ON-SCREEN EXERCISES: GETTING STARTED*

If you exited the program at the end of the previous session, refer to page 11 of Session 3 to review how to open the next session. If you are continuing immediately from Session 42, start with Exercise 43.2. Click the Next Exercise or Previous Exercise button if you are not at the correct exercise.

When you have completed the on-screen activities for Session 43, you will return to the text to complete two 1-minute and two 5-minute timings plus letters of application and a resume using the *Search and Replace* feature.

43.3   **ONE-MINUTE TIMINGS**

Goal: 40 WAM/2 errors

SI: 1.45

- Take two 1-minute timings.
- Use your most recent timing score to set a speed or accuracy goal.

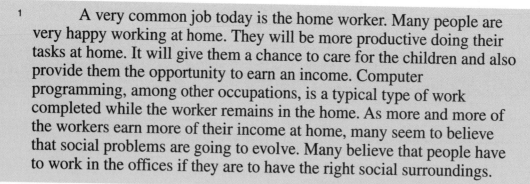

1   A very common job today is the home worker. Many people are very happy working at home. They will be more productive doing their tasks at home. It will give them a chance to care for the children and also provide them the opportunity to earn an income. Computer programming, among other occupations, is a typical type of work completed while the worker remains in the home. As more and more of the workers earn more of their income at home, many seem to believe that social problems are going to evolve. Many believe that people have to work in the offices if they are to have the right social surroundings.

43.4   **FIVE-MINUTE TIMINGS**

Goal: 30 WAM/2 errors

SI: 1.46

Take two 5-minute timings. If you finish the three paragraphs before time is up, start over with the first paragraph.

Unit

7

PROOFREADING & WORD PROCESSING TECHNIQUES

work as a medical assistant. Include three dates that you are open for a visit and designate mornings and/or afternoons.

Use the block-style letter format and include a copy notation to your instructor. Proofread your letter for wordiness and other language errors as well as punctuation and capitalization. When you have finished, save the letter as **042wprd**. Print and then close the document. Then trade printed copies with a classmate. Edit each other's documents for wordiness, adding your suggestions in pencil or pen. Include the note *Edited by (your name)*.

ENDING THE SESSION

Now you may print this session's files, continue to the next session, or exit the program. See page 182 in Session 39 to review the procedures.

Students in Online Classes

1. Use the timing feature.
2. If you do not have access to a classmate, ask a relative or friend to review your letter and comment on the things you were to address.
3. When finished, center the letter on the page vertically.

Ergonomic Tip
Take longer breaks from your computer every two hours—at least 15 minutes.

34

PROOFREADING AND WORD PROCESSING TECHNIQUES

Session Goals

1-Minute: 35 WAM/2 errors

Review error correction methods
Split and join paragraphs

34.1-34.2 ON-SCREEN EXERCISES: GETTING STARTED

If you are continuing immediately from Session 33, start with Exercise 34.2. Click the Next Exercise or Previous Exercise button if you are not at the correct exercise.

If you exited the program at the end of the previous session, refer to page 11 of Session 3 for instructions on entering the program and start with Exercise 34.1.

34.3 ONE-MINUTE TIMINGS

Goal: 35 WAM/2 errors

SI: 1.36

• Take two 1-minute timings on the following paragraph. If you finish in less than one minute, start over.

• Set either a speed or accuracy goal, based on your most recent timing score. (To review your timed writing scores, go to Session 7, page 27, for instructions on accessing your report.)

> 1   Never use a steel hammer to strike a chisel. Utilize either the solid rubber or wooden mallet. You can use the palm of your hand, of course, depending on the particular project. A mallet can be used in cases where the edge to be cut is across the grain. If, however, the cutting edge is with the grain, a mallet could easily split the wood. Remember to angle the chisel slightly when starting a cut. The angle makes smooth or pared cuts easier to do.

Mr. Charles VanThornout
Page 2
current date

Please contact me if you have any questions. My phone number is 602 555-0456, extension 6599; my e-mail address is rcassells23@emcp.net. We can also set up an initial visit to determine if you meet the criteria necessary for enrollment. I hope to hear from soon.

Sincerely yours,

Regina Cassells
CAPT Research Coordinator

xx/042prob

Enclosure

42.7

Document C

Two-Page Letter with Numbered Paragraphs

1 Open 042proa.
2 Change the bulleted paragraphs to numbered paragraphs.
3 Save the revised document as **042wprc**.
4 Print and then close the letter.
5 Click Next Exercise.

REINFORCING WRITING SKILLS

Have you ever read a letter that begins *I would like to take this opportunity to thank you…* or *I am writing this letter to tell you about the conference on Aging…*? These clauses are examples of using many words for what could be said in a few words. The first clause could be rewritten as *Thank you….* In the second clause the writer simply begins with *The conference on Aging opens November 15….*

One of the hazards of using extra "verbiage" (words) is that the writer's message becomes lost. The reader has to plow through meaningless phrases that only cause frustration. And, although most writers can recognize the problem of excessive words, they may omit that editing step because it takes a little extra time. Frequently, writers are satisfied with merely having completed the writing task.

When proofreading and editing your documents, it is critical that you take the time to cut out unnecessary words. Make it a challenge to reduce your sentences to the essential words that convey your meaning clearly and completely.

42.8

Document D

Composing and Editing a Business Letter

Compose a letter to a local medical clinic that is closest to your home or school. Ask if you can spend a half day with one of their medical assistants while on the job, which will provide you with a realistic appreciation of what medical assistants do. Include a brief paragraph about yourself and describe any medical expertise you have gained to date and why you are pursuing

Beginning with this session, you will use Paradigm's Word Processor (PWP) to prepare several paragraphs and sentences containing medical terminology. Most are automatically named, saved, and checked by the Paradigm Keyboarding (PKB) software. The program assigns a file name that includes four parts: 1) the session number; 2) **pro** for production documents; 3) a document designation (a, b, etc.); and 4) an extension consisting of a period and the letters rtf. In this session, Documents C, D, and E are named, saved, and checked by the PKB software.

Certain documents, including Documents A–B in this session, must be completed in PWP by itself. You are instructed to name and save these documents using a system similar to the filenaming system used by the PKB program: the session number, **wpr** for Word Processing Reinforcement, and a document designation (a, b, etc.). The program will automatically add the ".rtf" extension. The PWP software does not check these documents for errors. However, the program can time your keyboarding speed. You can have your WAM rate calculated by clicking the WAM 🖳 button before you begin keying the document and click on Stop 🖳 when you are finished.

Read the following information about Proofreading Techniques. Then prepare Document A. Instructions for Documents B–E also appear in the text.

Proofreading Techniques

Developing effective proofreading techniques is an essential skill whether you are writing your own documents or preparing documents for others. Proofreading requires knowledge and practice. The document is to be read slowly, word for word. For best results, proofread the document three times: (1) for content (check to see that all information from the original document has been included); (2) for punctuation and grammar; and (3) for meaning (this applies particularly to documents you write yourself). Good proofreaders focus on the following guidelines:

1 Know the basics of punctuation and grammar.
2 Pay attention to detail.
3 Use the proofreading method best suited to the material.
4 Allow sufficient time to proofread.
5 Use standard proofreaders' marks as much as possible.
    Note: A list of marks is provided after the index of this text.
6 Use an electronic spelling checker (when available) to catch basic spelling errors and a grammar checker (when available) to underscore possible grammatical errors.
7 After completing an electronic spelling check, proofread again for errors in word use and other kinds of mistakes that spelling checkers and grammar checkers miss.

Inserting Text: Review

Once you have created a document, you may want to insert information. By default, PWP is in the "insert" mode. This means that anything new that you key is added at the insertion point location and does not take the place of existing text.

If you want to insert or add something, simply key the new text at the desired location. If, however, you want to replace old text with new text, turn Overtype on by pressing **Insert**. When you press this key, the text you key replaces previous text, letter by letter. Accidentally keying over text you want to keep is easy, so be careful about remaining in Overtype mode. Overtype will stay in effect until you press **Insert** again or until you exit the program.

2 Proofread and correct any errors in the letter.
3 Click Check to automatically name (**042prob**), save, and check the letter.
4 Print the document.
5 To correct errors, click View Original. Make any necessary changes, then recheck the document.
6 Click Next Exercise.

Current date

Mr. Charles VanThornout
15128 Crown Ridge Drive
Sun City West, AZ 85374

Dear Mr. VanThornout:

Dr. Richard Parks has given me your name, with your approval, and indicated that your have the early stages of Macular Degeneration. It is possible that you could be eligible to participate in a current study, Complications of Age Related Macular Degeneration Prevention Trial (CAPT), which is sponsored by the National Consultants of Arizona, LTD. I am writing you to give you some information on this nationwide investigation. Please consider the following:

1. We have been told that you have the dry type of Macular Degeneration and have relatively good vision; consequently, this condition can convert to the wet type, which is associated with ~~bad~~ abnormal blood vessels and significant loss of vision.

2. Unfortunately, at the present time there is no effective treatment for this condition.

3. The government and the National Eye Institute are in the process of investigating ways to preserve vision in Macular Degeneration patients.

The CAPT study involves laser treatment on one eye and observing the other eye. Some initial studies have show that applying a light laser to deposits on the retina, called drusen, prevent growth of the abnormal blood vessels and loss of vision. It has been calculated that if this treatment is effective in reducing the rate of choroidal neovascularization by 30 percent, that it may reduce the rate of legal blindness by about 50 percent.

If you are interested in becoming a candidate in this study, please review the pamphlet enclosed with this letter. Dr. Dugell, Dr. Parks, and Dr. shipperly are the participating Ophthalmologists for the greater Phoenix area. The study site closest to you is in Glendale at 59th and Glendale Avenue.

Continued on next page

Deleting Text: Review

In PWP you can delete text by pressing the Backspace key to delete characters to the left of the insertion point. Or, you can press **Delete** to delete characters to the right of the insertion point.

34.4

Document A

Paragraphs

1   At a clear editing window, key the text shown in Document A. Use the default margins.

2   As you key the text, use the insertion point movement commands and the Insert/Delete functions to correct errors.

3   When the text is entered, complete the following steps to practice moving the insertion point. (**Note:** You will find the keys referenced in 3a–f in the bank of ten keys located between the alphabetic keyboard and the 10-key numeric keypad.)

   a   Press **Page Up** to move the insertion point to the top of the screen.

   b   Press **Ctrl + Right Arrow** to move the insertion point word by word until it reaches the last word at the end of the first paragraph.

   c   Press **Ctrl + Left Arrow** to move the insertion point word by word until it reaches the beginning of the first paragraph.

   d   Press **End** to move the insertion point to the end of the line.

   e   Press **Home** to move the insertion point to the beginning of the line.

   f   Press **Page Down** to move the insertion point to the bottom of the screen (last line of the document).

4   To save the document, click the Save button 💾 on the toolbar.

5   At the *Save As* dialog box, key **034wpra**, then press **Enter** or click Save. Your document has been saved. Then close the document by choosing File→Close.

Students in Online Classes

Commercial word processors such as Microsoft Word and Corel WordPerfect have the same functions as those presented here.

Document A

There are a number of medications on the market purported to reduce cancer risks. One product is Selenium, a nutrient found in our normal diet. Selenium enriched baker's yeast is a nutritional supplement that can be purchased over the counter.

Selenium has been known to protect against the development of many types of cancer, including colorectal cancer. Although it is not fully understood how Selenium works to inhibit cancer, it likely exerts a protective affect by working on many levels.

Splitting and Joining Paragraphs

To split a large paragraph into two smaller paragraphs, position the insertion point on the first letter where the new paragraph is to begin and press **Enter** twice. The first time you press **Enter**, the text is taken to the next line. The second time you press **Enter**, a blank line is inserted between the paragraphs.

To join two paragraphs, you need to delete the lines between them. There are two ways to do this. One is to position the insertion point on the first character of the second paragraph and press the Backspace key until the paragraphs join. (You may have to insert a space to separate the sentences.) The other method is to position the insertion point one space past the period at the end of the first paragraph and press **Delete** until the paragraphs join. When you join the two paragraphs, the lines of the new paragraph are automatically adjusted.

Mr. Hank Wrobleski
Page 2
Current date

Thank you for your interest in colon cancer prevention research. Should you choose to participate in the study, you would have a half hour appointment with a nurse from the Colon Cancer Prevention office in Sun City once every three months for two years.

Sincerely,

Patricia Leopard, M.D.

xx/042proa

Enclosure

Paragraph Numbering

In PWP you can create numbered paragraphs and lists the same way you create bulleted ones. The steps for activating and deactivating the numbering feature are as follows:

1 Choose Format→Bullets and Numbering. Click on the Numbered tab.
2 Click on the box displaying the style of numbers (or letters) you want. Then click OK.

From that point on, the line you are on will have a number at the beginning, and all lines of text keyed will hang indent with the first word of the previous line, not with the number. To create another numbered paragraph or item, press ***Enter***. To end numbering, press ***Enter*** twice.

To make a numbered list out of text already keyed, select the text to be made into a list, select Format→Bullets and Numbering, select the numbers tab, and click OK. PWP will insert a number at the beginning of each line after an ***Enter*** keystroke. To delete numbering, select the text, then go to the *Bulleting and Numbering* dialog box and click the box with no bullets or numbers, then click OK.

Edited Two-Page Letter with Numbered Paragraphs

42.6 Document **B**

1 At the *Session 42 Document B* screen, key Document B with the following specifications:
   a Press ***Enter*** six times. (This moves the insertion point to approximately line 7.) Then key the date.
   b Press ***Enter*** five times between the date and the inside address.
   c Create the numbered paragraphs by doing the following steps:
      1 Choose Format→Bullets and Numbering. Click on the Numbering tab.
      2 Click on the box displaying numbers with periods style. Then click OK.
      3 Key the numbered paragraphs, pressing ***Enter*** after each one.
      4 When you have keyed the last numbered paragraph, press ***Enter*** twice.
   d Insert a hard page where shown in Document B by choosing Insert→Page Break.
   e Create a heading for the second page as shown in Document B. Press ***Enter*** three times after the last line of the heading, then key the remainder of the letter.

Now you can practice deleting, inserting, and combining text as you complete the following documents using PWP.

Students in
Online Classes

Document B

Paragraphs with Proofreaders' Corrections

Open 034wpra by completing the following steps:

Following the Index at the back of this text is a one-page display of commonly used proofreader's marks. Before completing Document B, carefully review these marks.

1 Click the Open button 🖼 on the toolbar located at the top of the screen.
2 At the *Open* dialog box, double-click *034wpra*.
3 With the document open, make the indicated changes shown in Document B.
4 To save the document with the name **034wprb**, choose File→Save As.
5 At the *Save As* dialog box, you will see the filename *034wpra* (the file you opened and edited).
6 Move the insertion point to the *a* in the name. Delete the *a* and key **b**. The filename in the text box should now read *034wprb*.
7 Press **Enter** or click Save.
8 Close the document by choosing File→Close. Then click Next Exercise.

Document B

There are a number of medications on the market purported to reduce cancer *several* risks. One product is Selenium, a nutrient found in our normal diet. Selenium enriched *such* baker's yeast is a nutritional supplement that can be purchased over the counter.

Selenium has been known to protect against the development of many types of *shown* cancer, including colorectal cancer. Although it is not fully understood how Selenium works to inhibit cancer, it likely exerts a protective affect by working on many levels. *e*

Common Errors Found During Proofreading

Errors	Examples
Confusion of similar words	now/not; on/of/or; than/that; yes/yet
Confusion of suffixes and word endings	formed/former; pointing/point; type/types
Omissions in sequence of enumerated items	a/b/d/e; 1/2/4/5
Transposition of digits in numbers	451/541; 1998/1989
Transposition of letters within words	form/from
Misspelled names and words that sound alike	Clark/Clarke; Reed/Reid; knew/new
Errors in capitalization	capitalizing articles and conjunctions in titles
Errors in punctuation	missing or misplaced commas
Errors in word use	principal (head of a school) vs. principle (rule); advise (to suggest) vs. advice (a suggestion)
Errors in words that fall near margins	(because beginnings and endings of lines are often skimmed more rapidly)

Document A

Current date

Mr. Henry Wrobleski
12934 Buntline Drive
Sun City West, AZ 85374

Dear Mr. Wrobleski:

You recently had a colonoscopy where an adenomatous (pre-cancerous) polyp was found and removed. Pre-cancerous polyps can recur and, if not removed, have the potential for developing into colon cancer. You have taken the first step towards cancer prevention by having a colonoscopy.

I am participating in an important research project in conjunction with the University of Arizona Cancer Center aimed at finding ways to prevent colon cancer. The project, supported by the National Cancer Institute:

- Seeks to determine whether treatment with celecoxib (Celebrex), or selenium , or the combination of celecoxib and selenium can decrease the risk of developing recurrent colon polyps.
- Celecoxib is a safe non-steroidal anti-inflammatory drug (NSAID) used for the management of pain and inflammation associated with arthritis.
- Selenium is a dietary supplement.

I am enclosing, for your information, a brochure prepared by the Arizona Cancer Center about colon cancer prevention and the Celecoxib/Selenium Study. Your participation in this study is completely voluntary. I will continue to be involved in your care as a participating physician.

One of the nurses from the Colon Cancer Prevention office will be contacting you to see if you are interested in learning more about the project. If you prefer, you may call the Sun City Colon Cancer Prevention office (623 555-0080 or 1 800 555-6747) at your earliest convenience or fill out, detach and mail the response card from your brochure advising of the best time to reach you.

Insert a hard page break here.

Continued on next page

Omission of an entire line when a word appears in the same place in two consecutive lines	Turning it on is accomplished by moving the lever in. Turning off is done by moving the lever out.
	Turning it on is accomplished by moving the lever out.
Errors occurring at the bottom of a page	(Because the eye is tired or the reader skims too rapidly at the end of the page)
Omission of short words	(Short words such as **if**, **is**, **it**, and **in** when the preceding word ends in a similar letter or the following word begins with the same letter)

34.5 Document C

Sentences with Errors

1 At the *Session 34 Document C* screen, key the sentences shown in Document C.
2 Proofread the sentences and correct any errors you find. Watch for errors in word use.
3 Click Check 🔲. The PKB software saves and names the document as **034proc** and checks it for accuracy and keyboarding speed.
4 When checking is complete, you will see the WAM and Error counts displayed at the bottom of the screen. This score is saved in your Report and is the score used for grade calculation.
5 To print the document with the errors selected, click the Print button 🖨 on the toolbar. (Otherwise, you can print all Session 34 documents at the end of the session.)
6 To see your original document, click View Original 🔲.
7 With the original document displayed, you can correct any errors and have the document checked again (click Check), repeating the process until there are zero errors. Remember, however, that the first score is the one saved in the Student Report.
8 Click Next Exercise. This closes the document and displays the Document D screen.

Document C

Marion paid a great complement to the nurses and staff at the clinic.

Juanita and Doris Ann excepted their RMA certificates on Tuesday.

Most of our correspondence want to know how to deal with their ailments.

The Astro Medical Clinic is located in the capitol city of Madison, Wisconsin.

Their were far to many errors in the H&P exam report.

The personal in the clinic enjoyed working with the patients.

The doctor strongly advice the patient to stop smoking.

I here there are products on the market that can help people with back pain.

The medical assistances said that they liked it's use in managing electronic records.

Keeping up with knew medical terminology requires a great deal of attension.

With PWP, you can control page endings by inserting your own page breaks ("hard" page breaks).

Inserting Hard Page Breaks

PWP default settings break each page after approximately line 45. PWP automatically inserts page breaks in a document as you create or edit it. Since PWP does this automatically, you may find that page breaks sometimes occur in undesirable locations. To remedy this, you can insert your own page break.

The PWP page break, called a *soft* page break, displays as a dashed line across the screen. If you do not like where the soft page break is inserted in a document, you can insert your own. A page break you insert in a document is called a *hard* page break. To insert a hard page break in a document, do the following steps:

1 Position the insertion point where you want the break to occur.
2 Choose Insert→Page Break.

A hard page break displays as a line of dots across the screen. To repaginate (renumber the pages of) the document, select Print Preview, then select it again to return to the document, then move your insertion point to the top of the document using ***Ctrl + Home***.

Second-Page Heading

When a letter is longer than one page, it must have a heading on the second page. This heading begins one inch from the top of the second page. After the heading, press ***Enter*** three times, which leaves two blank lines between the heading and the body of the letter. The heading contains three lines of information: the addressee, the page number, and the date, as follows:

Mr. Neal Chomsky
Page 2 (Use either a number or the word)
June 15, xxxx

42.5

Document A

Two-Page Letter with Bulleted Paragraphs

1 At the *Session 42 Document A* screen, key Document A with the following specifications:
   a Press ***Enter*** five times and key the date.
   b Press ***Enter*** five times between the date and the inside address.
   c Enter the bullets as shown.
   d Insert a hard page where shown in Document A selecting Insert→Page Break.
   e Key the heading for the second page as shown in Document A. Press ***Enter*** three times after the last line of the heading, then key the remainder of the letter.
   f Press ***Tab*** between the copy notation and the person to receive a copy.
2 Proofread and correct any errors in the letter.
3 Click Check to automatically name and save the document as **042proa**, and check the letter.
4 Print the document.
5 To correct errors, click View Original. Make any necessary changes, then recheck the document.
6 Click Next Exercise.

34.6

Document D

Paragraphs with Errors

1 At the *Session 34 Document D* screen, key the three paragraphs shown in Document D.

2 Proofread the paragraphs and correct any errors you find. Watch for errors in word use.

3 Click Check 🔲. The PKB software saves and names the document as **034prod** and checks it for accuracy and keyboarding speed.

4 To print the document with the errors selected, click the Print button on the toolbar. (Otherwise, you can print all Session 34 documents at the end of the session.)

5 To correct errors, click View Original 🔲. Make any needed changes to the original document, then recheck the document (click Check). Repeat this process until there are zero errors.

6 Click Next Exercise. This closes the document and displays the Document E screen.

Document D

Everyone has cholesterol. It is a white, waxy fat found in you body's cells and bloodstream. Your body actually makes cholesterol. But to much cholesterol is dangerous.

Having high cholesterol is an major risk factor for a heart attack. To much cholesterol can clog the arteries that supply the heart with blood. Usually, hear disease happens when cholesterol, fat, and other substances built up and make "plaque" in the major artery of the heart, the coronary artery.

Plaque slows down the flow of blood to the heart, and less oxygen gets to the heart. This causes chest pains (angina). In some cases, a blood clot can form and led to a heart attach. After the age of 20, a person should be tested ever five years.

Tips for Proofreading Medical Material

- Proofread medical or difficult material *at least twice.* Read slowly; check for content (words left out or the wrong word), numbers, initials, and technical terms. Also, read for errors in punctuation and grammar.
- If possible, proofread with another person; one person reads from the original while the other makes proofreading changes on the keyed document. When reading from the original, indicate difficult spelling, paragraphing, format, and decimal points. Read numbers digit by digit; for example, 4,230.62 should be read aloud as "four, comma, two, three, zero, point, six, two."

34.7

Document E

Paragraph of Technical Material

1 At the *Session 34 Document E* screen, key the paragraph shown in Document E.

2 If possible, ask another student to read the paragraph to you while you proofread the text on the screen. Make any needed corrections.

3 Click Check 🔲. The PKB software saves and names the document as **034proe** and checks it for accuracy and keyboarding speed.

4 To print the document with the errors selected, click the Print button on the toolbar. (Otherwise, you can print all Session 34 documents at the end of the session.)

5 To correct errors, click View Original 🔲. Make any needed changes to the original document, then recheck the document (click Check). Repeat this process until there are zero errors.

1   A letterhead creates an image for a business. It is possible to hire a person or a design firm to design a letterhead for you, or you may decide to use a computer to make your own. By making your own, you have the flexibility to make it a "true picture" of you and your firm. There are several things you should keep in mind while designing your letterhead.

Keep in mind that your letterhead will make a statement about your firm. It will give the reader vital data and also create an image in the reader's mind about your firm. Do you wish the reader to obtain the mental image that your firm is "solid-as-a-rock conservative"? Or, do you wish your firm to be seen as "active, flashy, and fast reacting"? You must decide.

Vital data that must be included on your letterhead is the name of your firm, address, phone and fax numbers, and Web site address. There are certain placement guidelines that should be followed regarding the name and address of a business. For example, the firm's name, address, phone number, fax number, and Web site address may be centered at the top of the page. Left- or right-justifying at the top of the page is also very popular. When displaying this data, you may simply block the lines, or you may wish to be more creative and try such things as separating the data by bullets, clip art, and so on.

Many businesses have logos and slogans that may be used on the page. These two items may be placed anywhere on the page. A popular location to display a slogan is across the bottom of the page with the logo placed on the left- or right-hand side of the page.

You may wish to use different fonts when displaying your firm's data. Experts warn, however, to not use more than two fonts when designing your letterhead. Consider using both bold and plain fonts for variety. When picking fonts, keep in mind the image you are trying to present. Don't select a "flashy" type font if you are attempting to appear conservative.

TEXTBOOK EXERCISES: REVISING BUSINESS LETTERS

Most business letters take up only one page. Even if a sentence or two carries to the next page, you can easily adjust the top and/or bottom margins so that those sentences will print on the first page. However, sometimes you will write or prepare complex letters that require a second or even a third page. For those situations, consider the following guidelines:

- Keep a minimum of two lines of a paragraph at the bottom of a page.
- Keep a minimum of two lines of a paragraph at the top of a page (one full line plus three or more words).
- Do not place a paragraph heading on the bottom of a page and its accompanying text on the next page.
- Do not place the closing and signatures lines on a page by themselves.
- Do not hyphenate words between pages.

Aspirin and other NSAIDs have shown to be protective against colorectal cancer. Many people cannot take NSAIDs over a long period of time because of gastrointestinal side effects such as ulcers or bleeding. Most NSAIDs restrict two enzymes in the body called cyclooxygenase 1 and 2 (COX-1 and COX-2). The COX-1 enzyme normally protects the stomach and gastrointestinal lining. The COX-2 enzyme plays a role in inflammation and triggering pain. Using selected medications that restrict only COX-2 spares the protective effects of COX-1.

ENDING THE SESSION

Now you can print any files you have created, continue with the next session, or exit Paradigm Keyboarding with Snap.

Print

To print Exercises 34.1–34.7 proceed as follows:

1 Click the Close ⊠ button in the top right corner of the screen.
2 At your Paradigm Keyboarding with Snap Welcome page, point to Reports on the Snap menu bar, and click View Submissions Report.
3 At the View Submissions Report Wizard, click Show session files to see the drill lines text (Exercises 34.1–34.2), Show timings files to see the timings text (Exercise 34.3), and Show production files or Show unchecked production files to see the production documents.
4 Click Show Report.
5 Click the name of the file you want to print.
6 At the Word Processor dialog box, click Launch.
7 Click File, and then click Print.
8 At the Print dialog box, click OK.
9 Click the Close button to close the Paradigm Word Processor.
10 Click Home on the Snap menu bar to return to the Welcome page.

Continue

To continue on to the next session, click the Next Exercise button. This will take you to Exercise 35.1.

Exit

To exit, do the following:

1 Click the Close ⊠ button in the top right corner of the screen.
2 At your Paradigm Keyboarding with Snap Welcome page, click Logout.

Ergonomic Tip
Press your hand on a firm, flat surface for five seconds to relieve muscle tension.

Session 42

BUSINESS LETTERS

Session Goals

⏱ 1-Minute: 40 WAM/2 errors
5-Minute: 30 WAM/2 errors

✏️ Deleting unnecessary words

Inserting hard page breaks and numbered paragraphs

42.1-42.2 ON-SCREEN EXERCISES: GETTING STARTED

If you exited the program at the end of the previous session, refer to page 11 of Session 3 to review how to open the next session. If you are continuing immediately from Session 41, start with Exercise 42.2. Click the Next Exercise or Previous Exercise button if you are not at the correct exercise.

When you have completed the on-screen activities for Session 42, you will return to the text to complete two 1-minute and two 5-minute timings, plus several business letters in which you will learn word processing feature for inserting hard page breaks and numbering paragraphs.

42.3 ONE-MINUTE TIMINGS

Goal: 40 WAM/2 errors
SI: 1.45

- Take two 1-minute timings. If you finish before time is up, start over.
- Use your most recent 1-minute timing score to set a speed or accuracy goal.

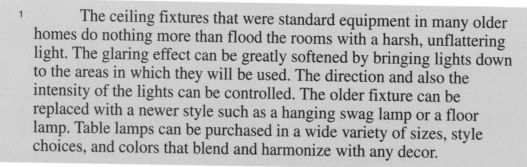

1   The ceiling fixtures that were standard equipment in many older homes do nothing more than flood the rooms with a harsh, unflattering light. The glaring effect can be greatly softened by bringing lights down to the areas in which they will be used. The direction and also the intensity of the lights can be controlled. The older fixture can be replaced with a newer style such as a hanging swag lamp or a floor lamp. Table lamps can be purchased in a wide variety of sizes, style choices, and colors that blend and harmonize with any decor.

42.4 FIVE-MINUTE TIMINGS

Goal: 30 WAM/2 errors
SI: 1.45

Take two 5-minute timings.

Unit

8

MEMOS AND E-MAIL

Identifying your reader is one of the first steps in creating a well-written document. Questions to ask yourself include the following:

- Who is my reader?
- What do I know about my reader that will help determine the best approach?
- Is the audience one person or a group?
- Is my reader a co-worker, a subordinate, a superior, or a customer?
- How is the reader likely to feel about my message?
- How much does the reader know already about my topic?

Answering these questions will help you choose the information to include in your document and the words and sentences to convey that information. For example, if you are describing the latest space mission and your readers are scientists or engineers, you will refer to principles of physics and use highly technical words that might be unfamiliar to the general population. You would also include more detail. A description of that space mission written for the local newspaper would have to relate the mission findings in language that the average reader could understand. You would describe results that would affect the general public.

Students in Online Classes

Document

41.8 **D** Rewriting a Letter for a Different Audience

> **Do not use the timing feature for this letter and do not center it vertically.**

Open Document 041prob and rewrite the body of the document for the parents of the deceased so that they understand the cause of Mindy Salazar's death.

Omit the date and inside address (assume that they will be added later). Use "Dear Mr. & Mrs. Salazar:" as the salutation. Use the same closing line (Sincerely,) and your name and title of RMA in place of Phillip Lahr, Pathologist. Save the letter as **041wprd** and print it, if requested by your instructor, then close the letter.

ENDING THE SESSION

Now you may print this session's files, continue to the next session, or exit the program. See page 182 of Session 39 to review the procedures.

Ergonomic Tip

Maintain the natural "S" curve of your spine when you are seated. Sit up straight so that the back rest of your chair fits the small of your back. This helps minimize backaches.

35

Session Goals

Memos E-mail

1-Minute: 35 WAM/2 errors
3-Minute: 30 WAM/2 errors

Indenting text,
Selecting text,
Changing alignment

Writing at the keyboard

35.1- 35.2 ON-SCREEN EXERCISES: GETTING STARTED

If you are continuing immediately from Session 34, start with Exercise 35.2. Click on the Next Exercise or Previous Exercise button if you are not at the correct exercise.

If you exited the program at the end of the previous session, refer to page 11 of Session 3 for instructions on entering the program.

35.3 ONE-MINUTE TIMINGS

Goal: 35 WAM/2 errors

SI: 1.36

- Take two 1-minute timings on the following paragraph.
- Set either a speed or an accuracy goal based on your most recent timing score. (To review your timed writing scores, go to Session 7, page 27, for instructions on accessing your report.)

> 1   Your ability to key at a very rapid rate will be a skill that you will never forget. It will be a skill that you will use almost all of the time if you work with computers. It will be an important skill if you end up using it only to access the Internet to do research, send e-mail messages, and interact with others in real time.

35.4 THREE-MINUTE TIMINGS

Goal: 30 WAM/2 errors

SI: 1.42

- Take two 3-minute timings on the following paragraphs.
- Set either a speed or an accuracy goal based on your most recent 3-minute timing score.

Based on the above findings, the cause of death is attributed to massive retroperitoneal bleeding with thrombocytopenia (29,000) arising from intravascular coagulopathy and hemophagocytosis-platelet phagocytosis, in a patient with acute lymphoblastic leukemia.

Sincerely,

Phillip Lahr, M.D.
Pathologist

xx/041prob

41.7

Document C

Letter with Wider Margins and Bulleted Items

1 At the *Session 41 Document C* screen, key Document C as a block-style letter with the following specifications:
   a Change the left and right margins to 1.5 inches.
   b Bullet the numbered items.
2 Proofread and correct any errors in the letter.
3 Click Check to automatically name and save the document as **041proc** and check the letter.
4 Print the document.
5 To correct errors, click View Original. Make any necessary changes, then recheck the document.
6 Click Next Exercise.

Document C

Mr. John Murray/17431 N. Camino Del Sol/Sun City West, AZ 85374/Dear Mr. Murray:/

This is a reminder of your CAPT (<u>C</u>omplications of <u>A</u>ge related macular degeneration <u>P</u>revention <u>T</u>rial) appointment at our Sun City Office. The following will be completed:/1. An ophthalmologic exam will be done by Dr. Park who will take photographs of both eyes./2. Dr. Park will then discuss with you whether this laser procedure would be beneficial to your condition. If you meet the study criteria, your randomized eye will have treatment that day./3.Your eyes will be dilated on the second visit, so it is highly recommended that you have a driver accompany you./I look forward to meeting you. If you have any questions, please contact me at 602-555-0490./Sincerely yours,/Walt Ciesla, M.D.

1   Each spring thousands of gardeners declare war on one bothersome weed that seems to plague everyone. This weed is the lowly dandelion plant. In earlier times, people savored all the virtues of this many faceted plant. Rather than referring to it as a weed, folks utilized the very fine herbal qualities. Some broths and tonics were made and utilized to restore health to persons who were ill. Even now, modern pharmacies continue to use extracts of this springtime plant in quite a number of medicines on the market for our use.

As a food, the dandelion is a big source of nutritious, healthy, and delicious food. It is quite rich in proteins, calcium, and iron. The plant contains more Vitamin A than spinach or green peppers. The durable leaves, which may be used in many delicious salads, should be picked before the first blossoms appear. The tender leaves, although tangy in taste, are very nutritious. If you carefully dry the leaves and boil them correctly, you can make delicious teas. You might wish to consume the new blossoms and make wines, salad garnishes, and snacks made from blossoms that have been dipped in a very tasty batter.

TEXTBOOK EXERCISES: PREPARING MEMORANDUMS AND E-MAIL

In terms of paper-generated documents (memorandums, letters, reports, and manuscripts), memos are the most frequently produced type of business correspondence. They are generally used to communicate internally within an organization. Memos can vary in length, but they are generally short.

The development of local area networks and the Internet has spawned a new type of memorandum: the e-mail message (an electronic memo). Just as the paper-generated memo is generally short, so too is an e-mail message. E-mail messages, however, are not limited to internal communications, and unless the recipients chose to print a copy of the e-mail message, it remains in an electronic format until deleted. E-mail messages far outnumber all types of paper-generated documents. The growth in use of e-mail as a means of communicating information is attributed to its speed, the universal use and access of microcomputers, and the user-friendly software for preparing these electronic memos. Paper-generated memos and e-mail messages are presented in this unit.

Memo Styles

Throughout this text, the term "memorandums" or "memos" means internal documents that are keyed, printed, and delivered via an organization's internal mail system. The term "e-mail" or "electronic memos" refers to documents that are transmitted electronically.

Memorandums may be prepared on preprinted memo forms, letterhead, plain paper, or memo templates available on some word processing software packages. The standard format is the block style, with guide words (DATE, TO, FROM, SUBJECT) and the message starting at the left margin (see the examples that follow). The order and placement of the guide words may vary from one organization to the next and among software packages that include preformatted document templates.

The traditional memo will be featured in this session. The order of the guide words for these memos is DATE, TO, FROM, SUBJECT.

Document B

1 At the *Session 41 Document B* screen, change the left and right margins to 0.5 inches.
2 Key the letter shown in Document B with the following changes:
   a Italicize the word *leukemia* wherever it appears in the document.
   b Instead of numbering the six paragraphs as shown, indent them 0.5 inches from the left and right margins with a double space between each of the conditions noted. See Session 35, pages 152–153, if you need to review the indenting feature.
3 Proofread and correct any errors in the letter.
4 Click Check. The program automatically names and saves the document as **041prob**, then checks for errors and calculates your WAM rate.
5 Print the document.
6 To correct errors, click View Original. Make any necessary changes, then recheck the document.
7 Click Next Exercise.

Document B

Current date

Fred Hafner, M.D.
Department of Pediatrics
University of Illinois
Urbana, IL 61952

Dear Doctor Hafner:

The postmortem examination performed on your patient, Mindy Salazar, resulted in the following findings:

1. Acute lymphoblasic leukemia, widely disseminated including bone marrow, spleen, liver, kidney, lungs, lymph nodes, and other visceral organs.

2. Hemophagocytosis and intravascular coagulopathy within the bone marrow, spleen, liver, and kidneys.

3. Bleeding diathesis (clinical thrombocytopenia).

4. Massive hemorrhage with hematoma formation in pelvic and lower abdominal retroperitoneal space.

5. Punctate petechiae within the ascending aorta, heart, and gastrointestinal tract.

6. Petechiae, with ecchymosis, both extremities.

Continued on next page

Formatting a Memorandum

The example that follows shows the format for a memorandum prepared on plain paper. Use the guidelines in the example that follows as you prepare Documents A–E.

> DATE: *tab* *tab* Current date
>   *ds*
> TO: *tab* *tab* Receiver's name *(first and last) plus title (optional)*
>   *ds*
> FROM: *tab* Sender's name *(first and last) plus title (optional)*
>   *ds*
> SUBJECT: *tab* TOPIC OF MEMO KEYED IN ALL CAPITAL LETTERS
>   *ds*
> This is the first line of the message, or body, of the memo. Typically, memos are short forms of communication, perhaps one or two paragraphs. The message should be written in clear, direct sentences using correct grammar, capitalization, and punctuation. Notice that there is a double line space between paragraphs.
>   *ds*
> If copies of the memo are to be sent to other individuals, arrange the names in alphabetic order at the end of the memo. Enter a "c" at the left margin to indicate "copies." Next press the **Tab** key and key the name of the first person on the list who is to receive a copy. Press **Enter**. For the remainder of the individuals who are to receive a copy, press the **Tab** key, key the person's name, and press **Enter**.
>   *ds*
> xx/memo *[your initials and the filename]*
>   *ds*
> Attachment
>   *ds*
> c   Person 1
>   Person 2
>   Person 3

Figure 35.1 Memorandum

35.5

Document A

Memo

1   At the *Session 35 Document A* screen, key Document A (next page) by completing the following steps:
   a   Key **DATE:**, then press **Tab** twice.
   b   Key the current date.
   c   Press **Enter** twice, key **TO:**, press **Tab** twice, then key **Fran Eron, Astro Clinical Newsletter Editor**.
   d   Continue keying the remainder of the memo. (You will need to press **Tab** once after FROM: and once after SUBJECT:.) Key your initials where you see the *xx* at the end of the memo. Press **Tab** between the copy notation and the names.
2   Proofread and correct any errors.
3   Click Check 🔲 to automatically name, save, and check the memo. (Note that the program names the memo **035proa** and saves it.)
4   To print the document with errors selected, click the Print button on the toolbar. Otherwise, you can wait until the end of the session to print all Session 35 documents.

Document A

1   At the *Session 41 Document A* screen, change the left and right margins to 1.75 inches. (See the preceding paragraph for step by step instructions.)
2   Key the business letter shown in Document A.
3   Proofread and correct any errors in the letter.
4   Click Check. The program automatically names and saves the document as **041proa**, then checks for errors and calculates your WAM rate.
5   Print the document.
6   To correct errors, click View Original. Make any necessary changes, then recheck the document.
7   Click Next Exercise.

Document A

Current date

Mr. Arthur Chosnyk
15215 Star Ridge Drive
Alexandria, VA 12454

Dear Mr. Chosnyk:

In checking our records, we find that you have a balance of $365 which is now 60 days overdue. Perhaps you have overlooked our bill. Please contact me if you have any questions about the charges. My local telephone number is 555-5488 Ext. 234 or you can e-mail me at ncameron@emcp.com.

It is important for you to clear your account as soon as possible. If your payment is already in the mail, please disregard this notice. If not, we would appreciate prompt payment.

Thank you for your cooperation.

Sincerely yours,

Norma Cameron, RMA

xx/041proa

Use the printed document for a reference in correcting errors (step 5). This will help you focus on the type of errors you are missing. Do this for Documents A, B, and C in this Session.

After checking letters A, B, and C in Session 41, center each one vertically as instructed in alternative 3, page 178.

5 To view the original document and correct errors, click View Original . Make your changes and recheck the memo until you have zero errors.

6 Click Next Exercise. This closes the document and displays the Document B screen. Read the information on "Selecting Text" and "Indenting Text from the Left Margin" before completing Document B.

Document A

DATE: Current date

TO: Fran Eron, Editor, Astro Clinic Newsletter

FROM: Dorothy J. Vandas, Office Manager

SUBJECT: WELL-CHILD CHECKUP APPOINTMENTS

ds

With the recent hiring of Dr. Earl Rynders, pediatric specialist, we will be scheduling additional well-child appointments. Well-child appointments will be scheduled at the ages of 2 weeks and 2, 4, 6, 12, 18, and 24 months. Each appointment generally takes 20 minutes. Dr. Rynders will be accepting well-child appointments on Tuesdays and Thursdays. Evening hours for appointments with Dr. Rynders will be added next month.

Attached is a brief resume describing Dr. Rynders's background. We are indeed fortunate to have Dr. Rynders on our staff.

xx/035proa

Attachment
c   Joann Dauer
      George Harper
      Jean Mooney

Students in Online Classes

Your WAM rate and the number of uncorrected errors you have the first time a document is checked are recorded in your Production Performance Report. By correcting the errors, even though the new score is not recorded, you will see the types of errors being made.

Indenting Text from the Left Margin

In PWP, all lines of text in a paragraph can be indented to a tab stop from the left margin.

To indent all lines of text in a paragraph, do the following:

1 Position the insertion point at the beginning of the first paragraph to be indented and choose Format→Paragraph.

2 Enter .5 in the window for Left Margin (your margins will be indented one-half inch) and click OK.

3 Move the insertion point to the beginning of the next paragraph; repeat step 1. Enter 0 in the window for left margin and click on OK (this puts the remaining paragraphs back to the original left margin).

Wise managers of money seem to have the ability or the foresight to make their money stretch a long way. Others spend haphazardly and always seem to be short of money long before the next salary check is due. What factors do the wise managers follow?

Food buying takes a large part of the salary check. In the area of buying groceries, one can save a large amount of money by wise and careful buying. There are many fine guides that a shopper can follow to economize and save money.

Probably the one best rule to attempt, at the outset, is to plan ahead. Plan all your meals in detail for a certain period, for example, a week or a month, but never day by day. After making the complete plan for your groceries, you are then ready to prepare your shopping list. Be sure that you have included all of the items required for cooking the meals to come. Many people forget to include the small items such as salt, pepper, and needed condiments. Once you have made a list, additional guides are very useful and helpful.

After making the major shopping list, you should compare prices. You should look at all the local advertisements in newspapers. Quite often, you will save considerable amounts of your money by comparison shopping. However, do not waste time or money for gas by driving your car from store to store. If you do this, you are defeating your purpose. After deciding where to do your shopping, your next step is that of doing the actual shopping.

TEXTBOOK EXERCISES: REVISING BUSINESS LETTERS

As you learned in previous sessions, the block-style letter is formatted with one-inch default margins. These defaults work well for most correspondence. However, there are times when you will need to change the left and right margins to visually balance the letter on the page. For example, a very short letter of ten lines would look better with wide margins. The larger areas of "white space" more closely match the white spaces above and below the text, creating a visually pleasing appearance.

Changing Margins

To change the left and right margins in PWP, complete the following steps:

1 Choose File→Page Setup.
2 Press *Tab* three times or click the left margin text box.
3 Key the new left margin setting in the Left text box.
4 Press *Tab* twice.
5 Key the new right margin setting in the Right text box.
6 Choose OK or press *Enter* to close the dialog box.

Indenting Text from the Left and Right Margins

Text in paragraphs can be indented from the left and the right margins in PWP by following the steps for indenting text from the left margin with one exception. You must also enter the amount of space to be indented in the window for the right margin.

35.6

Document B

Memo with Indented Text

1 At the *Session 35 Document B* screen, create Document B by completing the following steps:
   a Key the document using the ***Tab*** key to properly align the text after the headings. Key your initials where you see the *xx* at the end of the memo.
   b Indent the second paragraph 0.5 inches from the left margin.
2 Proofread and correct any errors.
3 Click Check to automatically name, save, and check the memo. (Note that the program names the memo **035prob** and saves it.)
4 To print the document with errors selected, click the Print button on the toolbar.
5 To view the original document and correct errors, click View Original. Make your changes and recheck the memo until you have zero errors.
6 Click Next Exercise. This closes the document and displays the Document C screen. Read the information on "Changing Alignment" before completing Document C.

Document B

DATE: Current date

TO: Fran Eron, Editor, Astro Medical Clinic Newsletter

FROM: Dorothy J. Vandas, Office Manager

SUBJECT: OPENING FOR A MEDICAL ASSISTANT

The Astro Medical Clinic has an opening for a medical assistant intern for 18 hours a week. We are offering minimum wage and flexible hours.

This position offers specific training in the following areas: registering patients, typing memos, e-mails, and correspondence, filing correspondence and some medical records, and scheduling appointments.

The contact person for this position at our clinic is Bill Hart. Please notify local schools providing Medical Assisting programs of this opening.

xx/035prob

Session 41

BUSINESS LETTERS

Session Goals

1-Minute: 40 WAM/2 errors
5-Minute: 30 WAM/2 errors

Changing margins

Writing for the reader

41.1- 41.2 ON-SCREEN EXERCISES: GETTING STARTED

If you exited the program at the end of the previous session, refer to page 11 of Session 3 of this book to review how to open the next session. If you are continuing immediately from Session 40, start with Exercise 41.2. Click the Next Exercise or Previous Exercise button if you are not at the correct exercise.

When you have completed the on-screen activities for Session 41, you will return to the text to complete two 1-minute and two 5-minute timings, plus several business letters in which you will use PWP to change margins.

41.3 ONE-MINUTE TIMINGS

Goal: 40 WAM/2 errors

SI: 1.45

• Take two 1-minute timings. If you finish before time is up, start over.

• Use your most recent 1-minute timing score to set a speed or accuracy goal. Note that with this session, the goal has been increased by 5 WAM.

> 1   To honor a deserving person in the community is a fine thing. A most interesting factor becomes apparent many times in the ugly form of jealousy for another's accomplishments. Most people can accept a high honor quite well (that is, if they were the ones to win). Those people who did not win may begin to hold a grudge against anyone who was a winner. Honors and awards must be given and accepted with a generous, happy spirit.

41.4 FIVE-MINUTE TIMINGS

Goal: 30 WAM/2 errors

SI: 1.42

Take two 5-minute timings. If you finish the four paragraphs before time is up, start over with the first paragraph.

Selecting Text

Text can be selected using the mouse. To use the mouse to select text, position the I-beam pointer on the first character of the text to be selected, hold down the left mouse button, drag the I-beam pointer to the last character of the text to be selected, then release the mouse button. The selected text will be displayed in reverse video. Another way to select text is to hold down the shift key and press the down arrow.

To deselect text with the mouse, position the I-beam pointer anywhere in the document outside the selected text, then click the left mouse button.

Changing Alignment

By default, paragraphs in a PWP document are aligned at the left margin and ragged at the right margin. This alignment can be changed. Text in a paragraph can be aligned at the left margin, between margins, at the right margin, or at the left and right margins.

Use the buttons on the style bar shown below to change the alignment of text in paragraphs.

To align text	Button
at the left margin	Align Left ▤
between margins	Center ▤
at the right margin	Align Right ▤
at the left and right margins	Justify ▤

To return paragraph alignment to the default (left aligned), click the Align Left button on the toolbar.

To change the alignment of existing text in a paragraph, position the insertion point anywhere within the paragraph and click the button on the toolbar for the desired alignment.

To align multiple paragraphs, select the text to be aligned, then click the desired alignment button.

35.7

Document C

Memo with Left and Right Alignment

1 At the *Session 35 Document C* screen, create Document C by completing the following steps:

 a Key the document with proper block-style memo formatting. (***Note:*** In this document and in certain documents in later sessions, the diagonal slash is used to indicate separations between heading parts or to indicate new paragraphs.)

 b Change the alignment to left and right justified for the paragraphs in the body of the memo after you have completed keying the document.

2 Proofread and correct any errors.

3 Click Check to automatically name, save, and check the memo as **035proc**.

4 To print the document with errors selected, click the Print button on the toolbar.

5 To view the original document and correct errors, click View Original. Make your changes and recheck the memo until you have zero errors.

6 Click Next Exercise.

REINFORCING WRITING SKILLS

Well-written paragraphs begin with a topic sentence and build to a clear conclusion. Each sentence is to tie in with the one before and after it, creating a sense of *unity*. Every sentence should also add information that helps explain or support the topic sentence.

The paragraph that follows contains both essential and unnecessary information. Read it carefully and decide which sentences can be omitted because they do not help explain the topic sentence. Then rekey the paragraph as you have changed it. If you notice some weak word choices, edit those as well. Save the file as **040wprd**. Then print the document, if required by your instructor, and close it.

40.8   **Document D** Edited Paragraph

The applicant's interview for a medical assistant position went well. She had a difficult time finding a parking place. Within minutes after meeting the human resources coordinator, she began to ask thoughtful question about the clinic. She was told that the clinic was previously located five blocks away. The human resources coordinator talked a lot about the clinic's history, its achievements and future plans. The applicant worried that someone else had already gotten the job. This clinic has been researching ways to improve its service to its patients. It also won an award for building design. By the time the interviewer began asking her questions, she knew a lot about the clinic. This knowledge helped her answer the human resources coordinator's questions about her potential role in the clinic, and she got the job.

ENDING THE SESSION

Now you may print this session's files, continue to the next session, or exit the program. See page 182 of Session 39 to review the procedures.

Ergonomic Tip
Shifting position in your chair rotates stress between different muscle groups allowing some to rest and recuperate.

Document C

(Current date)/TO: Connie Beckvall, Medical Office Assistant/FROM: Dorothy J. Vandas, Office Manager/SUBJECT: EQUIPMENT RESERVATION/Dr. Ellen Dobbs will be presenting information on diabetes at the next meeting of the Greater Phoenix Healthcare Workers Association. She has asked that we reserve a laptop and a computer projector for her to use for her presentation. Please reserve these two pieces of equipment for Dr. Dobbs on Wednesday, September 25, at 6 p.m. She will return the equipment Thursday morning by 8:30 a.m./Attached is a notice that includes the location of the presentation. Please make arrangements to have the equipment setup by 5 p.m. on Wednesday./your initials and filename/Attachments

35.8

Document D

Memo with Left and Right Alignment

1 At the *Session 35 Document D* screen, create Document D by completing the following steps:
  a Key the document with proper memo formatting and left and right alignment. (This time, change the alignment setting **before** keying the text.)
  b Indent the second paragraph in the body of the memo 0.5 inches from the left and right margins.
  c Key your initials where you see the *xx* at the end of the memo.
2 Proofread and correct any errors.
3 Click Check to automatically name, save, and check the memo as **035prod**.
4 Print the document with errors selected.
5 Click View Original. Correct any errors and recheck the memo until you have zero errors.
6 Click Next Exercise. This closes the document and displays the editing window where you can complete the Reinforcing Writing Skills activities.

Document D

(Current date)/TO: Fran Eron, Editor, Astro Medical Clinic Newsletter/FROM: Dr. John Gelsey/SUBJECT: COMMON KNEE PROBLEMS/Fran, please include the following in our next newsletter under the heading of "Common Knee Problems and Treatment Options." This month I'll address Meniscus Cartilage Tears.

> A sudden twist or repeated squatting can tear the meniscus. This may cause your knee to hurt or swell. Your knee may also catch or lock when you bend it.

Your surgeon may remove or repair damaged tissue, depending on its location. Torn tissue on the inside of the meniscus is usually removed. Torn tissue on the outer edge of the meniscus is often repaired because it received enough blood to allow proper healing.

xx/035prod

1 At the *Session 40 Document C* screen, key the business letter shown below.
2 Proofread and correct any errors in the letter. For a review of Proofreader's Marks, go to the chart that follows the last page of the Index. Though a document has been edited, it doesn't mean that all errors have been found.
3 Click Check. The program automatically names and saves the document as **040proc**, then checks for errors and calculates your WAM rate.
4 Print the document.
5 To correct errors, click View Original. Make any necessary changes, then recheck the document.
6 Click Next Exercise.

Document C

Current date

Martha Stitt-Gohdes, M.D.
220 River's Crossing
Athens, GA 30601-4707

Dear Doctor Stitt-Gohdes:

We will open our new <u>Riverside</u> medical center on January 1, 20xx. A 5-year strategic plan for operating this facility has been prepared by a consulting firm headquartered in Seattle. Our primary goal is to provide a state-of-the-art facility to better serve our patients.

lc I've contacted several Medical Center Chief Administrators in the East and Midwest who have been through the process of building a new facility. I've asked them for suggestions on what we can do to make sure that "no stone is unturned" to complete this project.

One suggestion has been made numerous times and that is that we bring in a third party consultant to review our strategic plan and the systems to be incorporated. Your name has been mentioned on more than one occasion to contact for such an endeavor.

Are you available to analyze our plan? If so, how soon could you begin reviewing what ~~has been proposed~~? How long would it take to review? ~~How much~~ would be the cost for your services? A brochure describing our new medical center is enclosed to give you an idea
of the size and scope of our operation.

it *What*

Sincerely yours,

Terrance Borman, M.D.
Chief Administrator

xx/filename

Enclosure

Use the printed documents for a reference in correcting errors (step 4). This will help you focus on the type of errors you are missing.

Many students and office workers handwrite documents and then key them on their computers. This process can be shortened if you can think and key at the same time—you don't need to prepare the handwritten copy first. The average individual writes at the rate of 10–12 WAM. You can double or triple this speed if you use the keyboard. It takes practice, but perfecting this skill is well worth the effort.

Beginning with Session 35, most of the sessions include an optional writing activity that strengthens your writing and grammar skills while giving you an opportunity to compose at the keyboard. With practice, you will find that it is much easier to create documents directly at the keyboard.

35.9

Document E

Composing a Memo

Let the system calculate your words-a-minute rate so that you have some idea of your composing speed.

1 At the word processor screen, click the WAM 🖳 button.
2 Note that the button was changed to the Stop WAM button. 🖳 When you finish composing the memo, click in this box.
3 Your WAM rate appears on the screen; click Print 🖨 on the toolbar.

At a clear editing window, compose a memo to the director of your school. Use your name in the FROM: section of the memo headings. The subject is "School Evaluation." Include the following in your memo:

Document E

- In the first paragraph, state your purpose (evaluating the strong and weak points about your school). Then identify two or three things you like about the school (for example, the curriculum, the buildings, the computer software and hardware, the faculty, the students, the administration).
- In the second paragraph, note two or three things you would like to see changed. Be sure to explain how/when these changes can be made and their impact on the school.

Proofread your memo and correct any errors. Save the memo as **035wpre**. Then print (check with your instructor) and close the memo.

ENDING THE SESSION

Now you can print any files you have created, continue with the next session, or exit Paradigm Keyboarding with Snap.

Print

Students in Online Classes

To print Exercises 35.1–35.9 proceed as follows:

1 Click the Close ❎ button in the top right corner of the screen.
2 At your Paradigm Keyboarding with Snap Welcome page, point to Reports on the Snap menu bar, and click View Submissions Report.
3 At the View Submissions Report Wizard, click <u>Show session files</u> to see the drill lines text (Exercises 35.1–35.2), <u>Show timings files</u> to see the timings text

Remember that documents with the filename wpr are not saved automatically. If you need to review the steps for saving a document, go to Session 34, page 143, steps 4 and 5 of Document A.

1   At the *Session 40 Document B* screen, key the business letter shown below. Insert the current date and include your initials and the filename (040prob) and make the corrections.
2   Proofread and correct any errors in the letter.
3   Click Check. The program automatically names and saves the document as **040prob**, then checks for errors and calculates your WAM rate.
4   Print the document.
5   To correct errors, click View Original. Make any necessary changes, then recheck the document.
6   Click Next Exercise.

Document B

Robert Gryder, M.D.
School of Medicine
Arizona State University
1452 University Drive
Tempe, AZ 84601

Dear Doctor Gryder:

Thank you for conducting the workshop on "Scanning the Future: Emerging Trends in the Medical Field" for our medical assistants and staff at the Astro Medical Clinic. The most frequent comment from the participants was "Let's have him back."

staff Our ~~people~~ appreciated the fact that they could see the logic in what you were sharing with us and how it would impact our work at the Astro Clinic. You made it clear to us that computer technology will play a much larger role in the medical profession from the office to the operating room.

Thank you again for conducting such an excellent program. You can be sure that we will be calling on you again. As you said, ten years ago one out of every $6 was spent on health care; it is now one out of every $5. More and more people will be entering the medical profession, and we must be prepared.

Sincerely yours,

Dorothy J. Vandas
Office Manager

Students in Online Classes

Use the printed documents for a reference in correcting errors (step 4). This will help you focus on the type of errors you are missing.

(Exercises 35.3–35.4), and <u>Show production files</u> or <u>Show unchecked production files</u> to see the production documents (Exercises 35.5–35.9).

4   Click Show Report.
5   Click the name of the file you want to print.
6   At the Word Processor dialog box, click Launch.
7   Click <u>F</u>ile, and then click <u>P</u>rint.
8   At the Print dialog box, click OK.
9   Click the Close button to close the Paradigm Word Processor.
10 Click Home on the Snap menu bar to return to the Welcome page.

Continue

To continue on to the next session, click the Next Exercise ⊡ button. This will take you to Exercise 36.1.

Exit

To exit, do the following:

1   Click the Close ☒ button in the top right corner of the screen.
2   At your Paradigm Keyboarding with Snap Welcome page, click <u>Logout</u>.

Ergonomic Tip

With the fist down, press against the knuckles of the closed hand. Resist for five seconds on each knuckle. Repeat series five times. This helps the circulation in your hands and fingers.

4 Print the document.

5 To correct errors, click View Original. Make any necessary changes, then recheck the document.

6 Click Next Exercise.

Document A

Current date

Mrs. Jayne VanWinkle, Chair
Medical Assisting Department
Estrella Mountain Community College
Dysart and Thomas Roads
Goodyear, AZ 85309

Dear Mrs. VanWinkle:

We have an opening at the Astro Medical Clinic for a medical assistant intern for 18 hours a week. We are offering flexible hours and minimum wage.

The position offers specific training in the following areas:

• Registering patients
• Preparing memos, letters, and medical reports
• Filing correspondence and medical records
• Scheduling appointments

A copy of this month's Astro Clinic Newsletter is enclosed. It includes additional details about the internship. In addition to the specific training noted above, we are contemplating adding accounting responsibilities to the internship. Students interested in this position are to send a letter of application and resume to: Mary Alcorn, Human Resources Coordinator, Astro Medical Clinic, Meeker Boulevard and Granite Valley Drive, Sun City West, AZ 85374.

If you have questions about this internship, please call me at (623) 555-4589 or e-mail me at DJV7524@emcp.net.

Sincerely yours,

Dorothy J. Vandas
Office Manager

wm/040proa

Enclosure

Session Goals

E-mail

1-Minute: 35 WAM/2 errors
3-Minute: 30 WAM/2 errors

Ideal sentence length

Bolding, italicizing and underlining
Review indenting and changing alignment

36.1-36.2   ON-SCREEN EXERCISES: GETTING STARTED

If you are continuing immediately from Session 35 start with Exercise 35.2. Click the next Exercise or Previous Exercise button if you are not at the correct exercise.

If you exited the program at the end of the previous session, refer to page 11 of Session 3 for instructions on entering the program.

36.3   ONE-MINUTE TIMING

Goal: 35 WAM/2 errors

SI: 1.38

- Take a 1-minute timing on the following material.
- Use your most recent timing speed to set a speed or accuracy goal. (To review your timed writing scores, go to page 27 of Session 7 for instructions on accessing your report.)

> 1   Rain is quite welcome when the land is dry. The earth's surface holds quite a bit of water, but in times of very dry weather it always seems to be in the wrong place, or it is of the type that can't be used. Normally, all regions of the United States receive adequate amounts of rain; however, there are particular periods when clouds don't release their moisture for long amounts of time.

36.4   THREE-MINUTE TIMING

Goal: 30 WAM/2 errors

SI: 1.38

Take one 3-minute timing on the following paragraphs. If you finish the two paragraphs before the time is up, start over with the first paragraph.

Common Letter Notations

In addition to the major sections of a business letter, there are several notations that are used if they are appropriate to a particular letter, as shown in Figure 40.1.

1 **Enclosure/attachment:** Indicates that a document or another item is included with the letter. Several styles are acceptable, including the abbreviation *Enc.*
2 **Copy (c):** Lists in alphabetical order the additional people who will receive copies of the letter. Either the word *copy* or the letter *c* is acceptable. The letter *c* is used in this text.

Letter Styles

A variety of letter styles are used today for both personal and business letters. The letter format presented in this book is the *block style*. In the block-style letter, all parts of the letter begin at the left margin. The block-style letter is popular because it is comparatively easy to learn, and it is the fastest letter style to set up. Once you have mastered the block-style letter, you will have little difficulty adjusting to other letter styles.

Using Bullets to Highlight Items

Sometimes letters include a list of items (words, phrases, or sentences) that are to be set apart from the body of the letter for special emphasis. These items can be numbered, or they can be preceded by a bullet. A bullet can take many shapes such as a circle, a square, a diamond, or an arrow.

You can create bullets of various types in PWP using the following steps.

1 Choose Format→Bullets and Numbering.
2 Click the box displaying the type of bullet you want. Then click OK.

From that point on, the line you are on will have a bullet at the beginning, and all lines of text keyed will hang indent with the first word of the previous line, not with the bullet. To create another bullet item, press **Enter**. To end bulleting, press **Enter** twice.

To make a bulleted list out of text already keyed, select the text to be made into a list, select Format→Bullets and Numbering, select the type of bullet you want, and click OK. PWP will insert a bullet at the beginning of each line after an **Enter** keystroke. To delete bulleting, select the text, then go to the *Bulleting and Numbering* dialog box and click the box with no bullets, then click OK.

40.5

Document A

Business Letter with Bullets

1 At the *Session 40 Document A* screen, key the business letter shown and insert the arrow bullets shown by completing the following steps:
  a Choose Format→Bullets and Numbering.
  b Click the box showing arrow-shaped bullets.
  c Key each paragraph of text shown. Each time you press **Enter**, a new arrow bullet will appear.
  d After keying the fourth bulleted paragraph of text, press **Enter** twice and then key the remaining text in Document A.
2 Proofread and correct any errors in the letter.
3 Click Check. The program automatically names and saves the document as **040proa**, then checks for errors and calculates your WAM rate.

1   Changes are often the cause of stress, whether you wanted these changes or they are thrust upon you. Change can be frightening and may call for some adjustment on your part. Change and stress are closely knit. You may experience stress as the result of changes that occur on a regular basis. These changes can be good or they can cause problems. Some of the common changes that cause stress are the death of a parent, the death of a child, the start of a new job, enrollment in a new school, asking someone for a date, or giving a speech.

You may also encounter stress by getting married or by having children. There are many other causes as well. It is best to confront stress when you have a problem managing it. Do not keep feeling bad about something that has happened to you on the job or at home. Work through the problems. Keep a positive outlook, and be prepared for the usual ups and downs in feelings. Work to handle your relationships with care. Learn to control stress.

TEXTBOOK EXERCISES: E-MAIL MESSAGES

The format for e-mail messages varies depending on whose software is being used. E-mail software also varies in the number of editing features available, such as bolding, italicizing, indenting, and spell checking. To take advantage of the features available in word processing software, some individuals create their e-mail messages in their word processor, then import the text to their e-mail software for transmission. Here's one example of an e-mail message:

TO: tmodl@emcp.com   C: bmitchel@emcp.com

SUBJECT: SIMILARITIES AND DIFFERENCES IN MEMOS AND E-MAIL

Tom, notice the similarities in the format of e-mail messages and memos. The "TO:" and "SUBJECT:" headings are used in both memos and e-mail messages. The heading labeled "C:" is used to identify individuals to receive electronic copies; in memos this information appears at the end of the document. The "DATE:" and "FROM:" headings found in memos don't appear on e-mail messages as this information is entered automatically by the e-mail software.

One feature that is unique to e-mail is how the name of the person(s) to receive the message is made up. The name generally includes a shortened form of the full name; for instance, in this example "tmodl" is short for Tom Modl. In addition to the person's name, there is an abbreviated form of the address; "@emcp" is short for "at EMC/Paradigm"—the place where Tom works. The designation "com" is short for a commercial business. If this were an educational institution, the designation at the end of the name/address would be "edu."

Figure 36.1 E-mail message

This is an example. Do not key.

Ohio Medical Society
15 Medford Avenue • Toledo, OH 57089 • (108) 555-1717
Fax (108) 555-2829 • Web site: www.emcp.com/omeds

Use the default margins of 1 inch top and bottom margins and 1 inch left and right margins

June 15, 2007   *keyed at line 7 or 3 lines below the last line of the letterhead; increase this space for short letters*

4 blank lines — but may be adjusted depending on length of letter

Denise Armstrong, M.D.   *Use the default of left alignment*
Cleveland Medical Clinic
8900 University Avenue
Cleveland, OH 44102   *1 space between the state abbreviation and ZIP code*
ds
Dear Doctor Armstrong:
ds
Thank you for submitting a paper to be presented at the Ohio Medical Society in Toledo on September 15. I read your paper with great interest and applaud the diligence you have applied to your research on treating heart disease with aspirin.
ds
Unfortunately, a similar study was submitted three weeks ago. While I wish we could allow both papers to be presented, the program committee has decided that due to the large number of papers, we must limit each topic to one presentation. You may wish to contact Drs. Teresa Lopez and Lee Wong at the Akron Cardiology Center, the researchers who are conducting studies similar to yours. Perhaps you can exchange some information.
ds
Thank you again for supporting your professional society. I have enclosed your paper along with a list of the meeting presenters.
ds
Sincerely yours,

3 blank lines

Kirsten Danforth
Executive Secretary
ds
cm/armstrng.ltr
ds
Enclosures
2 Enters
c *tab*   Margit Bergren, M.D.   *In alphabetic order*
   tab   Keith Holmes, M.D.

Figure 40.1 Block-style letter

Document A

E-Mail Message

1 At the *Session 36 Document A* screen, create Document A by completing the following steps:
   a Key the word **TO:**. Press *Tab* once; key the e-mail address of the person receiving the message.
   b Tab three times and key **C:**. Press *Tab* once and enter the e-mail address of the person who is to receive a copy of the message. Press *Enter*.
   c Key the word **SUBJECT:**, press *Tab*, and enter the subject of the e-mail message in all caps.
   d Complete the document.
2 Proofread and correct any errors.
3 Click Check to automatically name and save as **036proa**, and check the e-mail message.
4 Print the document with errors selected.
5 Click View Original. Correct any errors and recheck the e-mail message until you have zero errors.
6 Click Next Exercise. Once closed the Document B screen is displayed. Read the material on "Using the Bold Feature" before completing Document B.

Document A

TO: djvandas@emcp.com/C: rogergame@emcp.net /SUBJECT: "EMPLOYEE OF THE MONTH" PROGRAM/Dorothy, at our last Board of Directors meeting, it was recommended and approved that we institute an "Employee of the Month" program commencing with the opening of the addition to the Astro Medical Clinic on January 1. Employees throughout the Clinic are eligible for this award. Using your creative talents, would you please design a certificate to be used in conjunction with this program? At the bottom of the certificate provide two signature lines, one for the Chief Administrator and one for the Chief Surgeon.

Using the Bold Feature

One way to emphasize words or lines of text is to use the *Bold* feature. Bolding is often used to make key words and phrases stand out within a body of text. Bolding is also used in report headings to help set them apart from the text.

The Bold feature can be used to bold text as you key or to bold previously keyed material. To bold words as you key, complete the following steps:

1 Click the Bold button **B** on the style bar to turn bolding on. (Or press *Ctrl + B*.)
2 Key the word or words to be bolded.
3 Click the Bold button to turn bolding off. (Or press *Ctrl + B*.)

1   Many of the metal articles in everyday use are made of brass. A bookend or candlestick made of brass is quite common. But no one has ever heard of brass mines, because there are none. Brass is a blend, or mixture, of metals. Copper and zinc are usually mixed when making brass. These two metals are heated to their melting points, at which time they are joined together. After the mixture cools, it begins to harden. The copper and zinc have blended and formed a new metal with which one can make many creations.

    There are quite a few other alloys. In fact, almost none of the metal items we have are made of a single pure metal. The most common alloy by far is steel. Steel is chiefly iron. Since iron is not the strongest metal in the world, it must be combined with just the right amount of carbon for strength. The steel is then used to construct a number of objects such as cars, bridges, skyscrapers, and rails. The iron is also mixed with chromium and nickel to form stainless steel.

    Bronze is another common alloy. Bronze is made from the mixture of copper and tin. We call our pennies copper, but actually they are made of bronze. Another alloy called pewter is made of tin.

TEXTBOOK EXERCISES: PREPARING BUSINESS LETTERS

As you learn to prepare letters, work toward the following goals:

- Prepare a document that conveys a favorable image. This requires learning style and format guidelines.
- Prepare correspondence free from errors in spelling, punctuation, and word use.
- Prepare correspondence in mailable form at job-ready production levels of at least 25 WAM.

Parts of a Business Letter

A business letter has nine major parts, as shown in the illustration that follows:

1 **Letterhead:** Company logo, including the name, address, phone number(s), fax number, and Web site address.
2 **Date line:** Current date written as month, day, year (April 15, 2007). The international format lists the day, the month, then the year with no commas (15 April 2007).
3 **Inside address:** Receiver's name, title, department, company name, and address.
4 **Salutation:** Greeting that includes the receiver's name followed by a colon. In the *open punctuation* style, no punctuation is used after the salutation or the closing.
5 **Body:** Message of the letter, consisting of one or more single-spaced paragraphs with a double space between them.
6 **Closing:** Short farewell followed by a comma. The open punctuation style uses no punctuation.
7 **Signature line:** First and last names of the sender. Avoid using initials for your first name. The receiver may not know whether you are male or female.
8 **Title line:** Sender's business or professional title.
9 **Reference initials and filename:** Initials of person who keyed the document (included only if this person is not the sender) plus the name of the electronic file where the document is stored.

To bold previously keyed text, you would complete the following steps:

1   Select the text to be bolded (position the I-beam on the first character, hold down the left mouse button, drag to select the text, then release the button).

2   Click the Bold button (or press **Ctrl + B**).

3   Position the I-beam pointer outside the selected text and click the left mouse button to deselect the text.

36.6

Document B

E-Mail Message with Bolded Items

1   At the *Session 36 Document B* screen, create Document B by completing the following:

a   Use the same formatting steps for TO:, C:, and SUBJECT: as those in Document A.

b   Set the document for left and right margin (justify) alignment.

c   Bold the word **Lucent** each time it appears.

2   Proofread and correct any errors.

3   Click Check to automatically name and save as **036prob**, and check the e-mail message.

4   Print the document with errors selected.

5   Click View Original. Correct any errors and recheck the e-mail message until you have zero errors.

6   Click Next Exercise. The Document C screen is displayed. Be sure to read the section on "Using the Italicizing Feature" before completing Document C.

Document B

TO: dlopez@emcp.com /C: edondero@emcp.net /SUBJECT: VISIT TO MINNEAPOLIS/Dr. Lopez, I'll be in Minneapolis over the Thanksgiving vacation to visit my parents. I'm scheduled to leave Phoenix at 2:15 and will arrive at 6:30 p.m. on Tuesday, November 22. I'm scheduled to depart on Sunday, November 27. Even though it is not finished, is there any chance of touring the addition to the University of Minnesota Medical Center? I realize it's a holiday weekend, and you may have other plans./In case we don't get together, please send me your fax number. I found an article on a new drug called Lucent that is being tested to reverse wet macular degeneration. The initial findings for Lucent are encouraging. I talked with Dr. Park at our Clinic in Phoenix, and he is optimistic that Lucent will help his patients.

Using the Italicizing Feature

Italicizing is another of the features available to highlight words to make them stand out within a document. Italicizing is frequently used for book, newspaper, and magazine titles plus key words such as names and headings.

Session Goals

🕐	**1-Minute: 35 WAM/2 errors** **3-Minute: 30 WAM/2 errors**
✏️	**Building paragraphs**

Inserting bullets

40.1-40.2 ON-SCREEN EXERCISES: GETTING STARTED

If you exited the program at the end of the previous session, refer to page 11 in Session 3 to review how to open the next session. If you are continuing immediately from Session 39, start with Exercise 40.2. Click the Next Exercise or Previous Exercise button if you are not at the correct exercise.

When you have completed the on-screen activities for Session 40, you will return to the text to complete two 1-minute and two 3-minute timings, plus several business letters in which you will use the bullet feature to highlight text.

40.3 ONE-MINUTE TIMINGS

Goal: 35 WAM/2 errors

SI: 1.43

- Take two 1-minute timings. Start over if you finish before time is up.
- Use your most recent timing score to set a speed or accuracy goal.

1   Roller blading can provide hours of exciting fun. If there is a nearby paved lot, you are ready. Roller blades and protective equipment are needed. Skating requires lots of energy or zest to keep moving for a long period of time. The beginning skater should only skate for a short time and not get too tired. After some time has passed, the skater should be able to skate for hours without ever getting tired.

40.4 THREE-MINUTE TIMINGS

Goal: 30 WAM/2 errors

SI: 1.43

- Take two 3-minute timings. If you finish the three paragraphs before time is up, start over in paragraph one.
- On the second attempt, try to increase your speed while maintaining your accuracy.

To use the italicizing feature complete the following:

1 Click the Italicizing button on the style bar to turn italicizing on. (Or press **Ctrl + I**.)
2 Key the word or words to be italicized.
3 Click the Italicizing button to turn italicizing off. (Or press **Ctrl + I**.)

To italicize previously keyed text, do the following:

1 Select the text to be italicized (position the I-beam on the first character, hold down the left mouse button, drag to select the text, then release the button).
2 Click the Italicizing button (or press **Ctrl + I**).
3 Position the I-beam outside the selected text and click the left mouse button to deselect the text.

36.7

Document C

E-Mail Message with Indented Paragraphs and Italicized Items

1 At the *Session 36 Document C* screen, create Document C by completing the following steps:
 a Bold the names of the herbal medicines as shown.
 b Indent the information regarding each of these tools 0.5 inches from the left and right margins. The directions for indenting both the left and right margins appear in Session 35 on page 153.
 c Italicize the source of the herbal medicines.
2 Proofread and correct any errors.
3 Click Check to automatically name and save as **036proc**, and check the e-mail message.
4 Print the document with errors selected.
5 Click View Original. Correct any errors and recheck the e-mail message until you have zero errors.
6 Click Next Exercise. Before completing Document D, be sure to read the Section on "Using the Underlining Feature."

Document C

TO: plahr@emcp.com /C: none/SUBJECT: HERBAL MEDICINES/Phyllis, here is what I put together as brief explanations for four herbal medicines. /**Ginseng:** Ginseng root consists of the dried main and lateral root and root hairs of *Panax ginseng*. It is sold as a tonic for invigoration in times of fatigue. There are no known side effects when taken in the recommended dosage/**Ginkgo:** Ginkgo is extracted from the *Ginkgo biloba* leaf. It is marketed for the treatment of memory deficits, to improve concentration, and to increase learning capacity. Few side effects are known to occur, but they may include stomach or intestinal upset, headaches, and allergic reactions. Ginkgo also can increase blood clotting time./**Echinacea:** The *echinacea pallida* root is used as supportive therapy to flu-like symptoms. It should NOT be used when a person has tuberculosis, multiple sclerosis, AIDS, HIV infection, or other diseases that alter the immune system./**Garlic:** Garlic bulbs (clove) are often used as supplements to dietary modifications to treat high blood lipid levels. The side effects of garlic include only rare instances of gastrointestinal symptoms./Since many of our patients request information

Continued on next page

8 At the Print dialog box, click OK.

9 Click the Close button to close the Paradigm Word Processor.

10 Click Home on the Snap menu bar to return to the Welcome page.

Continue

To continue on to the next session, click the Next Exercise button. This will take you to Exercise 40.1.

Exit

To exit, do the following:

1 Click the Close ⊠ button in the top right corner of the screen.

2 At your Paradigm Keyboarding with Snap Welcome page, click Logout.

Ergonomic Tip

Place fingertips on shoulders, bring elbows together in front of your chest, and lift them. Then allow elbows to swing open. This will help you relax your upper body muscles.

about herbal medicines, perhaps Dorothy J. Vandas could prepare a leaflet that could be printed and given to patients requesting information about herbal medicines.

Using the Underlining Feature

Underlining is commonly used in the headings of a report to call the reader's attention to the content of the text that follows. Like italicizing, underlining is also used with book, magazine, and newspaper titles. Also, key words are often underlined to get the reader's attention.

A word of caution about the use of **bolding**, *italicizing*, and underlining: These features are to be used sparingly. If overused, they will detract from their purpose, which is to call the reader's attention to what is being presented.

To use the underlining feature complete the following:

1   Click the Underlining button **U** on the style bar to turn underlining on. (Or press *Ctrl+U*.)
2   Key the word or words to be underlined.
3   Click the Underlining button to turn underlining off. (Or press *Ctrl+U*.)

To underline previously keyed text, do the following:

1   Select the text to be underlined (position the I-beam on the first character, hold down the left mouse button, drag to select the text, then release the button).
2   Click the Underlining button (or press *Ctrl+U*).
3   Position the I-beam outside the selected text and click the left mouse button to deselect the text.

REINFORCING WRITING SKILLS

Communicating with people in writing is much more difficult than communicating in person. On a face-to-face basis, the speaker knows immediately if the message is not being communicated correctly. Body language, facial expressions, and questions provide instant and ongoing feedback. But a writer does not enjoy that advantage. Instead, the writer must rely on clear sentences and carefully chosen words to convey the intended meaning.

One simple way to help the reader get your message is to keep sentences at a reasonable length— 15 to 25 words. Readers tend to get lost in sentences that are too long, and very short sentences create a "choppy" rhythm.

Focus on creating sentences of the target length as you complete the next document. First, compose the e-mail message at the computer. Then edit your document for clear meaning, correct punctuation, and accurate word choices. Check the sentence length and edit accordingly.

36.8   **Document D**   Compose an E-Mail Message

Compose an e-mail message to your instructor. Use your name in the C: (copy) heading. The subject of the e-mail message is "Paradigm Word Processing Features." In the body of the e-mail message, identify the Paradigm Word Processing features that you've used to date that have been the most helpful. Explain how and why. In the second paragraph, talk about features that have been the most difficult to master and why. Include any suggestions you have for

Have you ever seen a document containing a paragraph that is half a page or more in length? Research demonstrates that most people will read a long paragraph quickly, paying little attention to detail. Yet those details frequently contain information that is important for the reader.

Technical reports, medical reports, scientific research, and other academic documents often include long paragraphs due to the complexity of the information. However, general correspondence, business documents, and college assignments usually can be structured with shorter paragraphs of up to nine or ten lines. As with short sentences, brief paragraphs tend to increase readability.

39.8 **Document D** **Personal Business Letter**

Students in Online Classes

Compose a letter to a friend or relative living in another city. Your purpose is to get information on the medical-related job market. Are jobs available, and if so, what types of jobs are they? What are the experience and education requirements? Explain what kind of a job you are seeking. Describe your qualifications and include when you could start working.

In your letter use some of the word processing features you have learned so far, including indenting, justification, underlining, italicizing, and/or bolding. Pay particular attention to your word choice and paragraph length. Are your words accurate and short? Are the sentences and paragraphs of ideal length?

Proofread and correct any errors. Save the letter as **039wprd** and print a copy, unless you are to print all documents at the end of the session. Then close the document.

1. Calculate your WAM rate using the timing feature (See page 156, Doc. E if you need help).
2. After getting your WAM rate, center the letter vertically using the same procedures as in Documents A, B, and C.
3. Save the letter. See page 143, steps 4 and 5, for help if needed.

ENDING THE SESSION

Now you can print any files you have created, continue with the next session, or exit Paradigm Keyboarding with Snap.

Print

To print Exercises 39.1–39.8 proceed as follows:

1 Click the Close ☒ button in the top right corner of the screen.
2 At your Paradigm Keyboarding with Snap Welcome page, point to Reports on the Snap menu bar, and click View Submissions Report.
3 At the View Submissions Report Wizard, click Show session files to see the drill lines text (Exercises 39.1–39.2), Show timings files to see the timings text (Exercises 39.3–39.4), and Show production files or Show unchecked production files to see the production documents (Exercises 39.5–39.8).
4 Click Show Report.
5 Click the name of the file you want to print.
6 At the Word Processor dialog box, click Launch.
7 Click File, and then click Print.

making the learning easier. Underline the word processing features discussed in both paragraphs.

In your message, use some of the word processing features you have learned—for example: indenting, bolding, italicizing, and changing alignment. Check your sentence length and make adjustments. Proofread the e-mail message and make necessary corrections. Save the completed message and name it **036wprd**. Print 036wprd, then close the document.

Students in Online Classes

Calculate your WAM rate. If you need help, see the instructions on page 156, Session 35, Document E.

ENDING THE SESSION

Now you may print this session's files, continue to the next session, or exit the program. See pages 156–157 of Session 35 if you need to review the procedures.

Students in Online Classes

Documents with the filename wpr are not saved automatically. If you need to review the steps for saving a document, go to Session 34, page 143, steps 4 and 5 of Document A.

Ergonomic Tip

Vary tasks during the day to break up repetitive routines. This improves your ability to concentrate.

Document C

1 At the *Session 39 Document C* screen, key the personal business letter making the changes as noted. For a review of Proofreader's Marks, go to the chart that follows the last page of the Index.
2 Proofread and correct any errors.
3 Check the letter; the program names it **039proc** and saves it, displays uncorrected errors, and calculates the WAM rate.
4 Print the letter.
5 To correct errors, click View Original. Make any necessary changes, then recheck it.
6 Click Next Activity.

Document C

Students in Online Classes

Current date

Ms. Dorothy J. Vandas
Office Manager
Astro Medical Clinic
14926 Camino Del Sol
Sun City West, AZ 85374

> After you have checked the letter, follow the instructions in alternative 3 on page 178 to center the letter vertically on the page.

Dear Ms. Vandas:

three years ago DeeAnn Davis and Mary Ruiz are medical assistants at the Astro Medical Clinic. I was in the same medical assisting program as DeeAnn and Mary. After completing the program, I moved to Grand Forks, North Dakota, to work as a medical assistant at *the* University Clinic. After two years I relocated to my present address. *Medical*

I've kept in touch with DeeAnn and Mary, and they keep telling me how impressed they are with the Astro Medical Clinic. The doctors, nurses, and staff members are so *They tell me that* pleasant and helpful. The facility is so well equipped with state-of-the-art medical and computer systems and software.

beginning I'll be in the Phoenix area on the 15th of next month for seven days. Can you please arrange a half day tour of the Clinic for me at a date and time that is convenient to you? *for* My phone number is (312) 555-2534 and my e-mail address is (*insert your e-mail address*).

Sincerely yours,

(your name)
(your address)

Session 37

Review

1-Minute: 35 WAM/2 errors
3-Minute: 30 WAM/2 errors

Choosing effective words

Review indenting, bolding, italics, underlining, and changing alignment

---

37.1- ON-SCREEN EXERCISES: GETTING STARTED
37.2

If you are continuing immediately from Session 36, start with Exercise 37.2. Click the Next Exercise or Previous Exercise button if you are not at the correct exercise. If you exited the program at the end of the previous session, refer to page 11 of Session 3 to review how to open the next session or to continue from where you left off.

37.3 ONE-MINUTE TIMINGS

Goal: 35 WAM/2 errors

SI: 1.35

- Take two 1-minute timings.
- Work on improving either speed or accuracy, depending on your most recent timing score.

1   Snowshoes add two dimensions to the feet. Snowshoes are big and add a lot of weight. To compensate for size, you must use your eyes, as well as your brain, to pick the way. Normally, in walking through the forests, most of us look ahead about ten feet. When walking with snowshoes, it is best to look ahead about 20 or 30 feet. The size of the shoes requires that a person turn bigger corners and also allow more room to maneuver. Most brush and bramble bushes are a big problem and should be avoided.

37.4 THREE-MINUTE TIMINGS

Goal: 30 WAM/2 errors

SI: 1.39

Take two 3-minute timings. If you finish the three paragraphs before the time is up, start over with the first paragraph.

Personal Business Letter

Document B

1 At the *Session 39 Document B* screen, key the personal business letter shown in Document B. Bold the text as shown.
2 Proofread and correct any errors in the letter.
3 Click Check. The program automatically names and saves the document as **039prob**, then checks for errors and calculates your WAM rate.
4 Print the document.
5 To correct errors, click View Original. Make any necessary changes, then recheck the document.
6 Click Next Activity.

Document B

Current date

Students in Online Classes

After you have checked the letter, follow the instructions in alternative 3 on page 178 to center the letter vertically on the page.

David McGuire, M.D.
Midelfort Medical Clinic
122 Whipple Street
Eau Claire, WI 54704

Dear Doctor McGuire:

For my presentation next month on "Computer Assisted Less Invasive Knee Surgery," I'll bring the following equipment with me: a **laptop computer** with **25GHz wireless notebook adaptor** and a **computer projector**. Would you please make arrangements for the following items: a **high intensity overhead projector,** access to a **wireless network**, and a **large screen**.

I look forward to sharing with your surgeons what we are doing at the Carter Institute in both research and applications in total knee replacement. We have had patients with total knee replacement who are walking unassisted two weeks after the surgery.

Can you estimate the number of surgeons attending the workshop? I want to ensure that I have sufficient materials for each participant.

Sincerely yours,

Julian Munoz
12450 Greenway
Glendale, AZ 83456

1 A wood chisel may be used to remove extra wood when another tool will not do the job efficiently. The wood chisel can also be used to make precision wood joint cuts.

Never use a steel hammer to strike a chisel. Use either a solid rubber or wooden mallet. You can also use the palm of your hand, of course, depending on the particular project. A mallet can work in cases where the edge to be cut is across the grain. If, however, the cutting edge is with the grain, a mallet could easily split the wood. Remember to angle the chisel slightly when starting a cut. The angle makes smooth or pared cuts easier to do. Cutting on the angle leaves the piece of wood much smoother when cutting either with or against the grain.

To make a vertical cut against the grain, tilt the chisel off to one side to initiate a sliding action to the flat cutting edge. A surface that is wider than the chisel is easier to cut if the chisel is pressed against the cut-out portion. The procedure will provide a guide for that portion of the chisel when cutting out the new portion or edge. Always remember to cut with the grain so that any excess or extra wood will split away in a straight line and not cause a further problem to the woodcutter.

37.5 TEXTBOOK EXERCISES: FORMATTING TEXT IN MEMOS

Document A

Memo with Italicized Words

1 At the *Session 37 Document A* screen, key the memo shown in Document A with the following specifications:
   a Insert the current date.
   b Italicize the text as shown in Document A.
   c Be sure to key your initials at the end of the memo followed by the document name.
2 Proofread and correct any errors in the memo.
3 Click Check. The program saves the document as **037proa**, then checks for errors and calculates your WAM rate.
4 Print the document with errors selected.
5 To correct errors, click View Original. Make any necessary changes, then recheck the document until you have zero errors.
6 Click Next Exercise.

Document A

Memo to Medical Assistants/from Dorothy J. Vandas, Office Manager/subject: RELEASING MEDICAL RECORDS.

Attached is a two-page insert for your Office Manual of our updated procedures for Releasing Medical Records. Please dispose of the old copy that you have in your Office Manual. Patients, or their legal representative, may inspect, obtain copies of, or have copies of their Astro Medical Clinic medical records sent to another medical facility. Astro Medical Clinic is required to obtain an original, complete, and properly executed *Authorization for Disclosure of Health Information* form before the clinic may provide a copy of a patient's records to anyone, including the patient. /xx/037proa/Attachment

Remember: You are responsible for watching for and correcting any intentional errors in spelling, spacing, or arrangement that appear in the documents. This helps you become a **thinking** keyboarder.

39.5

Document A

Personal Business Letter

1 At the *Session 39 Document A* screen, key the personal business letter shown in Document A. Italicize the text as shown in Document A.
2 Proofread and correct any errors in the letter.
3 Click Check. The program automatically names and saves the document as **039proa**, then checks for errors and calculates your WAM rate.
4 Print the document.
5 To correct errors, click View Original. Make any necessary changes, then recheck the document.
6 Click Next Exercise.

Document A

Students in Online Classes

Current date

Ms. Rena Coleman
EMC/Paradigm Publishing Company
875 Montreal Way
St. Paul, MN 55104

Dear Ms. Coleman:

Thank you for sending me the catalog of medical textbooks published by EMC/Paradigm Publishing Company. I'm in the process of building a personal library for medical assisting for reference and for increasing my skills.

Please send me *Medical Assisting - Administrative and Clinical Competencies* and *Medical Terminology, 2nd Edition* shown on pages 47 and 49 in your catalog. Please send the texts and bill to my home address listed below.

I've used several of your texts while in school. They were well written, comprehensive, organized in a logical manner, and contained helpful visual aids throughout.

Sincerely yours,

Ms. Marie Sanchez
13487 Conquistador Drive
El Mirage, AZ 85781

> After you have checked the letter, follow the instructions in alternative 3 on page 178 to center the letter vertically on the page.

37.6

Document B

Memo with Bolded Words

1 At the *Session 37 Document B* screen, key the memo shown in Document B with the following specifications:
  a Bold the names as shown in Document B.
  b Key your initials at the end of the memo followed by the document name.
  c For the copy notation, key **c**, press *Tab*, then key the name.
2 Proofread and correct any errors in the memo.
3 Click Check to automatically name and save as **037prob**, and check the document for errors.
4 Print the document.
5 To correct errors, click View Original. Make any necessary changes, then recheck the document.
6 Click Next Exercise.

Document B

Memo to Dorothy J. Vandas, Office Manager/from Don Monroe, Space Coordinator/subject: CHANGES IN WORKSTATION LOCATIONS

The new addition to the Astro Medical Clinic will open next Monday. Those Medical Assistants moving to the new addition are as follows: **Connie Gutierrez, Marion Hobart**, and **Miki Horton**. All items from their current workstations will be moved over the weekend to their new locations.

Connie has been assigned to l03 West, Marion to 214 West, and Miki to 318 West. It would help if items to be moved are boxed and placed on top of their current workstations before they leave on Friday afternoon.

xx/037prob

c   Connie Gutierrez, CMA
      Marion Hobart, CMA
      Miki Horton, RMA

37.7

Document C

Edited E-Mail Message with Left and Right Indent and Underlined Words

1 At the *Session 37 Document C* screen, key Document C as follows:
  a Instead of numbering the five paragraphs indent them 0.5 inches from the left and right margin with a double space between each paragraph.
  b Underline the words that appear at the beginning of each of the five paragraphs.
  c Be sure to add your initials and the filename at the end of the memo.
2 Proofread and correct any errors.
3 Click on Check to name and save as **037proc**, and check the document.
4 Print the document with errors selected.
5 Click View Original. Correct any errors and recheck until all errors are corrected.
6 Click Next Exercise.

This happened one other time prior to the time you joined the staff at the Astro Medical Clinic. I believe the form that was submitted by the Astro Medical Clinic to Medicare and Blue Cross/Blue Shield had incorrect information. The bookkeeper at that time checked and sure enough it contained incorrect information.

ds

Would you please check the forms submitted to see if the information provided was correct? Also, for the past year, I've received checks from Blue Cross/Blue Shield for the portion of the bill they cover. I then endorsed the checks and sent them to the Clinic. Is there a way to have the checks mailed directly to the Clinic? Thanks for any help you can provide.

ds

Sincerely yours,

3 blank lines

Ms. Trish Huston
12516 Greasewood Drive
Surprise, AZ 85365

Figure 39.1 Personal business letter

Centering Text on the Page

Typically, commercial word processing software packages include a command allowing the user to center documents, such as a letter, on a page vertically. This command can be set at the beginning of a document or after it is completed. If your word processing software, like PWP, doesn't have the vertical centering feature, there are three alternatives available when dealing with letters. They are as follows:

1 Print the letter as is. There will usually be more blank space at the bottom of the letter than the top depending on the number of lines in the body of the letter.

2 "Guesstimate." If the letter appears to be short, add more space before the date and between the date and inside address. Instead of pressing **Enter** 5 times after inserting the date, press **Enter** 6–8 times. When you reach the end of the letter and you are still too high on the page, you can add blank lines between the complimentary close and the signature line. The individual signing the letter can then write her or his name a little larger. (In PWP, you can view the position of your text on a piece of paper by choosing File→Print Preview.)

   It is also possible to increase the width of the left and right margins, which reduces the line length and makes the letter seem longer. However, adjusting margins even with word processing commands adds time to the production of the letter and thus is something to avoid.

3 Key the letter and then count the number of lines from the date line through the last item on the page. Subtract this number from 54, the number of lines left on the page after taking away the one inch top and bottom margin default. Divide the remainder by two, go to the beginning of the date line, press **Enter** that many times. What you have done is place an even number of blank lines at the top and bottom of the letter.

Check with your instructor on which alternative you are to follow in preparing letters. Follow that alternative for all letters that take up less than one full page. As you will see later, there's no problem when working with two-page letters.

TO: casiclovan@emcp.com/C:djvandas@emcp.com/Subject: Fees for Mailing Medical Records/Here is the information you requested regarding the fees for reproduction costs and mailing medical records:

1. Mailing Medical Records: If the medical record in being mailed to the patient, then the patient will be charges for mailing costs.

2. Reproduction Charges: If the reproduction charges are greater than $100, the prepayment will be required before a patient's records can be mailed.

3. Sending Records to Another Medical Facility: All fees will be waved if the patient is requesting her/him records be sent directly to another medical facility.

4. Accessing Time: Patientss are to allow five working days for requests to be processed. An employee of the Medical Records Department will contact the patient when the records are ready for pickup or mailing.

5. Picking Up Medical Records: If the patient plans to come to the Medical Records Department to pickup her/his records, they are to bring a photo ID.

Dr. Siclovan, please call me at extension 2544, if you have any questions about our fees for mailing medical records.

REINFORCING WRITING SKILLS

In Session 36, you read that for readability and comprehension purposes, the ideal sentence length is 15 to 25 words. Another factor that promotes clear communication is word choice. In addition to choosing words that accurately say what you mean, it is important to choose simple, common words that everyone understands. Do not fall into the trap of selecting long, obscure words just to make your message seem more important. Some of the most powerful written statements consist of very short words, as in the following example:

If it is to be, it is up to me.

As you complete Document D, concentrate on keeping sentences in the 15- to 25-word range and use simple words that communicate directly and forcefully.

Document

37.8

D E-Mail Message with Left and Right Margin Alignment

Assume that you are creating this e-mail message in your word processor and will then import it to your e-mail software for transmission.

Compose an e-mail message to your instructor on the topic AN IDEAL VACATION. The e-mail message is to have at least two paragraphs. Write about where you would like to go for an ideal vacation and what you would do. Include the names of places, the length of the vacation, the time of year, and transportation. Be sure to explain why you consider this to be an ideal vacation.

1   To avoid consumer problems, some decisions should be made before buying a product. The first major point is to decide if you and your family really need that new product or new service. If the answer is yes, then the next step is to shop around and compare prices. A good library will have publications that give helpful comparisons among similar products. Check on the firm with which you are dealing; call the Better Business Bureau for more information. Make certain that a guarantee is in writing. Before you sign a contract, read it to make sure that you understand it fully. If you have any doubts at all, it would be wise to wait and think about the purchase a little longer.

When you buy a product or a service, be sure that you understand the method of payment if it is to be a credit purchase. Know exactly when each payment is due, how much interest is being charged, and how many months the payments are to be made. Read all tags and labels to learn all about the product before you use it. If you have any problems with the product or service, speak with the seller first. If you find that a seller does not give the proper satisfaction to a problem, there are many consumer protection groups and agencies you can contact.

TEXTBOOK EXERCISES: PREPARING PERSONAL BUSINESS LETTERS

A personal business letter is a letter from an individual to a business. Examples of personal business letters are the letters individuals write to companies requesting information or complaining about a product or service.

In this session, you will review the formatting guidelines for preparing personal business letters. In Figure 39.1, below, note that the return address is placed below the keyed sender's name. Note also that the personal business letter is keyed on plain paper, not on company letterhead. The letter is centered vertically on the page for a visually pleasing appearance.

current date
4 blank lines

Linda Fields, Bookkeeper
Astro Medical Clinic
14926 Camino Del Sol
Sun City West, AZ 85374
ds

Dear Miss Fields:
ds

Yesterday I received a bill from the Astro Medical Clinic indicating that I had a balance of $10.41 due for my protime that was done the 15th of last month. Between Medicare and Blue Cross/Blue Shield my medical bills have been covered 100 percent.
ds

Continued on next page

Copy yourself for this e-mail message. Use your instructor's e-mail address as well as yours. Align your e-mail message at the left and right margins. When you have finished the message, proofread it and correct any errors. Save the document as **037wprd**. Print the e-mail message for your instructor, then close the document.

ENDING THE SESSION

Now you may print this session's files, continue to the next session, or exit the program. See pages 156–157 of Session 35 if you need to review the procedures.

Ergonomic Tip

With arms hanging at your sides, gently circle shoulders forward and then backward. This helps relax your upper body muscles.

39

PERSONAL BUSINESS LETTERS

1-Minute: 35 WAM/2 errors
3-Minute: 30 WAM/2 errors

Centering text on a page

Improving paragraph readability

39.1- ON-SCREEN EXERCISES: GETTING STARTED

39.2

If you are continuing immediately from Session 38, start with Exercise 39.2. Click the Next Exercise or Previous Exercise button if you are not at the correct exercise.

If you exited the program at the end of the previous session, refer to page 11 of Session 3 for instructions on entering the program.

39.3 ONE-MINUTE TIMINGS

Goal: 35 WAM/2 errors

SI: 1.38

- Take two 1-minute timings.
- Use your most recent timing score to set a speed or accuracy goal. If you finish before time is up, start over. (To review your timed writing scores, go to Session 7, page 27, for instructions on accessing your report.)

> 1   Most clouds move usually from west to east as they cross an area of land. If there should be a high pressure system holding around the West Coast, it will divert the clouds and moisture northward into the Canadian Rockies. Many experts think that the climate over the whole earth is becoming warmer and drier. These experts state that the one thing that will suffer most will be rainfall.

39.4 THREE-MINUTE TIMINGS

Goal: 30 WAM/2 errors

SI: 1.42

Take two 3-minute timings. If you finish the two paragraphs before time is up, start over with the first paragraph.

Session 38

PRODUCTION PROGRESS CHECK: MEMORANDUMS AND E-MAIL

Session Goals

1-Minute: 35 WAM/2 errors
3-Minute: 30 WAM/2 errors

Apply features presented in Sessions 35–37

Ideal paragraph length

38.1- 38.2 *ON-SCREEN EXERCISES: GETTING STARTED*

If you are continuing immediately from Session 37, start with Exercise 38.2. Click the Next Exercise or Previous Exercise button if you are not at the correct exercise. If you exited the program at the end of the previous session, refer to page 11 of Session 3 to review how to open the next session or to continue from where you left off.

When you have completed the on-screen activities for Session 38, you will return to the text to complete a production progress check on memos and e-mail.

38.3 ONE-MINUTE TIMINGS

Goal: 35 WAM/2 errors

SI: 1.40

- Take two 1-minute timings.
- Work on improving either speed or accuracy, depending on your most recent timing score.

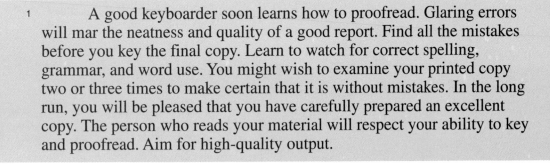

1   A good keyboarder soon learns how to proofread. Glaring errors will mar the neatness and quality of a good report. Find all the mistakes before you key the final copy. Learn to watch for correct spelling, grammar, and word use. You might wish to examine your printed copy two or three times to make certain that it is without mistakes. In the long run, you will be pleased that you have carefully prepared an excellent copy. The person who reads your material will respect your ability to key and proofread. Aim for high-quality output.

38.4 THREE-MINUTE TIMINGS

Goal: 30 WAM/2 errors

SI: 1.39

Take two 3-minute timings. If you finish the three paragraphs before time is up, start over with the first paragraph.

9

LETTERS

1   Many people are growing herb gardens. The herb plants provide a variety of new seasonings, fragrances, and flavorings. Growing herbs is quite similar to growing a vegetable garden. You should select an area for your herb garden that is sunny, as herbs demand an abundance of sunlight to make them sweet and flavorful.

To supply enough herbs for a family of four, you would need a garden space of at least 12 to 18 square feet. If you do not have enough room, it is always easy to grow an abundance of herbs in an ordinary window box or in small clay flower pots. If grown inside, the herbs should be placed in a window that receives full sunlight at least half of the day. In cases where sunlight is not available, a fluorescent-light garden will give you a plentiful harvest of herbs. To promote compact growth, it is a good idea to snip the plants back on a regular basis.

Herbs placed with other plants add charm and grace with the rich foliage. Freshly picked herbs can either be dried or frozen for future use. Many good cookbooks offer directions for using a variety of herbs.

TEXTBOOK EXERCISES: PRODUCTION PROGRESS CHECK— MEMORANDUMS AND E-MAIL

Now that you have completed the instruction on preparing memos and e-mail messages, it is time to assess how quickly and accurately you can key these documents. Each completed document is to be "mailable," which means that it could be sent either by an internal mail system or electronically without any further corrections.

Your goal is to key each memo in mailable form at 25 WAM or higher. If you are below 25 WAM and/or are missing errors that should have been corrected, your instructor may ask you to repeat documents.

It is your responsibility to review each document and the instructions before keying. The memos may be missing required features such as the date or reference initials and filename. In addition, there may be punctuation, spelling, or capitalization errors.

38.5

Document A

Memo with Italicized Words

1 At the *Session 38 Document A* screen, key Document A in the memo format. Italicize *"Optical Disk System"* whenever it appears.
2 Proofread and correct any errors in the memo.
3 Click Check to automatically name and save as **038proa** and check the memo.
4 Print the document.
5 To correct errors, click View Original. Make any necessary changes, then recheck the document.
6 Click Next Exercise.

Students in Online Classes

If you are below 25 WAM and/or have uncorrected errors, use the timing feature in the word processor to repeat documents. The timing feature will not identify your errors, but it will calculate your WAM rate. Proofread your document(s) and circle errors.

Now you may print this session's files, continue to the next session, or exit the program. See pages 156–157 of Session 35 if you need to review the procedures.

Ergonomic Tip

The next time you buy eyeglasses, tell your optometrist or optician about your computer use patterns. This is especially important if you wear bifocals to minimize having to tilt your head to see the screen.

Document A

To: Dorothy J. Vandas, Office Manager/From: Alberto Gomez, Medical Records Administrator/Subject: Demonstration of the Optical Disk System for Creating, Maintaining and Updating Medical Records/Dorothy, please notify Department Heads that a demonstration has been set for our new Optical Disk System. The demonstration is two weeks from today in Room 109 from 1 – 4:30 p.m. Representatives of the firm that sold us the Optical Disk System will demonstrate its use. Ample time has been provided to ask questions and make recommendations to adjust the system to meet our needs. It is imperative that all department heads are in attendance.

Memo

38.6

Document B

1   At the *Session 38 Document B* screen, key Document B in the memo format. Bold the names of the three candidates.
2   Proofread and correct any errors in the memo.
3   Click Check to automatically name and save as **038prob**, and check the memo.
4   Print the document.
5   To correct errors, click View Original. Make any necessary changes, then recheck the document.
6   Click Next Exercise.

Document B

To: Dr. Mitchell Giangobbe, General and Vascular Surgery/From: Ken Larson, Human Resources/Subject: Medical Assistant Candidates/Dr. Giangobbe, attached are the resumes of the top three candidates for the Medical Assistant position in your Department. All three candidates have been awarded their CMA. Angelica Sumano and Gary Vierra have worked with vascular surgery doctors in Phoenix. Donna Reed recently moved to Phoenix from Ohio where she was employed as a medical assistant at the Cleveland Medical Institute. /After reviewing the resumes, please let me know whether you want to interview all three or just two of the candidates. Also, what is the best date and time for interviews?/Attachments

Turn Over for page 173

38.7 E-Mail Message with Left and Right Indent and Underlined Words

Document C

1 At the *Session 38 Document C* screen, key Document C as follows:
   a Left and right indent the three training areas 0.5 inches with a double space between each of the training areas.
   b Underline the names of the training areas.
2 Proofread and correct any errors.
3 Click Check to name and save as **038proc**, and check the document.
4 Print the document with errors selected.
5 Click View Original. Correct any errors and recheck until all errors are corrected.
6 Click Next Exercise.

Document C

TO: mmildenberger@emcp.com/C: ccooper@emcp.com/Subject: Software Training /Dr. Mildenberger, per your request, I've surveyed the department heads and the medical assistants to determine their needs for software training. The three areas that were identified most frequently are as follows:/Accounting: The medical assistants want to go more in depth with our accounting software package to take advantage of the features available especially in the accounts receivable area./Internet Explorer: The medical assistants need to know how to access information from the Internet related to medical issues./PowerPoint Presentations: The medical assistants are being asked to prepare PowerPoint presentations for the doctors and administrative staff. Inserting graphics and pictures into presentations as well as designing the program for maximum effectiveness are critical elements./We will begin offering these training programs on the first of next month. The programs will be staggered so that the medical assistants can attend all three training sessions.

38.8 E-Mail

Document D

Compose an e-mail message to your instructor (copy yourself) consisting of at least two paragraphs, each with four or more sentences. Select one of the following topics:

1 My favorite summer sport(s) or my favorite winter sport(s)
2 My hobby
3 If I were to buy a new car today, it would be a _____.
4 How to stay in shape

Use your instructor's actual e-mail address and yours as well. Use the timing feature in PWP so that your WAM rate can be calculated. Proofread and correct any errors made and save the document as **038wprd**. Print a copy of the e-mail message for your instructor, then close the document.

Writing Checklists/ Proofreader's Marks

Use the two checklists below whenever you write your own documents. Evaluate your first draft according to the checkpoints. Then make any necessary changes before you print the final draft.

Composition Checklist

- ☐ Did I order my thoughts in a sensible way?
- ☐ Did I group related paragraphs together?
- ☐ Did I group related pieces of information in a single paragraph?
- ☐ Did I start a new paragraph for each new idea?
- ☐ Did I begin each paragraph with a topic sentence or a connecting sentence?
- ☐ Did I vary sentence structure and length?
- ☐ Did I break up overly long sentences?
- ☐ Did I make my subject and verb agree?
- ☐ Did I use pronouns correctly and without bias?
- ☐ Did I take care not to split verb phrases?
- ☐ Did I put modifiers next to the words they modify?
- ☐ Did I use correct punctuation?

Style Checklist

- ☐ Did I use language suitable for my intended reader?
- ☐ Did I use everyday language?
- ☐ Did I avoid slang, cliches, and phoniness?
- ☐ Did I avoid sexist language?
- ☐ Did I use strong, lively words?
- ☐ Did I use concrete rather than abstract words?
- ☐ Did I use the active voice?
- ☐ Did I eliminate redundancies?

Proofreaders' Mark	Example	Revised
# Insert space	lettertothe	letter to the
ℒ Delete	the commands is	the command is
lc / Lowercase	he is Branch Manager	he is branch manager
(cap) or UC ☰ Uppercase	Margaret simpson	Margaret Simpson
# New paragraph	The new product	The new product
no # No paragraph	the meeting.	the meeting. Bring the
	Bring the	
∧ Insert	pens clips	pens, and clips
⊙ Insert period	a global search	a global search.
⊐ Move right	With the papers	With the papers
⊏ Move left	access the code	access the code
⊐⊏ Center	Chapter Six	Chapter Six
∩ Transpose	It is raesonable	It is reasonable
(sp) Spell out	475 Mill Ave.	475 Mill Avenue
... Stet	I am very pleased	I am very pleased
(do not delete)		
⌒ Close up	regret fully	regretfully
ss Single-space	The margin top	The margin top
	ss	is 1 inch.
	is 1 inch.	
ds Double-space	Paper length is	Paper length is
	set for 11 inches.	
		set for 11 inches.
ts Triple-space	Use options from	Use options from
	the File drop-down	
	menu	
		the File drop-down menu
bf Boldface	Boldface type	**Boldface** type
	provides emphasis.	provides emphasis.
(ital) Italics	Use italics for terms	Use *italics* for terms
	to be defined.	to be defined.
ᴴ∧ insert hyphen	phase in plan	phase-in plan
m̂∧ M dash	two models one	two models--one
	two hyphens, no	
	spaces	

PWP QUICK REFERENCE

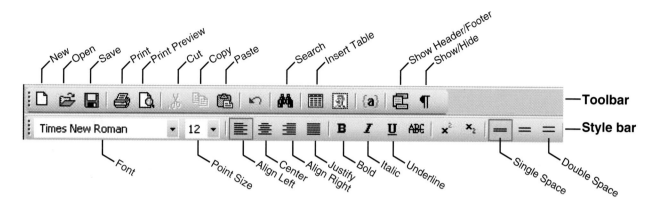

Opening a PWP Document

Many times you will want to open a document that has been saved. You may want to bring it back to the screen to add more text, review the document, or make corrections. To open a saved document, complete the following steps:

1   At the PWP window, click the Open button on the toolbar or choose File→Open. **Note:** You can select a pull-down menu such as File from the top of the screen by either clicking it with the mouse or by pressing the **Alt** key and the underlined letter key at the same time.

2   At the *Open* dialog box a list of documents is displayed. Note: If you cannot locate your document, check the Look in box located toward the top of the dialog box, and make sure the drive listed in the box is the same drive where you saved your documents. The *Open* dialog box lists all documents saved in folder in alphabetic (or numeric) order.

3   Position the mouse pointer on the document name and click the left button to select the document.

4   Press Enter or click Open to open the document. **Note:** You can also double-click (two clicks in quick succession) with the left mouse button on the document name to open the document.

Saving a PWP Document

You can save a newly created document in PWP by taking the following steps:

1   Choose File→Save As.

2   At the *Save As* dialog box, key in the document name in the File name text box, then click Save or press **Enter**.

You can save an opened document in PWP by doing *one* of the following steps:

1 Choose File→Save.
2 Clicking the Save button on the toolbar.
3 Pressing *Ctrl* + *S*.

Naming a PWP Document

A document name in Windows can be from 1 to 255 characters in length. It can contain letters (uppercase or lowercase), numbers, spaces, periods, and some symbols. PKB automatically adds a period and three-character extension to a file name. You will receive specific instructions for naming files in the text.

Printing a PWP Document

1 Open the document you wish to print.
2 Click the Print button on the toolbar or choose File→Print.
3 Click OK in the *Print* dialog box.

Closing a PWP Document

To close a document in PWP,
1 Save the document.
2 Choose File→Close.

Deleting a PWP Document

To delete a document in PWP,
1 Click the Open button on the toolbar or choose File→Open.
2 At the Open dialog box, position the arrow pointer on the name of the document you wish to delete, and then click the right mouse button.
3 At the pop-up menu that displays, click Delete with the left mouse button.
4 At the question asking if you are sure you want to delete the document, click Yes.
5 Click the Cancel button to close the Open dialog box.

Note: In PWP, you cannot delete a document that is currently opened.